An illustrated analysis of
Pottery & Porcelain
Prices at Auction
1999-2003

2004 Edition

Editor John Ainsley

An illustrated analysis of
Pottery & Porcelain
Prices at Auction
1999-2003

2004 Edition

Edited by John Ainsley

First published in Great Britain 2003 by
Antiques Information Services Ltd. Wallsend House,
P O Box 93, Broadstairs, Kent CT10 3YR
Telephone: 01843 862069
Fax: 01843 862014
Email: john.ainsley@antiques-info.co.uk

Further details about the Publishers may be found on our website at
www.antiques-info.co.uk

ISBN: 0-9546479-0-4

Whilst every care has been exercised in the compilation of this guide, neither the
editor nor publishers accept any liability for any financial or other loss incurred by reliance
placed on the information contained in Pottery & Porcelain Prices at Auction

Printed by Buxton Press Limited
Palace Road, Buxton, Derbyshire SK17 6AE

Contents

Introduction

The Project

The idea for a new approach to price guides was first formulated about five or six years ago. Two years of negotiations and discussions began and eventually we were able to put into place the actual gathering of information. Four years later the process of gathering sufficient information to produce a book was completed. It was now possible to commence the project. However even in the months of 2003 and right into November information was continuously gleaned from auctions throughout the country to ensure that this 2004 Edition would be as up-to-date as possible when we went to press in late November. Hence this work will continue to address the needs of both the professional user and the collector for several years to come, after which another edition will be published.

Acknowledgments

In the last six months up to December 2003, the process of forming the book began and a very dedicated and highly motivated team spent hundreds of hours on the project. I must mention in particular, Brenda Turner, who processed the thousands of photographs and keyed in and shared in the editing of every caption. There are over 3,030 illustrations in this book at the final count, not to mention the many hundreds of further images which had to be processed and from which the final choice was made. Great praise is due also to my wife, Angela, for the countless hours, frequently at weekends, spent in compiling the Index. This is exacting work but it was pursued with a remorseless determination in order to meet our print deadline.

There would have been no book without the co-operation of the many auctions up and down the country who have, over several years, made their contributions. As busy as they are they have always found the time to help when I have made a special request or pestered for more images. Every caption in the book is headed up by the name of the supplying auction. It is the very least they deserve.

Dedication

Finally, I should like to dedicate this pilot work to the many thousands of both amateur and professional enthusiasts up and down the country and indeed world-wide, as well as their forebears throughout history, even into pre-dynastic times, who live or who have lived with a great love for ceramics and all of the fire-baked clay vessels, be they terracotta, the tin-glazed or lead-glazed products of history, or the stonewares, or the finer porcelains themselves which have now graced this earth for more than a thousand years.

Price Guides in General

This work is quite unique - the idea untested. Previously general or even specialist price guides have usually followed the tried and tested formula of the A-Z format. In ceramics this will usually mean a start with say, *Adams* and a conclusion with *Worcester* or even *Zsolnay*. And even then within the overall A-Z format there is a second level of the A-Z format which identifies the various pieces and shapes. These usually commence with *animals* and conclude with *wall pockets*. As an alternative, pottery and porcelain are often separated out and the main A-Z format follows the animals-to-wall-pockets principle except in certain pockets of the books which might look in particular at *Clarice Cliff* or *Wemyss*. Or porcelain for example may have a book of its own. These formulae are not being challenged. They have a logic and play a significant role in providing information to us all.

With regard to the prices or the price ranges quoted these are based on the informed opinions of experts from the auctions and retail industry. However it is quite clear that they do not represent actual sales. Indeed there are thousands of examples year in and year out where sales results are significantly above or below those that were anticipated.

A New Rationale

Here for the first time ever are the actual hammer prices at auction from a mass of defined market situations representing the sales of over 3,030 lots. These have been placed in seven price bands and in actual price order in the price range £240,000 down to only £5. The price bands are somewhat arbitrary; they have to be. This is not a criticism but straightforwardly a technical means of dividing the work into sections which not only aid the analyses but also provide a simple and straightforward format which will help the reader to keep their bearings.

These 3,031 illustrations have not only been chosen to represent the various price ranges but also to represent a distinctive time period associated with the history of ceramics. Examples will be found which represent some of the very earliest artefacts from pre-dynastic Egypt right through into the twenty first century with some of the very latest collectibles which can be found in the last sections. To ensure a sensible time window in respect of the market the lots illustrated have been taken from sales occurring between 1999 and 2003, a very credible four years. It will be shown later however that in some of the very fast moving areas where fashion is flinging the old ideas of values out of the window that credibility itself may be stretched to breaking point. Four years is a long time in politics! More of this later.

The rationale is the rationale of the market. This has been given absolute priority. If you have ever tried to study the market from previous price guides you will be aware of the difficulties. The very A-Z format is a weakness in itself bearing no relationship to the market which is a straightforward matter of when an item was sold, where it was sold and what it sold for! And as these singular points tend not to sway those publishers who produce price guides then one might suggest that they are unlikely to provide total market satisfaction to users although they do provide an extremely useful guide to prices and to the history of ceramics.

Here, in this work, for the first time ever, the actual numeric price order, overseeing the various price ranges, representing the extremely expensive right down to the very cheapest lots to be found *is* the essential market ingredient which aids a grasp of the fundamental elements which *are* the market at the various levels. Here for the first time ever, one can study and analyse the market in many ways. For example, the reader can browse any of the price ranges or check out a particular price. Or, using the comprehensive *Index*, it is possible to make for example a market study of Worcester or Doulton or Beswick, prices at auction, or analyse Satsuma or English Delft or creamware. Even patterns and figures are listed, such as Moorcroft's *Anemone* or Clarice Cliff's *Orange House* or Royal Doulton's *Pearly Boy*.

Each section of this volume is preceded by an Editor's analysis and it is recommended that this analysis is studied along with the images and the captions themselves. It must be made clear that this analysis is not definitive and is therefore not intended to be obtrusive. The reasoning behind these thoughts are straightforward. Any analysis in respect of the information contained is not and never can be a science. So complex is the information provided that analyses may follow numerous paths at various levels. Hence, the Editor's analyses will become personalised around the editor's interest and the editor's level of knowledge. A myriad of readers will each seek their own analyses based on their own knowledge and their own peculiar or broad interests. For example, a specialist ceramics dealer will take a broad interest, particularly within his operational theatre. Alternatively a collector of eighteenth century soft paste porcelains, such as Bow, Chelsea or Worcester may concentrate on this area and may find that he or she is able to question certain attributions or even fill in gaps where lots remain unattributed. At the same time of course they will be familiarising themselves with the market. Or a collector or dealer specialising in Royal Doulton figures will have many examples from across a huge price range and across the country from which to choose. Auctions results become a fascinating area of study when they are presented in this way.

Auctions Prices in the context of the Market

Auction prices are often considered to be the wholesale side of the market as opposed to the more obvious retail outlets such as fairs, markets, shops and antiques centres. Certainly, the trade, not all mind you, buy at auction. And if they are to resell their purchases then they need to work on a sensible margin. However, auctions are not wholesale outlets with unlimited supplies of various lines. Indeed dealers at auction, in a free market situation are inevitably competing with other dealers and collectors and their margin is usually the adding on of a reasonable profit in the knowledge that, if they buy sensibly, then they should be able to sell. When very desirable lots come to auction, those of extremely fine quality or rarity, then canny prices can go out of the window as dealers and collectors compete. In general one cannot be definitive on how auctions fit into the trilogy of outlets, except to say that, in general, there is a higher standard of goods sold at fine art auctions than in the average antiques and collectors fair or antiques centre. This is because it is not worth the auctioneers time to store, sell and take a percentage for goods having little value. Alternatively at specialist fairs, and particularly those that are datelined and vetted, or in the top-of-the-range antiques shops or antiques centres, the quality and rarity and hence the desirability of goods exceed by far the goods at the average auction. But then of course there are specialist auctions! Drawing lines is virtually impossible. However if one should offer any advice on where to buy it is that one should not discount any area of the real market. The most successful dealers or collectors will leave no stone unturned in their endeavour to find either their stock or to add to their collection. Specifically, boot fairs nowadays are by their nature a 99% palpable waste of time, unless of course you find them enjoyable! They rather compare well with purchasing a lottery ticket! In any event the best advice one can ever give in respect of buying is to go for the very best you can afford. You will hear this repeated again and again by experts. Better to buy one item for £200 than ten at £20 each which could provide you with a space problem and little investment potential.

The Arithmetic of Buying and Selling at Auction

The reader may already be asking themselves why we haven't rationalised the prices in order to state categorically the actual price paid by the buyer in each case. The reason is straightforward. About 99% of auctions in the UK actually publish only their hammer prices. The final price paid by the buyer is a matter of a private invoice which is not accessible to the press.

Buying at auction

Auctions add on the following charges. Firstly there is a buyer's premium, which can vary, depending on the hammer price. Usually there are differing price bands which decrease as the hammer price increases. For example you may pay 15% on top of a hammer price of say £1,000 but only 10% on top of a hammer price of £30,000. In addition there is VAT to be paid on the premium and in some cases VAT may be due on the hammer price as well, depending on the age and origin of the lot. This is why throughout this book we advise that you add on average about 15% to the hammer prices stated to gauge the approximate price paid by the buyer. The auction catalogue will always explain the terms and conditions relating to buying at auction.

Selling at auction

The final cost to the vendor again can never be in the public domain and is a matter of a final statement along with a cheque for an item that has been sold. Again there is a premium to pay which on average will be at least 10-15% of the hammer price. Then there is the VAT and in addition there may be charges related to a photograph or photographs in the catalogue, storage and even insurance. We would suggest that if you use this price guide to gauge how much you would receive if you were to sell an item, that this time you subtract about 15% from the hammer price. This is an important market statement. The buying and true selling prices will vary by about 30%. Again the auction catalogue will always explain the terms and conditions relating to selling at auction. If in doubt, auctions are always willing to explain their operations. And on viewing days, staff are usually on hand to offer information or advice on the lots themselves.

How to use this Book.

Whilst this book provides an ideal browsing medium, it is recommended that both the full **Introduction** and the **Section Analyses** are read at an early stage. A very significant part of this work are the captions to the images. These conclude always with the month and year of sale being from 1999 to 2003. This four year period represents an extremely credible period but at the same time certain hammer prices must be treated with caution. There are undoubtedly, lots which have sold, say in 1999 or 2000 which in 2004 are likely to fetch considerably more than they did then. The Section Analyses point up examples.

In addition whilst every effort has been made by the Editor to check out the attributions within the captions, there exists the possibility, even though extremely unlikely, that a wrong attribution has been made. Auction cataloguing is an extremely difficult and arduous task and even specialists cannot know everything. However, great care is usually taken and 'labelling' is in most cases very accurate. Incidentally, many auctions will rescind a sale within a set period of the purchase if the buyer can show inaccuracies in the catalogue description. Disputes usually revolve around damaged, restored or reproduction lots.

Readers should also be aware that in some cases captions have been rationalised in order to solve technical editing requirements related to space. Sometimes syntactical changes have been made and abbreviations used which did not occur in the original auction catalogue. And on occasions the Editor has used his discretion to omit descriptive detail which would be tedious and which would not materially influence the price. In all cases the Editor has ensured that changes in meaning have not occurred and that the content of a caption remains true to the original version. Factory names have occasionally been rationalised. For example, *New Hall* has been used rather than *Newhall*. Foreign spellings also varied considerably in the original catalogues and these have been, where possible, standardised to ensure the integrity of the Indexing system.

Despite the huge range of pictures included covering four years of auctions sales, there *will* be gaps in the A-Z of ceramics, although we hope there are few and that these missing manufactories are perhaps less relevant than all of the mainstream factories covered. However, as this work is essentially a guide to what is selling at auction, then what is not appearing at auctions is a market point in itself. For example, why there is no Daniel is perhaps a mystery, but it is quite understandable that a little known pottery such as Upchurch hasn't appeared. A further related point is the vast amount of Worcester or Royal Worcester, as well as the ubiquitous Royal Doulton, Moorcroft and Clarice Cliff which is included. Regardless of their abiding presence they always manage to hold their prices. In fact the rarer appearance of certain pottery and porcelain compared to the ubiquitous appearance of others is a market statement in itself. Those considering buying pottery and porcelain should consider the investment implications of the rare or the common, or if nothing else, the storage implications of buying from a never ending market supply!

One final point. Damage has never really been desirable, particularly in the finer porcelains, except when rare. And obviously for rarer English Delft it is more or less irrelevant. But creeping into today's market is a respect for rarer pieces, whatever their condition. Witness the £1,750 (392) paid for a substantially riveted *Kangxi* vase on page 26. And there are other examples! An additional market point is the possible reappearance of certain lots in the same or a different auction at a later date and how they faired. Readers should also be on the look out for the appearance of similar items appearing in different geographical locations on similar dates which fetch almost identical prices. This shows quite clearly that, with auctions always attended by specialist dealers and collectors that the market is indeed very wise.

John Ainsley

The Editor welcomes correspondence on any aspect of this work. Please send to: The Editor, Antiques Information Services Ltd, Wallsend House, P. O. Box 93, Broadstairs, Kent CT10 3YR.

Section 1

Sample Analysis

Readers should not, as explained in the **Introduction**, consider this analysis definitive. Rather it represents the opinions of the Editor based on his own knowledge and experience. Many, many more pages than this could be written if the information provided in the following pages were to be analysed in greater depth. It is of necessity a sample only. Each reader will therefore use the information provided to construct their own analyses around their own interests and experiences.

This section, as only to be expected, is the smallest in the book covering only 134 lots. Here can be found both the extremely rare and the extremely grand. Let us begin with the grand. The reader should look for those lots whose quality is so sumptuous that they must of necessity be rare. Manufacturers at this level had to employ the very best designers, artists and gilders, in an exorbitant amount of time and effort to bring these lots to completion. Images 3, 5, 12, 38, 85 and 97 typify this level of quality. It is to be expected that famous names of artists and decorators will nearly always be present in this price range.

Continuing on the porcelain theme, when you can marry the famous William Billingsley of Pinxton fame with the currently very marketable name of Nantgarw as at 6, then the resulting £30,000 hammer price is hardly surprising. You can follow the Nantgarw trail through the **Index** but even within this section you can check out the 2003 prices of a quite undistinguished pair of Nantgarw plates at *Canterbury Auction Galleries*, which fetched a staggering £9,400 (49) and a London decorated Nantgarw plate (72) which fetched £7,500. In addition to Nantgarw it is worth analysing the prices in this section for Chelsea, Derby, Worcester, Sévres and Meissen. Frequently the value is not necessarily in the quality but rather the rarity of quite simple objects. For example see images 8, 11, 16, 50. One of the most incredible lots in this section is 46. What drives the price of the Newhall hybrid hard-paste mug is the riveting presence of the name Fidelle Duvivier!

Another fascinating lot is the Girl-in-a-Swing French hen at 122. It is the Editor's opinion that at only £5,200 hammer it has yet to reach its full potential. Here surely is an excellent investment, probably more so than the Lowestoft wash basin at 59 which fetched £8,500.

Prices can also be incredibly high for Chinese or Japanese porcelain, witness the Kakiemon tankard at 13, the famille rose hawks at 10 or 22 or the cockerels at 88. However, you would need to be an acknowledged expert to comprehend why the Chinese export tureen and stand at 27 fetched an amazing £14,000. Strides tell us that it is apparently a rare pattern!

Pâte-sur-pâte prices continue to strengthen. The process of manufacture is incredibly time-consuming and therefore extremely expensive. Two Louis Solon pieces are on page nine at 14 and 21. And see also for example, 37. Pâte-sur-pâte can be of such stunning quality and rarity. With a market now desperate to acquire such pieces it can be difficult to keep up with current values. An auction recently told us of a piece that was coming up for sale which they were estimating at £3,000-4,000. Having studied the prices for the purposes of this volume, we suggested that they at least double their expectations. The lot was eventually sold for £12,000!

At this point it is worth drawing attention to the extremely rare Wedgwood & Bentley blue jasper plaque at 2 and the black basalt figures at 52. Rarely do these particular bodies figure in this price range.

Space now demands that we turn to pottery and at this juncture it is worth noting that extensive ironstone dinner services can fetch a fortune. And they don't have to be Mason's either. At 35 the reader can view a 123-piece Hicks & Meigh service which fetched £11,000.

Nothing now exceeds the importance, in strictly market terms, of English Delft. Image 1 is really out of place or rather out of time in this volume having been sold almost ten years ago. Yet to our knowledge not a finer piece has tested the market since. The exciting thing about English Delft is that it is not always obviously valuable. For example the beaten up cat at 4, which fetched a hammer price of £45,000 despite its poor condition, is a case in point. Most people would walk past such an object, which after all is very small at only 5in high, without a second glance. Even it were noticed I doubt if most people would pay more than a pound or two. Five pounds or more and probably 99% of the population would rather spend the money on a Dinky toy or a beefburger and a cup of tea! Examples of English Delft can also be found in this section at 20, 40, 42, 56, 60, 74, 84, 89, & 110. They average about £12,000 each!

There are quite a few examples of Martin Brothers in this volume and readers can follow this up through the **Index.** However the pick of these has got to be image 9 which fetched £23,000 at *Woolley and Wallis* in Salisbury in May 2003. Incidentally it would appear that this particular bird, or one very similar, is on the move again at the same auction with an estimate of £20,000-30,000 and due to be auctioned after we have gone to press. Hopefully we will be able to report on this in a later edition. Will it fetch more or less?

Other important results in this section are, the incredible Barnstaple slipware jug illustrated at 7 which fetched £28,000, the high price paid for a 1918 Pilkington Lancastrian vase by Richard Joyce shown at 68, a creamware Toby at 81 which fetched £6,500, and a further creamware cricketing item which fetched £5,200 and is illustrated at 121. It is also worth mentioning the Staffordshire rabbits at 86 and leopards at 129. For many of us, one piece of Staffordshire is much like another, but then we ourselves would be the 'rabbits' if we were to allow ourselves to harbour such thoughts! As we pass on through the spectacular let us spare a thought for the more ubiquitous names which never-the-less grace the auctions scene. Do not therefore overlook the world record price of £19,000 (15) paid for a pair of Moorcroft Florian vases or on the same page a Royal Doulton character jug at £16,000. In addition there is another piece of Moorcroft at 58 which fetched £8,500 and there are several other Royal Doulton character jugs to be found in this section. You can expect and therefore not be surprised to note that Clarice Cliff also makes an appearance.

This analysis would not be complete without a mention of majolica. Be it Minton, George Jones or Wedgwood, this section can boast well over a dozen lots which have fetched between £5,000 and £11,500. The demand, particularly in the USA remains insatiable for a ceramic type, which ten years ago you could hardly give away. I wonder, will there be a new 'majolica' in the next decade?

Two Goldscheider figures appear here, a life-size terracotta black youth at 41 by Haniroff which fetched £10,000 and a life-size negro boy at 123, with restorations at £5,200. However, perhaps the most surprising is the £5,500 paid for a 1969 Guy Sydenham, Atlantis Range Poole Pottery lamp base at 105. Will this be a good investment? Who knows?

Hammer Prices £240,000-£15,000

Phillips, London. London Delftware marriage dish with a nativity scene, dated 1638 in two places,reverse with potter's initials R.I. and bride and grooms initials, 41.5cm dia. £240,000. June 94.

Sotheby's, Billingshurst. Fine set of 6 Wedgwood & Bentley blue jasper 'Herculaneum' oval plaques, c1778, overall 12in. £61,000. Sep 99.

Hy. Duke & Son, Dorchester. A suite 5 Royal Crown Derby vases, painted with flowers by Leroy. £58,000. Sep 01.

Halls Fine Art, Shrewsbury. A rare Delft tin glazed earthenware cat, 17thC, 5in high. £45,000. Mar 03.

Mellors & Kirk, Nottingham. Pair of Derby ice pails, covers and liners, painted with views, impressed 2E, painted crown, crossed batons, D, 299 and script titles in blue, exhibition labels, 24cm, c1797-1800. £32,000. Apr 03.

Woolley & Wallis, Salisbury. Fine and rare Welsh porcelain campana vase, painted by William Billingsley, marked 'NANTGARRW' painted in red, c1813-23, 27.5cm. £30,000. Nov 02.

Bonhams, London. Barnstaple slipware jug by Thomas Fields, dated 1757. £28,000. June 03.

Hy. Duke & Son, Dorchester. Very rare and early Worcester mug decorated with exotic birds amongst foliage in polychrome in the Imari manner, 3.25in high. £26,000. Sep 02.

Woolley & Wallis, Salisbury. Large and impressive Martin Brothers bird, ebonised wood base, neck with brass reinforcer, incised R W Martin & Brothers, London & Southall ll 1900, 37cm high. £25,000. May 03.

Phillips, Scotland. Pair of Chinese Famille Rose Hawks, 25.3cm. £25,000. June 00.

Bristol Auction Rooms, Bristol. First period Worcester pair of gugglets, c1753-55, blue painted in 'The Lange Lijzen' pattern, 24cm, one with rim chips. £24,000. July 03.

Woolley & Wallis, Salisbury. Fine Flight Barr and Barr solitaire set painted with scenes from the works of Shakespeare, every scene titled, mark 'Flight Barr & Barr Royal Porcelain Works, Worcester'. 'London House, 1 Coventry Street' painted in script, cup, saucer and tray impressed marks, paper labels for Albert Amor, c1820-30. £23,000. Feb 03.

Woolley & Wallis, Salisbury. Japanese Kakiemon tankard of European form, moulded with panels of dragons and chrysanthemum on unglazed 'fish roe' ground, karakusa scroll to the handle, c1670, 14cm. £21,000 May 01.

Richard Wintertons, Burton on Trent. A pair of Mintons pate sur pate plaques signed L. Solon (18(80), in period gilt Florentine frames, 17 x 15cm. £20,000. Sep 01.

Prices quoted are actual hammer prices which excluded the buyer's premium. Adding 15% will give an approximation to the buying price.

Gorringes, Lewes. Pair of early Moorcroft florian vases with Japanese carp amidst underwater foliage, 11.75in. £19,000. Oct 99.

Woolley & Wallis, Salisbury. Pair of Derby models of wild boars, bases applied with flowers and enamelled details, c1755, 16.5cm wide, bases with stencilled marks 'Bt. at Dr. Wake Smarts Sale, April 1895, Lot 103, Chelsea China'. £19,000. May 01.

Woolley & Wallis, Salisbury. Pair of Sevres biscuit figures of Cupid and Psyche, after models by Falconet, marked with incised 'F', bases with blue crossed 'L's enclosing 'K' for 1763 and above a 'P'. £16,500. June 00.

Phillips, London. Doulton. Baseball player. A prototype character jug, D6624, by David Biggs, c1970, 21cm. £16,000. Nov 99.

Bonhams, London. Pair of Chamberlain shell painted ice pails, covers and liners, c1810. £16,000. June 03.

Bonhams, London. A fine London Delft pill slab, c1700. £16,000. June 03.

Bonham's, London. A monumental Minton Pâte-sur-pâte Vase by Louis Solon, c1899, entitled 'The Idol Seller'. £15,000. July 02.

9

Hammer Prices £15,000-£9,800

Tring Market Auctions, Herts. Pair of 18thC Chinese figures of hawks, very af, 10.5in high. £15,000. Jan 03.

Woolley & Wallis, Salisbury. Chelsea figure of Bajazzoo, from the Commedia dell' Arte series after Meissen original, c1755, red anchor mark, 16cm. £15,000. Sep 01.

Sotheby's, Billingshurst. Pair of Chinese moulded yellow 'mallow flower' dishes marks and period of zonzheng. £14,000. Sep 99.

Henry Duke & Son, Dorchester. Meissen 'Tulip' tea and coffee service, late 1750s. £14,000. Jan 02.

Bearne's, Exeter. Pr Chelsea Chinese pheasants, probably workshop Wm Duesbury, red anchor marks, c1750-52, 21cm damaged, £14,000. July 03.

Stride & Son, Chichester. Chinese export tureen and stand. £14,000. Feb 03.

Woolley & Wallis, Salisbury. Blue printed Spode from Bill Coles collection, many rare patterns. £13,000. Mar 00.

Gorringes, Lewes. Pair of Canton floor vases, Kuang Hsu, shishi lug handles and applied dragons, 4ft 6in high. £13,000. May 03.

Sworder & Sons, Stansted Mountfitchet. A pair of gilt bronze mounted porcelain vases, probably French, late 19thC, formed as two carp, 17in. £12,600. Mar 01.

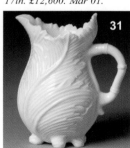

Bonhams, London. A Chelsea milk jug, c1745-49. £12,500. June 03.

Woolley & Wallis, Salisbury. Pair Meissen pagoda figures, gilded details, crossed swords and incised marks, second half 19thC, 31.5cm high, 32cm wide. £12,200. June 00.

Sotheby's, London. Minton majolica garden seat, circa 1867. £11,500. July 02.

Woolley & Wallis, Salisbury. Fine Coalport dessert service, richly gilded, painted with sprays of flowers, fruit, gilt borders with 'C' scrolls, c1820-25. (41) £11,500. Nov 01.

Sotheby's, Billingshurst. Hicks and Meigh ironstone extensive dinner service, c1815-22, comprising 123 pieces. £11,000. Nov 00.

Clarke Gammon, Guildford. Victorian majolica pottery jardiniere on stand, 44.25in high. (Probably by George Jones) £11,000. June 00.

Bonham's, London. A French pâte-sur-pate plaque by Louis Solon dated 1869. £11,000. July 02.

Sotheby's, Billingshurst. A fine pair of Worcester Flight, Barr & Barr candlesticks, c1820, 6.5in high. £10,500. Jan 01.

Phillips, London. Doulton George Washington by Stan Taylor, D6669, 19cm. (special certificate) £10,500. Nov 99.

Sotheby's, Billingshurst. Rare Delftware 'Fazackerly' palette puzzle jug, Bristol or Liverpool, c1760, 20cm. £10,000. Nov 00.

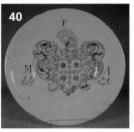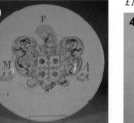

Woolley & Wallis, Salisbury. Rare early English Delft armorial plate dated 1653, painted in blue, yellow and ochre with the initial letters P, M & A, 1653, 22.5cm. £10,200. Nov 01.

Phillips, London. Doulton. Baseball player. A prototype character jug, D6624 by David Biggs, c 1970, 18cm. £10,000. Nov 99.

Stride & Son, Chichester. Pr Chinese Export plates, with image of Table Mountain, South Africa with Dutch flagged ships off coast, 23cm. £9,800. May 01.

Bristol Auction Rooms, Bristol. A Goldscheider large terracotta figure of a black youth, stamped marks, No. 1419/148/12 and signed 'Haniroff' (?), 125cm. £10,000. Sep 02.

Bonhams, London. English Delft Queen Caroline commemorative plate, dated 1738. £9,800. June 03.

Trembath Welch, Gt Dunmow. A c1790 Newhall mug by Fidelle Duvivier, labels to underside, chip to rim, 14cm high. £9,500. July 03.

Mellors & Kirk, Nottingham. Worcester Flight, Barr & Barr campana vase, c1820. £9,500. Dec 02.

Bonhams, London. Minton majolica cabaret service, dates 1873 and 1874. £9,500. June 03.

Canterbury Auction Galleries, Kent. Pair Nantgarw oval plates, probably by Thomas Pardoe, 10 x 14.25in, c1820. £9,400. Aug 03.

Woolley & Wallis, Salisbury. Worcester blue and white jug, 'scratch cross' type, (minute chip) c1755, rare birds to the reverse. £9,200. Dec 99.

Phillips, London. Doulton. George Washington by Stan Taylor, 19cm. (special certificate) £9,000. Nov 99.

Woolley & Wallis, Salisbury. A rare and finely modelled pair of black basalt figures of Lord Rodney and Admiral Hood, each incised 'Stephen F', 30.5cm, probably early 19thC. £9,000. Dec 99.

Hogben Auctioneers, Folkestone. Clarice Cliff Persian pattern inspiration wall plate. £8,900. Feb 01.

Woolley & Wallis, Salisbury. Large pair of Chinese famille rose quatrelobed vases and covers with dog of Fo knops and animal mask lifts, Qianlong 1736-95, 65.5cm. (Body cracks) £8,800. Nov 02.

Woolley & Wallis, Salisbury. William De Morgan Persian tile panel each three tile frieze depicting a peacock above a vase of flowers, in later wood frame, 61cm high. (One tile cracked and museum restored, minor chips. £8,600. May 03.

Sotheby's, Billingshurst. A dated delftware punch bowl, possibly Liverpool, 1775, inscribed 'Drive on my Jolly Fellows, the season is begun, God send a Plentous Harvest, with the approaching Sun, March 17th 1775, James Duke'. £8,500. June 00.

Hamptons, Godalming. Pair famille rose bowls, Yongzheng period. £8,500. Sep 00.

Sotheby's, Billingshurst. Claremont, a large Moorcroft flambe vase, 1928, blue painted signature and date, impressed 'Made in England', 12in high. £8,500. Mar 01.

Bonhams, London. Early Lowestoft wash basin, c1759-60 . £8,500. June 03.

Phillips, London. Liverpool Delft mug, printed by Sadler, c1762. £8,200. Feb 01.

Wintertons Ltd, Lichfield. Rare pair of Derby chocolate cups and covers and one stand, c1794, each enamelled with oval black on moonlight titled scenes, blue crown cross batons mark and no. 231, 11.5cm high. £8,000. May 03.

Hogben Auctioneers, Folkestone. One of a pair of fine Berlin 19thC vases, 36in high. £8,000. Feb 01.

Bonhams, London. Royal Worcester ewer by George Owen and Harry Chair, c1909. £8,000. June 03.

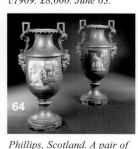

Phillips, Scotland. A pair of very large ormolu mounted Sevres style vases, 94cm high. £7,800. June 01.

Woolley & Wallis, Salisbury. Large Minton majolica model of a grey heron, modelled by Paul Comolera, 'P. Comolera' moulded to the base, 1917 and Minton impressed, date cipher for 1876, 100cm. (Minor damages) £7,800. Sep 01.

Prices quoted are actual hammer prices which excluded the buyer's premium. Adding 15% will give an approximation to the buying price. Illustrations are in price order.

Tring Market Auctions, Herts. A Minton majolica water fountain in the form of two putti with a dolphin, impressed 'MINTON', 26in high, af. small restoration. £7,800. May 02.

Phillips, Scotland. One of a pair of George Jones majolica comports, modelled as an oak tree with animals around the base. £7,700.

11

Hammer Prices £7,600-£6,200

Woolley & Wallis, Salisbury. Pilkington Lancastrian vase by Richard Joyce, in copper lustre with Toucans amongst pomegranates and foliage on a ruby lustre ground, painted artist cypher datemark 1918, impressed mark, 32cm high. £7,600. May 03.

Woolley & Wallis, Salisbury. Rare Staffordshire creamware equestrian group of Hudibras, of Ralph Wood type, c1780, modelled astride a brown glazed horse, 28cm high. £7,600. Nov 02.

Sotheby's, Billingshurst. Large Mintons majolica flower holder, after A. Carrier Belleuse, modelled as a classical woman in brown robes reading a book, impressed marks, c1873. £7,500. Apr 00.

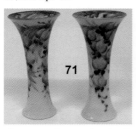

Gorringes, Lewes. A pair of Moorcroft Macintyre pale pink and mauve wisteria vases with flared rims, 7in. £7,500. Dec 00.

Woolley & Wallis, Salisbury. London decorated Nantgarw plate, centre painted with four doves, 'C' scroll and foliate border, painted with sprays of pink roses on a gold seeded ground, 'Nantgarw CW' impressed, c1814-23, 25cm. £7,500. Nov 01.

Gorringes, Lewes. Harlequin set of 11 late 19thC and early 20thC Meissen monkey band figures, all dressed in brightly coloured costumes on gilded rococo bases, including harpsichord and cello players, largest 5.75in, smallest 4.75in. (some with minor damage) £7,100. Feb 01.

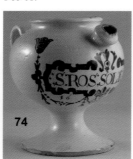

Woolley & Wallis, Salisbury. Good Lambeth Delft wet drug jar dated 1679, body inscribed below the spout 'S: Ros: Sol:-Cv: Ag' within a baroque cartouche and above initials 'A-G' and the date 1679, flared foot, 28cm. £7,000. Feb 03.

Canterbury Auction Galleries, Kent. Minton majolica two handled tureen and cover with a foot-long 'lobster' on top, dates from June 1870, 13.5in overall. £7,000. Nov 99.

Sotheby's, London. A good pair of Worcester Barr, Flight and Barr jardinieres, circa 1810. £6,800. July 02.

Woolley & Wallis, Salisbury. c1755 Chelsea figure of Scaramouche, from the Commedia dell'Arte series after Meissen, red anchor mk. 14.5cm. £6,800. Sep 01.

Prices quoted are actual hammer prices which excluded the buyer's premium. Adding 15% will give an approximation to the buying price.

Sworder & Sons, Stansted Mountfitchet. A Chelsea red anchor plate, 7.5in. £6,600.

Bearne's, Exeter. William de Morgan six tile panel, each tile 15cm square, impressed mark, 'DM Merton Abbey', c1885, odd minor flake at margins. £6,600. July 03.

Sotheby's, London. Wedgwood majolica oval game pie dish cover, c1882. £6,500. July 02.

Sotheby's, Billingshurst. Staffs creamware, Wood type 'Prince Hal' Toby jug, early 19thC, 39.5cm. £6,500. Nov 00.

Woolley & Wallis, Salisbury. Pair of Staffordshire models of lions, recumbent on bases with Pratt colours, late 18thC, 21.5cm. (one with small chip and fire cracks to base) £6,400. Nov 02.

Hy. Duke & Son, Dorchester. 18thC Caughley miniature tea and coffee service with chinoiserie scenes, 'S' mark. £6,400. Sep 02.

Cheffins, Cambridge. 18thC Delft plate, 'Success to the John & Mary, John Spencer', 23cm dia. £6,400. Apr 03.

Sotheby's, Billingshurst A pair of Staffordshire pottery rabbits, c1870, each modelled munching at green lettuce leaves. £6,200. June 00.

Woolley & Wallis, Salisbury. Delftware blue and white two handled vase, painted with cattle, houses and haystacks, mid 18thC, 21cm high. (rim chip, scroll to one handle lacking and an 11cm hairline) £6,200. May 03.

Woolley & Wallis, Salisbury. Pair of Chinese porcelain models of cockerels, rockwork bases with a blue glaze, Qianlong, c1760, 39cm. £6,200. Nov 02.

Sotheby's, Billingshurst. A rare Delftware polychrome sparrow beak jug, probably London, c1765. £6,200. Sep 00.

Bearne's, Exeter. Worcester Barr, Flight and Barr part tea and coffee service: teapot, cover and stand, milk jug, sugar bowl, 2 plates, 11 cups, 11 saucers and 4 coffee cans each painted with 'Fancy Birds', and insects in the manner of 'Doctor' George Davis, impressed BFB and crown, c1810, together with 7 matching Spode coffee cans, c1815. £6,200. July 03.

90

Gorringes, Lewes. Victorian Minton majolica fox and heron group, inspired by Aesop's fable, 8.25in. (some damage & repair). £6,200. June 03.

91

Louis Taylor, Stoke on Trent. Royal Doulton, 'Bluebeard' HN410, Introduced 1920 withdrawn 1936, by Ernest Light. £6,000. June 03.

92

Louis Taylor, Stoke on Trent. Royal Doulton. The swimmer HN 1270, designer L. H., intro 1928, withdrawn 1938. £6,000. Dec 00.

93

Woolley & Wallis, Salisbury. A rare Worcester teapot and cover, transfer printed in brick red with 'The Fishing Party' to one side and 'The Singing Lesson' to the reverse, c1755-60. 14.5cm long. £6,000. Mar 00.

94

Cheffins, Cambridge. 19thC George Jones majolica cheese dish/cover, impressed marks and numbered 5204, 31.5cm high. £5,800. Feb 00.

95

Sotheby's, Billingshurst. Mason's ironstone dinner service, c1820. Painted in underglaze blue, iron-red, green, pink and gilding with a central floral spray within a conforming border with stylised flowerhead edge. £5,800. Nov 99.

96

Gorringes, Lewes. George Jones majolica jardiniere, PODR for 1876 and numbered 3499 and 30, 14in. £5,800. Sep 00.

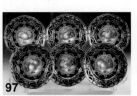

97

Sotheby's, Billingshurst. Set of six Royal Worcester plates, c1921, each painted in the centre by Richard Sebright, 22cm. £5,800. June 01.

98

Louis Taylor, Stoke on Trent. A set of six porcelain plaques by J E Dean, painted with cockfighting scenes, each signed, 4.75 x 6.5in. £5,800. June 03.

99

Sotheby's, Billingshurst. Charles Vyse pottery group, c1929, incised C.Vyse Chelsea 1929, 12.25in high, ebonised wood base. £5,800. Mar 00.

100

D M Nesbit & Company, Southsea. Clarice Cliff 'Blue Firs' Lotus jug. £5,800. July 00.

101

Dreweatt Neate, Newbury. Swansea porcelain 'London' shape part tea service, pattern No. 411, printed iron-red mark, iron-red pattern no., c1818. (slight damage) (54) £5,800. Nov 01.

The numbering system aids the editorial analysis as well as providing a reader reference

Hammer Prices £6,200-£5,500

102

Woolley & Wallis, Salisbury. Chelsea figure of Mezzetino, from the Commedia dell' Arte series after a Meissen original, c1755, 15.2cm. £5,600. Sep 01.

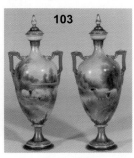

103

Andrew Hartley, Ilkley. Pair of Royal Worcester porcelain vases and covers by Harry Davis, shape No H/247, 10in high. £5,600. Oct 01.

104

Sotheby's, London. A George Jones majolica 'Punch' bowl, c1875. £5,500. July 02.

105

Sotheby's, Billingshurst. Rare Atlantis range Poole Pottery stoneware lamp base, post 1969, Guy Sydenham, monogrammed, impressed and incised mark, 28.25in high. £5,500. Mar 01.

106

Hamptons, Godalming. A pair of still life painted porcelain plaques, by Le Bel. £5,500. Apr 03.

107

Phillips, London. Doulton. The Marriage of Art and Industry, by Peggy Davies, No 6 of 12. Produced 1958 for the Brussels Exhibition, decorated in a special matt green glaze developed for this piece. £5,500. Nov 99.

108

Gorringes, Lewes. Pair of 19thC Sevres porcelain and ormolu mounted vases and covers with fete gallant and riverscape panels, one indistinctly signed Bestrey, 31in. £5,500. June 00.

109

Sworder & Sons, Stansted Mountfitchet.Four 16th/Early 17thC Venetian albarelli, enamel coats of arms and inscribed 'Dia-Sebestens, Hyerae-copos, Adipis-Eqvi, Locd-Sqville' substantial chips 7.25in. £5,500. Feb 02.

110

Cheffins, Cambridge. Ten dated Delft plates, initialled W over IE and 1700, crowned cartouches supported by griffins, 22.5cm. (2 damaged) £5,500. Apr 03.

Hammer Prices £5,400-£5,000

111

Woolley & Wallis, Salisbury. 2 Royal Worcester plaques, one with a basket of fruit, signed Sebright, the other a bowl of flowers and glass of wine, signed E. Phillips, pink marks, c1913, 10cm. in gilt frames. £5,400. Feb 03.

112

Bearne's, Exeter. Worcester Flight, Barr & Barr, pedestal jar and cover, applied bands with pearls, probably by John Barker, 23.5cm, impressed and script marks, c1815. (repair) £5,400. July 03.

113

Woolley & Wallis, Salisbury. A large pair of Chinese Canton famille rose baluster vases and covers, mid 19thC, (one lid with small re-glued chip, one vase with rim chip and hair crack, 62cm high. (4) £5,400. June 00.

114

Sotheby's, Billingshurst, West Sussex. Clarice Cliff Isis vase, c1930-1934, Red Autumn (Balloon Trees), 10in high. £5,400. Oct 00.

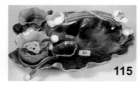

115

Thos Mawer & Son, Lincoln. George Jones, majolica strawberry dish as a lily leaf, cream jug and sugar basin, sifter spoon, leaf serving spoon to dish. £5,400. Apr 02.

116

Sotheby's, London. A Royal Worcester two-handled potpourri vase and cover, circa 1926. £5,200. July 02.

117

Woolley & Wallis, Salisbury. Belleek armorial tea service of 'Echinus' design, as sea urchins and coral, tray with crest and motto 'Per Mare Per Teras' for Alexander fam. of Co. Armagh, first period marks. (10) £5,200. Sep 02.

118

Hamptons, Godalming. Pair of very large Meissen figures of a gallant and his lady, mid 19thC. £5,200. July 00.

119

Louis Taylor, Stoke. Royal Doulton.Windmill lady, no No. should be HN 1400, designer L.H., intro 1930, withdrawn 1937. £5,200. Dec 00.

120

Woolley & Wallis, Salisbury. Large Safavid pottery dish, decorated in Kraak style in blue with black outlines, seal mark, c17thC, 43.5cm. (Hair cracks) £5,200. Sep 01.

121

Woolley & Wallis, Salisbury. Rare creamware cricketing and racing jug, printed with a view of a cricket match and the reverse with a view of the Oatland Stakes at Ascot, makers Fletcher & Co. Shelton, c1795, 17.7cm. (Some staining and old restoration) £5,200. Sep 02.

122

Dreweatt Neate, Newbury. 'Girl in a Swing' gilt metal mounted bonbonniere and hinged cover, French hen sitting on her brood, 5cm. 1749-54. £5,200. June 03.

123

Gorringes, Lewes. Goldscheider figure of negro boy, signed and entitled 'Checo', 4ft 7.5in. (one toe and one finger restored, two chips to jacket, minor paint flaking) £5,200. June 03.

124

Sotheby's, Billingshurst. George Jones majolica 'Punch' bowl, c1875, shape 3468, moulded reg. lozenge, 28.5cm wide. (repair to hat, head of Punch, small chip to one foot) £5,100. June 01.

125

Dreweatt Neate, Newbury. Minton majolica oyster stand with 4 tapering tiers of oyster shells, finial with 3 fish and an eel, mounted to revolve on foot with rim, 27cm high, c1865, unmarked. (rim chips) £5,000. June 03.

126

Phillips, London. A Bristol teapot and cover, c1772-76. £5,000. Feb 01.

127

Phillips, Scotland. A pair of Sevres gilt metal mounted vase & covers, 49.5cm. £5,000. Nov 99.

128

Sotheby's, London. Very rare Minton's majolica squirrel vase, c1877. £5,000. July 02.

129

Stride & Son, Chichester. Pair of Staffordshire pottery leopards. £5,000. June 00.

130

Woolley & Wallis, Salisbury. Pair of Chinese blue and white Fitzhugh pattern ice pails and covers, each with crest for Larken, c1800, 23cm high. £5,000. June 00.

131

Clevedon Salerooms, Bristol. 19thC Meissen porcelain Pagoda nodding figure. £5,000. Sep 00.

132

Gorringes, Lewes. Minton majolica crab dish/cover, 16in. (dish damaged and repaired) £5,000. May 03.

133

Phillips, Scotland. A pair of 19thC Austrian pottery deer, 120cm high. £5,000. Sep 99.

134

Louis Taylor, Stoke. Royal Doulton Grotesque bird jar and cover by C. Noke. £5,000. Dec 01.

Sample Analysis

It will be useful to commence this section by once again following a porcelain theme as there are some notable lots. Firstly, witness the pair of Bow recumbent lions at 137. These are almost certainly unmarked and could turn up almost anywhere. Only the experts who have studied the eighteenth century soft-paste porcelains or the auctions who are familiar with handling such lots are likely to appreciate their significance. Whilst £4,800 is a lot if money it is important to note that this is a pair and it is likely that they will prove to be a good investment, or if the buyer was a dealer, show a significant profit. Staying over £4,000 in this section are examples of Minton, Spode and even Copeland, although the latter only achieves a hammer price of £4,400 because it is a 64-piece service. See 151, 159 and 160. Actually the three Spode garden pots at 160 with a hammer price of £4,200 is quite a surprise. Continuing through the section, it is noteworthy that half a dozen Royal Crown Derby coffee cans and saucers (162) fetched a staggering £4,200 hammer, whilst dating from only 1934. And at 224 yet another set from 1939 fetched an incredible £3,200. The point is clear. Quality, subject and one must assume rarity is more important than age. Note also that porcelain does not have to be grand to fetch a small fortune. The first period Worcester creamboat at 216 or the Bow plate at 218 and the Worcester mug at 275 serve as examples. For the porcelain enthusiast there is much to study in these pages.

In case there is any doubt, those readers who would perhaps consider themselves beginners in the study of ceramics should understand that pottery prices across the market usually outdo those of porcelain. I recall many years ago, following the tragic and early death of the well-known Davenport collector, Trixie Iwass, that when her entire collection came to auction, it wasn't the porcelains, although some of those pieces were extremely rare, but rather the creamwares and pearl-wares, the coloured bodied earthenwares, the black basalts, the canewares and the terracottas which fetched the best prices.

Let us now turn our attention to pottery. Never under-estimate the appeal of terracotta, witness the pair of Austrian figures at 135, which brought £4,800 hammer at Gorringes, Lewes, three years ago. Other lots of special interest are the Fremington bowl at 139 and the spectacular yellow-glazed pottery West Country jug at 158, weighing in at £4,200. Other surprising heavyweights perhaps are the Liverpool printed creamware jug at 248 and the Iznik (Turkish) late sixteenth century pottery dish at 252. Readers should also be aware that the days are long gone when slipware such as that at 317 could be had for a few hundred pounds and nineteenth century examples for £30 or £40. It took £2,300 to net this very simple eighteenth century combed slipware bowl. Incidentally, the clay cribbage board at 153 was an absolute surprise at £4,300 and surely one of the rarest and most desirable of simple pottery objects ever to appear in recent years and certainly the only ceramic object ever to have been described simply as clay!

Let us now trawl through the section for items that have caught the editor's eye. Remember we are only embracing a sample analysis. Hundreds of pages of analytical text covering every illustration in this section could be written if one had the knowledge to comment on all of the lots shown. Consider the English Delft in this section say at 136, 200, 265 and 324. They might be compared with the extremely high priced English Delft in Section One. Or they might be compared with all of the tin-glazed earthenwares appearing in this volume. We worked out an average cost for the English Delft in Section One at £12,000. It is possible, using the *Index* to find a useful average cost for Delft at auction during the last few years.

Remember the pair of Staffordshire pottery rabbits at 86 in Section One which fetched £6,200? Here are yet another pair of nineteenth century Staffordshire rabbits which fetched £4,700. (140) One should also take note of 145, a record for blue and white. This well-and-tree meat dish, the Durham Ox, fetched £4,600 at Dreweatt Neate in Newbury back in 2000. This record has certainly been broken since as we know of a nineteenth century Spode pot pourri which sold for £5,000 at Clevedon Salerooms, Bristol in September 2003.

Wemyss cats are always pricey and £4,000 hammer at 176 or £2,800 hammer at 249 are cases in point. The blue and white Caughley mask jug at 214, (porcelain £3,300) is quite a surprise. I remember these fetching under a hundred pounds twenty years ago so they have proved a sound investment. Italian maiolica does not often figure in this price range but see 320 and 325. Rarely now do even single albarelli even in the very worst of condition, go for less than £500. Check out albarelli in general through the *Index*.

You must expect majolica in this price range. There are at least twenty five pieces in these pages, ranging from £4,600 to £2,100 hammer. Majolica has seen perhaps the greatest market movement of any ceramic type in the last ten years. And the interest shows no sign of abating. The question is however, when will it peak?

Look also at these quite surprising pieces. A Lenci pottery figure which fetched £4,700 hammer at Wintertons in Lichfield in 2001, see 138: a Clarice Cliff Isis jug, football pattern £4,600 in 1999, (143): a Ruskin sang de boeuf bottle vase, dated 1924, £4,400. (152): a Moorcroft Lustre Prunus Blossom vase (161) at Canterbury Auction Galleries in 2002 which fetched £4,200 and a Chinese eighteenth century famille rose pillow at £4,000, (168) even though damaged.

Then there was the astonishing Chinese armorial soup tureen and stand (171) at Stride & Sons, Chichester in July 2003 which also fetched £4,000 and the same price was paid for only four Liverpool Delft wood block tiles (172) which also fetched £4,000 hammer at Phillips in London in 2001.

Martinware rarely fetches less than a small fortune nowadays. You can study quite a number of pieces in this volume. Remember the £25,000 bird on page 9? See also here the double-sided smiling grotesque faced jug at 181, which fetched £3,800 more than three years ago and which should certainly well exceed this figure if it were to reappear in the market in 2004. It seems almost hair-brained that a Moorcroft *Harebell* florian vase with crack should fetch £3,800 but it did at 186. And it also seems quite surprising that a Staffordshire goat should fetch £2,400 at 294. But it was, after all, by Ralph Wood.

In this section look out for Wedgwood Fairyland Lustre. There are quite a few examples. Chase them up through the *Index*. And do not forget to check out the ubiquitous Royal Doulton. In this section there must be well over a dozen examples starting with *The Mask*, c1924 at £3,800 through to *The Princess of Wales* by Eric Griffiths at £2,185.

Incidentally, whilst you are browsing this section it is worth taking a look at the William de Morgan lots at 237, 308, 314 and 347.

Hammer Prices £4,800-£4,200

Gorringes, Lewes. Pair 19thC Austrian cold painted terracotta figures, Arab warrior & companion. £4,800. June 00.

Hamptons, Godalming. Rare English delft (attributed to Brislington) punch bowl, 1680-90, 'China men in grasses', 34cm. £4,800. Mar 02.

Mellors & Kirk, Nottingham. Pair of Bow recumbent lions, 8cm high, 1753-55. (one with small chip) £4,800. Apr 03.

Wintertons, Lichfield. Lenci pottery figure, 'Lenci' mark in reverse impressed to base, a.f. 15.75in. £4,700. May 01.

Cheffins, Cambridge. Pair of mid 19thC Staffs rabbits, 22cm wide. £4,700. Feb 02.

Hamptons, Godalming. Stilton majolica dish/cover, George Jones, c1870. £4,600. July 03.

Wintertons, Lichfield. Pair of Worcester Flight Barr & Barr vases, c1810, script London Warehouse, 1 Coventry Street, impressed FBB crown mark, 17cm high. (slight chip to base). £4,600. July 03.

Gorringes, Bexhill. Clarice Cliff Bizarre Isis jug, football pattern. £4,600. Oct 99.

Sworders, Stansted Mountfitchet. Majolica cheese dish, George Jones. £4,600. Feb 00.

Dreweatt Neate, Newbury. Well-and-Tree meat dish, the Durham ox. A record beast from the early 19thC. £4,600. July 00.

Great Western Auctions, Glasgow. Carlton Fairy vase. 23cm high. £4,600. Feb 00.

Halls, Shrewsbury. Set of ten Toby jugs, Allied Commanders 1st World War, Wilkinson Ltd, Royal Staffordshire Potteries. £4,500. Mar 03.

Diamond Mills & Co, Felixstowe. Pair of late 19thC porcelain vases, pierced panels with vase shaped vignettes of Chinese figures, 14.75in. £4,500. Oct 01.

Sotheby's, London. A large English ironstone vase, circa 1820-30. £4,500. July 02.

Andrew Hartley, Ilkley. Pair Sevres porcelain & gilt metal vases, the body painted with a roundel depicting Napoleon and troops, signed Lancry, early 20thC, vase 20in high. £4,400. Aug 01.

Gorringes, Lewes. Copeland 64 piece part tea, dinner and coffee service with various hunting scenes after Lionel Edwards, incl. 2 tureens, 5 meat plates. £4,400. Dec 00.

Gorringes, Lewes. Ruskin sang de bouef vase,15in, dated 1924, £4,400. Feb 01.

Clevedon Salerooms, Bristol. Clay cribbage board, 8in long, damage to underside, impressed Betsey Cuppells 1780. £4,300. Feb 02.

Sotheby's, Billingshurst. Pair Minton majolica sweetmeat stands c1870, as three agate shells issuing from bearded masks with cherub, 11.75in. £4,200. July 99.

Eastbourne Auction Rooms, Sussex. Majolica crab dish and cover. (some damage) £4,200. Dec 2001.

Bearne's, Exeter. Pair of Barr, Flight & Barr, Worcester spill vases, beak ring handles, views of St Dennis Priory, Hants and Nunnery Castle, Somerset, 9cm high, impressed and painted marks, c1815. £4,200. July 03.

Sworder & Sons, Stansted Mountfitchet. A pair of 19thC French porcelain vases. £4,200. Nov 00.

Andrew Hartley, Ilkley. 19thC West Country, yellow glazed pottery jug, inscribed with verses of friendship and goodwill, dedicated to Mrs Ann Gammond Hollowill, 1868 from Thos. Bear, 11in high. £4,200. Aug 03.

Hamptons, Marlborough. Pair of 19thC Minton vases. £4,200. Nov 99.

Mellors & Kirk, Nottingham. A fine Spode garniture of three garden pots and stands. £4,200. Feb 03.

Canterbury Auction Galleries, Kent. Moorcroft lustre pottery vase, 16.5in, in green/blue/pink with Prunus blossoms on buff ground. £4,200. June 02.

Bearne's, Exeter. Fremington bowl/cover, 27cm, impressed, incised dates 1770 and 1855, firing cracks and minor flakes. £4,700. July 03.

162

Wintertons, Lichfield. Royal Crown Derby animal coffee set, date code for 1934, by C Gresley, red printed mark, each piece signed, pattern no. A292/3/4. £4,200. Jan 03.

163

Bearne's, Exeter. Worcester box/cover in the manner of George Owen, 8cm, puce backstamp and datecode for 1903. £4,100. July 03.

Prices quoted are hammer prices which excluded the buyer's premium. Adding 15% will give an approximation to the buying price.

164

Eastbourne Auction Rooms. George Jones majolica tazza, 4in. (damage) £4,100. Dec 01.

165

Gorringes, Lewes. Pair of early 19thC Ironstone vases/ covers, possibly Masons, ball knops and wolf masks, 22in. (restoration) £4,100. Dec 01.

166

Phillips, London. Worcester mug by James Ross, c1770-75. £4,100. Feb 01.

167

Rupert Toovey, Washington, Sussex. Wedgwood Fairyland lustre Picnic by a River pattern porcelain plaque, 11 x 25.2cm. £4,000. Sep 02.

168

Woolley & Wallis, Salisbury. Chinese famille rose pillow, modelled as a smiling boy kneeling with elbows on the ground, 18thC, 43cm long. (damage) £4,000. June 00.

169

Cheffins, Cambridge. 19thC George Jones majolica game dish, impressed marks, pattern 2628, 26cm. £4,000. Feb 01.

170

Phillips, London. Wedgwood, Liverpool-printed creamware Royal Commemorative teapot /cover, c1761. £4,000. Feb 01.

171

Stride & Son, Chichester. Chinese armorial soup tureen, 35cm, and stand, 39cm, crest of three suns, Pierson family. £4,000. July 03.

172

Phillips, London. Four rare Liverpool Delft wood block tiles, c1756-7. £4,000. Feb 01.

173

Wintertons, Lichfield. Set 4 Meissen figures, of the four Continents, Africa, America, Europe and Asia, c1870-80, 26-32cm. £4,000. May 02.

174

Gorringes, Lewes. 18thC group of a lady immortal on naturalistic base with a deer, 10in. £4,000. Apr 01.

175

Sotheby's, Billingshurst. 96 piece Derby pt dinner service, c1795, patt. 32, Angoulême flower sprigs. £4,000. Apr 01.

176

Amersham Auctions, Bucks. Wemyss pottery cat, green inscription to base, 12.75in. £4,000. Oct 02.

177

Canterbury Auc. Galleries, Kent. 19thC Minton majolica heron and fish pattern ewer. £4,000. Apr 03.

178

Rupert Toovey, Washington, Sussex. Wedgwood Fairyland lustre Sycamore Tree pattern porcelain vase and cover, 25cm high. £4,000. Dec 02.

179

Potteries Specialist Auctions, Stoke. R. Worcester, By a Short Head. £3,900. Mar 03.

180

Gorringes, Lewes. Minton majolica game dish, cover with gun dog, hare and bird panels, impressed mark and numbered 96L, date code for 1864, 12.5in. £3,900. Sep 00.

181

Gorringes, Lewes. Martinware jug with double sided smiling grotesque face, date 10-1890 and marked R W Martin & Bros, London & Southall, 7in. £3,800. June 00.

182

Gorringes, Lewes. Royal Worcester leadless glaze cabinet plate by Charles Baldwyn with ptarmigan flying over pine trees, 11.75in. £3,800. June 2001.

183

Andrew Hartley, Ilkley. A pair Worcester Flight Barr & Barr porcelain vases, scenes of Durham Cathedral, 8.75in high. £3,800. Apr 02.

184

Gorringes, Lewes. George Jones majolica novelty teapot modelled as a hen, number 3203, 10.5in. (tiny chip to beak) £3,800. Jan 02.

185

Sotheby's, London. A pair of Bow figures allegorical of 'Liberty' and 'Matrimony', circa 1760. £3,800. July 02.

186

Louis Taylor, Stoke on Trent. Wm. Moorcroft florian ware three handled vase, 'harebell'. (base crack) £3,800. Dec 02.

187

Ambrose, Loughton. Royal Doulton 'The Mask' c1924-38, HN 656, monogram 'W', 17.2cm. £3,800. Sep 00.

17

Hammer Prices £3,700-£3,300

188

Phillips, London. William Reid & Co coffee pot/cover, Sadler, c1760. £3,700. Feb 01.

189

Phillips, Scotland. Minton majolica centrepiece, 29.5cm. £3,600. Nov 99.

190

Woolley & Wallis, Salisbury. Worcester mug, with a three quarter portrait of Admiral Boscawen holding a map titled Louisbourge, unmarked, c1760, 8.5cm. £3,600. Mar 00.

191

Sotheby's, Billingshurst. 1st WW toby jugs 1915-19 by Sir F Caruthers Gould, H M King George V, Lord French, Rt Hon David Lloyd George, Admiral Jellicoe, Admiral Beatty, Lord Kitchener, Marshall Foch and Marshall Joffre. £3,600. Sep 00.

192

Phillips, London. Doulton. Prototype jockey (circa late 1950s) seated in a red and black riding garb, saddle over knee. £3,600. Nov 99.

193

Gorringes, Lewes. Pair of Victorian majolica ewers with swan necks, bull rushes, mark 414T and 32 below, 17in. £3,600. Sep 00.

194

Canterbury Auc. Galleries, Kent. Rabbits supporting a 19thC majolica cabbage leaf tazza, 9.5in. £3,600. Apr 00.

195

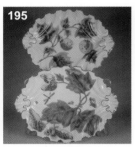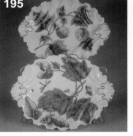

Woolley & Wallis. 2 similar Chelsea oval dishes, painted with large green leaves and colourful fruits. 24.5cm. (damage). £3,600. June 00.

196

Mellors & Kirk, Nottingham. George Jones majolica daisy pattern Stilton keeper, imp'd marks, painted 5204, c1880, 33cm. £3,600. Apr 03.

197

Louis Taylor, Stoke on Trent. Royal Doulton 'Negligee', HN 1228. £3,600. June 03.

198

Gorringes, Lewes. Moorcroft Macintyre tyg with red forget me nots and yellow flowers, blue green ground, green W Moorcroft signature, imp'd 140, 7.5in. £3,600. Mar 01.

199

Rupert Toovey, Washington, Sussex. Wedgwood Fairyland Lustre octagonal porcelain bowl, Fiddler in Tree pattern, interior Ship and Mermaid, 22cm dia. £3,500. Dec 02.

200

Phillips, Scotland. English Delft bowl, 22.5cm. £3,500. June 00.

201

Louis Taylor, Stoke on Trent. Royal Doulton 'The Winner', HN 1407. £3,400. Sep 2001.

202

Andrew Hartley, Ilkley. George Jones majolica cheese dish and cover, painted mark 5253 and impressed mark, 7.5in high. £3,400. Apr 00.

203

Andrew Hartley, Ilkley. Pair Royal Worcester vases by H Stinton, shape No. 293/H, signed, 7.5in. £3,400. Aug 02.

204

Canterbury Auc. Galleries, Kent. 18thC Chinese Armorial part tea service in 'Famille Rose', quartered armorials surmounted by arm holding a sword and worded 'Pour Mon Dieu', (10). £3,400. June 00.

205

Gorringes, Lewes. Wedgwood Fairyland lustre plate by Daisy Makeig-Jones, central Imps on a Bridge panel within a floral border, W560, 10.5in. £3,400. Feb 00.

206

Andrew Hartley, Ilkley. Pearlware tankard, 18th/19thC, inscribed Swansea, 5.75in high. £3,400. Dec 02.

207

Gorringes, Bexhill. Clarice Cliff dish, orange roof cottage. £3,400. Oct 99.

208

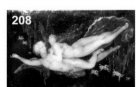

Louis Taylor, Stoke. Birks & Co. Pate sur pate plaque, 10.25 x 7in. £3,400. Dec 02.

209

Hamptons, Godalming. Martin Brothers vase, with grotesque fish, incised marks, dated 6/1897. £3,400. July 02.

210

Mellors & Kirk, Nottingham. George Jones & Sons majolica oval game pie dish and cover. £3,400. Feb 03.

211

Gorringes, Bexhill. Meissen clock/stand, blue crossed swords, incised numerals to stand, c1880, 23in high incl. stand. £3,400. July 03.

212

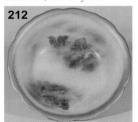

Andrew Hartley, Ilkley. Royal Worcester porcelain bowl, Highland Cattle, H Stinton, 11.25in. £3,300. June 00.

213

Hamptons, Godalming. Pair of George Jones majolica candlesticks, c1870. £3,300. Jan 2003.

214

Sotheby's, Billingshurst. Caughley blue and white mask jug, c1785. £3,300. Oct 99.

Gorringes, Lewes. Wedgwood Fairyland lustre plaque, poss. Daisy Makeig Jones, plaque 4.25 x 9.75in. £3,300. Sep 00.

216

Halls Fine Art, Shrewsbury. Worcester famille rose style creamboat, c1753-54, 4.25in long. £3,300. Jul 03.

217

Mellors & Kirk, Nottingham. Worcester Flight, Barr & Barr double inkwells, 10.5cm, c1820. £3,200. June 03.

218

Phillips, London. Bow plate, c1754-57, printed in red. £3,200. Feb 01.

The numbering system aids the editorial analysis at the beginning of each section as well as providing a reader reference.

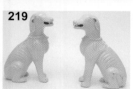

219

Gorringes, Lewes. Pr 18thC Chinese blanc de chine hounds 9.75in. £3,200. Mar 03.

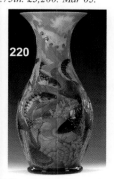

220

Mellors & Kirk, Nottingham. Moorcroft Carp vase by Sally Tuffin. £3,200. Feb 03.

221

Hamptons, Godalming. An 18thC English Delft flower pot. £3,200. Mar 01.

222

Hamptons, Godalming. Japanese Satsuma, Meiji, 5cm high x 11cm dia., gilt seal mark. £3,200. May 01.

223

Gorringes, Lewes. Pair of Chelsea gold anchor figures of a Shepherd/Shepherdess, 12in. (restorations and one af.) £3,200. Apr 01.

224

Mellors & Kirk, Nottingham. Set of six Royal Crown Derby coffee cans/stands, seascapes with shipping by W E J Dean, all signed, printed mark, pattern 0981, date code 1939 & 40, cased. £3,200. Apr 03.

225

Andrew Hartley, Ilkley. Royal Worcester vase by C Baldwyn of ovoid form with flared rim and leaf capped lug handles, 13in high. £3,100. Apr 00.

226

Gorringes, Lewes. Royal Worcester vase painted with rams in highland landscape, H. Davis, F106, date code for 1914, 9.75in. £3,100. Dec 00.

227

Louis Taylor, Stoke on Trent. Royal Doulton, Windmill Lady HN 1400. £3,100. Sep 02.

228

Gorringes, Lewes. Chinese export porcelain punch bowl, 15.75in. £3,100. Oct 02.

229

Hamptons, Godalming. Large Chinese porcelain 'Nine-peach' vase, base bearing an underglaze blue seal mark. £3,100. Jan 02.

230

Phillips, London. Doulton Prototype,19thC working man about to embark to America, mid 1960s. £3,000. Nov 99.

Hammer Prices £3,300-£3,000

231

Mellors & Kirk, Nottingham. Blue printed pottery footbath, floral 'sheet' prints, 24.5cm high, printed Semi-China mark, c1830. £3,000. June 03.

232

Sotheby's, Billingshurst. Pair of Meissen porcelain vases, encrusted with fruit, 2nd half 19thC, 36cm. £3,000. June 01.

233

Phillips, London. Worcester bowl, c1757, printed in grey, three chinoiseries subjects. £3,000. Feb 01.

234

Andrew Hartley, Ilkley. Royal Worcester porcelain vase, 13.25in high. £3,000. Sep 99.

235

Rupert Toovey, Washington, Sussex. R. Doulton Titanian ware porcelain vase, 1916-29, polar bear, cub in arctic landscape, Harry Allen, 'Beyond Man's Footsteps', 31.5cm. £3,000. Aug 03.

236

Phillips, London. Creamware Coal Trade Commemorative jug, c1775. £3,000. Feb 01.

237

Woolley & Wallis, Salisbury. William De Morgan dish, 'Winged Lions Fishing' design 1178, c1890, 36cm. (invisible crack 5.5cm) £3,000. June 00.

238

Gorringes, Lewes. Cased R. Worcester set 6 coffee cans and saucers, painted game birds by Jas. Stinton, with 6 silver spoons. £3,000. Feb 01.

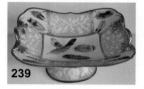

239

Stride & Son, Chichester. Chamberlains Worcester dessert service, painted studies of feathers, 16 plates, tureen, fruit stand, 3 dishes. Worn gilding. £3,000. Nov 02.

240

Gorringes, Lewes.18thC Meissen figure Scaramouche c1744, blue crossed swords mark, 5.25in. £3,000. Feb 01.

Hammer Prices £3,000-£2,600

Sothebys, Billingshurst. 'The Veiled Bride', Copeland parian, c1887. £3,000. Feb 01.

242

Lambert & Foster, Tenterden. Barr Flight & Barr Worcester porcelain, pair of funnel shaped vases. £2,900. Dec 00.

243

Gorringes, Lewes. 19thC Delft tulip vase, with bird handles, chipped, monogram L.E., 8in. £2,900. Apr 01.

244

Hamptons, Godalming. George Jones majolica centrepiece. £2,900. Sep 02.

245

Gorringes, Lewes. William Moorcroft jardiniere in Spanish pattern, signature mark, 9.5in. £2,800. Feb 00.

246

Gorringes, Lewes. Late 18th/ 19thC earthenware hare's head stirrup cup in Chinese style, 6.5in. £2,800. Mar 01.

20

247

Woolley & Wallis, Salisbury. George Jones Majolica strawberry dish, impressed mark, pattern No 3423/11, Rd. mk. S, 1875, 38cm. £2,800. Mar 00.

248

Phillips, London. Liverpool printed Creamware jug, c1790. £2,800. Feb 01.

249

Gorringes, Lewe. Wemyss cat painted with pink dog roses, green glass eyes, one foot restored, 12.25in high. £2,800. Apr 00.

250

D Duggleby, Scarborough. Wedgwood Fairyland lustre vase, 'The Imps on a bridge' pattern, 26.5cm, printed marks and painted No. 25360M. £2,800. Apr 02.

251

Canterbury Auc. Galleries, Kent. Two 19thC Staffs figures of leopards, 7.25in. Badly damaged in the Blitz and repaired. £2,800. Aug 01.

252

Sworders, Stansted Mount-fitchet. Late 16thC Iznik pottery dish, 12in. (old rim restorations) £2,800. May 01.

253

Bristol Auction Rooms. Chien Lung famille rose porcelain garniture of 5 vases. 28cm and smaller. £2,800. Oct 01.

254

Eastbourne Auction Rooms, , Sussex. A Majolica centre piece. (damaged) £2,800. Dec 2001.

255

Hyperion Auctions, St Ives, Huntingdon. Clarice Cliff tea for two. £2,750. July 99.

256

Wintertons Ltd, Lichfield. Derby yellow ground teacup and saucer, c1790, scenes by Zachariah Boreman, puce cross batons mark above no. 122, 7cm. £2,700. May 03.

257

Woolley & Wallis, Salisbury. Japanese Satsuma bowl, the exterior with figures in landscapes on a butterfly strewn ground, marked Kozan, Meiji, 1868-1912, 10.75cm. £2,700. Mar 00.

258

Louis Taylor, Stoke. Minton majolica teapot. (some damage) £2,700. Mar 02.

259

Louis Taylor, Stoke. Birks & Co. Pate sur pate plaque, 'The Three Graces', 6.75 x 11in. £2,700. Dec 02.

260

Louis Taylor, Stoke. Ralph Wood 'Thin Man' toby jug. (damaged) £2,700. Dec 01.

261

Trembath Welch, Great Dunmow. Set 19thC Persian glazed tiles as an arched surround depicting figure groups, some damage, gross height 55cm. £2,700. Nov 99.

262

Dee, Atkinson & Harrison, Driffield. Goldscheider pottery figure, by Stefan Dakon, minor chips, base inscribed 'Dakon', c1920, 15in high. £2,700. Sep 99.

263

Gorringes, Lewes. William Moorcroft Pansy tobacco jar with screw-on lid, impressed W963 and signed in green, 5.5in. £2,700. Feb 00.

264

Hogbens, Folkestone. Royal Worcester c1920s charger by Charles Baldwin, Swans in Flight. £2,700. Mar 00.

265

Peter Wilson, Nantwich. Delft 'Gardeners Arms' armorial plate, dated 1747, probably Liverpool. £2,700. Feb 03.

266

Richard Winterton, Burton on Trent. Pair of Mintons Art Pottery chargers painted with children, signed F Broughton, dated 1875. £2,600. Nov 01.

267

Gorringes, Lewes. George Jones majolica and brown basalt sweetmeat dish, c1868, impressed with monogram and entitled Kumassie, 9in high. £2,600. June 01.

268

Sotheby's, Billingshurst. Wedgwood fairyland lustre Melba bowl, 1920s, exterior with the Garden of Paradise pattern, interior with Jumping Faun, printed mark, painted Z4968, 8in. £2,600. June 02.

269

Dreweatt Neate, Newbury. Pr Chinese Canton baluster vases/covers, 62cm, c1860. (one cracked) £2,600. Apr 00.

270

Gorringes, Lewes. Pair of 19thC Wedgwood 2 colour jasper ware vases/covers, base stamped Wedgwood and HKV, 10.25in. £2,600. Oct 00.

271

Mellors & Kirk, Nottingham. Moorcroft vase, c1930. £2,600. Dec 02.

272

Hamptons, Godalming. Mason's Ironstone part dinner service c1840s, some damage. (70) £2,500. July 00.

273

Sotheby's, Billingshurst. 'Indian Sporting Series' a group of Spode blue printed dinnerwares, early 19thC. £2,500. Nov 99.

274

Woolley & Wallis, Salisbury. Miniature jewelled Coalport gold ground part tea service, green printed marks 6476 or V7350/258, early 20thC. (10) £2,500. June 00.

275

Woolley & Wallis, Salisbury. Documentary Worcester mug inscribed G. Bibby in underglaze blue, c1780, 11.5cm. £2,500. June 00.

The illustrations in these pages are in descending price order. The price range is indicated at the top of each page.

276

Canterbury Auc. Galleries, Kent. Copeland Parianware after R Monti - 'The Bride', 14.5in. £2,500. Aug 03.

277

Canterbury Auc. Galleries, Kent. Minton majolica two handled tureen and cover with a foot-long 'lobster' on top dates for June 1870, 13.5in overall. £2,500. Nov 99.

278

Gorringes, Lewes. Pair of Minton majolica table salts as clam shells on sea monster bases, surmounted by putti, 7in. £2,500. Apr 00.

279

Canterbury Auc. Galleries, Kent. Minton majolica teapot in the form of a monkey in a blue costume holding a large fruit, 6in high, date code for 1878. £2,500. Oct 01.

280

Woolley & Wallis, Salisbury. Copeland majolica life size model of two squirrels, 2nd half 19thC, 56cm (some restoration) £2,500. June 00.

281

Sworders, Stansted Mountfitchet. Royal Worcester vase and cover, shape no. 2149, by Frank Roberts, signed, date coded for 1902, 20in high. £2,500. Dec 01.

282

Locke & England, Leamington Spa. Pair of early William Moorcroft Cornflower pattern vases. £2,500. Nov 02.

283

Andrew Hartley, Ilkley. Pair of Stevenson & Hancock porcelain bottle vases and covers, signed H.S. Hancock, 9.75in high. £2,500. Apr 02.

284

Hamptons, Godalming. Export porcelain punch bowl, Mandarin style c1775, 36cm. £2,500. Nov 01.

285

Gorringes, Lewes. Clarice Cliff Applique Arignon pattern lotus jug, 11.5in. (two cracks) £2,500. June 01.

286

Gorringes, Lewes. George Jones majolica cheese dome, applied foliage, wicker fence decor, 12in. £2,500. Sep 00.

287

Thos Mawer & Son, Lincoln. R Worcester. Pair of pattern 302 vases, 17cm, and pattern 1286 vase/cover, 20cm, all date coded 1923. Raymond Rushton. £2,500. Feb 03.

288

Hamptons, Godalming. Coalport 'jewelled' vase and cover, c1895, green printed marks and gilt No. V2682, 32cm high. £2,500. Sep 01.

289

Gorringes, Lewes. Martinware stoneware vase, marked 4-1880 R.W. Martin & Bros London & Southall, 13.75in. £2,500. July 01.

290

Gorringes, Lewes. Pr 19thC Meissens vases each painted with lovers in landscapes, 11.5in. £2,400. Mar 01.

291

Phillips, Scotland. Wedgwood Fairyland lustre bowl by Daisy Makeig-Jones. £2,400. Nov 00.

292

Woolley & Wallis, Salisbury. Japanese Satsuma box and cover, signed Kyozan, 8.5cm wide. £2,400. Mar 00.

293

Hamptons, Godalming. Set 4 Derby figures of the seasons, c1775, by Pierre Stephan, 22.7 -24.3cm. £2,400. Sep 01.

294

Gorringes, Lewes. Ralph Wood model of a goat, in coloured glazes, 1775/85, 6.5in. £2,400. Oct 02.

Hammer Prices £2,400-£2,250

Sworders, Stansted Mount-fitchet. George Jones majolica cheese dish. £2,400. Feb 00.

296

Dockree's, Manchester. Pair Wedgwood 'Fairyland Lustre' vases Daventry pattern, after Daisy Makeig-Jones, shape no 3150, 8in. £2,400. May 00.

297

Peter Wilson, Nantwich. Pair of late 19thC Imari vases, with cartouches of humming birds, quail and flowers, gilts, 22in high. £2,400. Apr 00.

298

Phillips, London. Doulton. Prototype of an 18thC court musician. (early 1950s) £2,400. Nov 99.

299

Gorringes, Lewes. George Jones majolica sweetmeat dish, c1868 as a camel, base impressed with monogram and entitled Kumassie, 9in high. £2,400. Oct 2000.

300

Sotheby's, Billingshurst. Mandarin. Royal Doulton Titanian figure 1918-1936, by Charles Noke, painted, printed and impressed marks, 10.25in. £2,400. June 01.

301

D Duggleby, Scarborough. Pr Wedgwood vases, printed marks, painted pattern mark 25486A, impressed 2046, 28cm high. £2,300. June 03.

302

Mellors & Kirk, Nottingham. Pr R. Worcester vases, stags and other animals by Robert F Perling after Sir Edwin Henry Landseer, 44.5cm, moulded and printed marks and (18)72, £2,300. June 03.

303

Louis Taylor, Stoke. Pair of Royal Worcester two-handled vases/covers. £2,300. Dec 00.

304

Gorringes, Lewes. Royal Doulton figure of a seated buddha, impressed 12.19, 4.25in. £2,300. Apr 01.

305

Gorringes, Lewes. Victorian majolica vase as bulrushes beside a heron with a fish in its beak, unmarked, 15.5in. £2,300. Feb 00.

306

Hamptons, Godalming. A Swansea? creamware botanical dessert service, c1800, by Thomas Pardoe, 16 pieces. (some slight damage) £2,300. Sep 01. This attribution may be unsafe and is under investigation.

307

Gorringes, Lewes. Chelsea - Derby group, two young lovers, seated with a lamb, 8.5in high. £2,300. Dec 00.

308

Gorringes, Lewes. Late 19thC William De Morgan Cadogan style teapot with copper lustre glazed birds amidst foliage, impressed Merton Abbey mark, 8in. £2,300. Sep 00.

309

Dreweatt Neate, Newbury. Bow set of figures of the Four Seasons, tallest 17.5cm, three with anchor & dagger marks, c1765. (minor damage and restoration) £2,300. June 02.

310

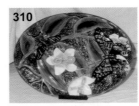

John Taylors, Louth. George Jones Majolica wall plaque. £2,300. Feb 00.

311

Hamptons, Godalming. Japanese Satsuma bowl, Meiji period, with flowers in a key fret border, interior decorated with butterflies, 10cm high x 15.5cm dia., seal mark to base, Kyoto. £2,300. May 01.

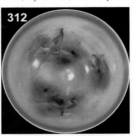

312

Andrew Hartley, Ilkley. Royal Worcester porcelain bowl, pheasants inside and outside, signed by Jas Stinton, 8.5in wide. £2,300. Sep 99.

313

Gorringes, Lewes. Royal Worcester vase with panel of orchids, signed Roberts, No 2057, 8.25in. £2,300. Feb 00.

314

Rupert Toovey, Washington, Sussex. William de Morgan bottle vase, c1888-1897, 39cm high. £2,300. Dec 02.

315

Dockree's, Manchester. Cornflower vase, 12.75in high, stamped to the base 'Moorcroft', Made in England and signed 'Moorcroft 1928 in u/g blue. £2,300. May 00.

316

Dreweatt Neate, Newbury. Japanese Satsuma oval bowl by Yabu Meizan, 16.7cm wide, signed. £2,300. June 03.

317

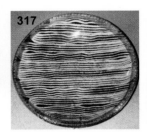

Clevedon Salerooms, Bristol. Early 18thC slipware bowl, 15in. £2,300. Mar 01.

318

Sotheby's, Billingshurst. Henry VIII, Royal Doulton ltd edn, 1933, HN1792, Charles Noke, no. 16/200, 11.5in. £2,300. June 01.

319

Richard Winterton, Burton on Trent. A group of Walton figures including a deer and a pair of circus performers. (all damaged) £2,250. Apr 03.

22

Sworders, Stansted Mount-fitchet. Montelupo Maiolica, 17thC, 31cm. £2,200. July 03.

Phillips, London. Doulton. Prototype of a gentleman enjoying a drink. (mid 1970s) £2,200. Nov 99.

Prices quoted are hammer prices which excluded the buyer's premium. Adding 15% will give an approximation to the buying price.

Gorringes, Lewes. A Bow figure of a seated Lady florist wearing a white dress with puce floral decoration and blue trimming, c1758, 5.25in high. £2,200. Dec 00.

Louis Taylor, Stoke. Set of Royal Doulton Tolkien figures and stand. £2,200. June 03.

Wintertons, Lichfield. Early 18thC English delft jar, probably Bristol, 3.5in. (slight wear to rim) £2,200. Feb 02.

Hamptons, Godalming. Pair of 18thC Italian maiolica Alberellos. £2,200. May 00.

Rupert Toovey, Washington, Sussex. Spode pearlware tree and well dish, Indian sporting series. £2,200. Dec 02.

Sworders, Stansted Mount-fitchet. An early 19thC Spode porcelain part dessert service. £2,200. Sep 01.

Mellors & Kirk, Nottingham. Pair John Walton pearlware models of lion & unicorn, 17cm, mark impressed on a scroll, c1820. £2,200. Apr 03.

Gorringes, Lewes. Meissen dessert service. A pair of tureens, covers and stands, 4 oval dishes, 2 square dishes & 15 plates. £2,200. Apr 01.

Gorringes, Lewes. Pair of 19thC Meissen pot pourri vases each having two satyr masks and surmounted by three frolicking putti, 8in high. £2,200. Feb 01.

Sotheby's, Billingshurst. 1920s Wedgwood fairyland lustre Imperial bowl, Daisy Makeig-Jones, black script patt. no. Z4968, 9.5in. £2,200. June 01.

Gorringes, Bexhill. R. Crown Derby 65 piece Japan pattern dinner and coffee service, Patt. no. 1128. £2,200. Oct 01.

Phillips, London. Doulton. Prototype of HM The Queen, mid 1950s. £2,185. Nov 99.

Phillips, London. Doulton. HRH The Princess of Wales, HN2887, Eric Griffiths, 1982 No 1500/1500 £2,185. Nov 99.

Gorringes, Lewes. Early 19thC Staffordshire figure of a winged mermaid. (wings chipped and paint flaking) 9.25in. £2,100. Mar 01.

Hammer Prices £2,200-£2,100

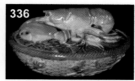

Rosebery's, London. Minton majolica pate tureen and cover. £2,100. Jan 00.

Canterbury Auc. Galleries, Kent. Clarice Cliff pottery Fantasque Bizarre Lotus pattern vase. £2,100. Apr 00.

Hamptons, Godalming. Fine satsuma dish, meiji, painted with palace. £2,100. July 03.

Mellors & Kirk, Nottingham. Pearlware Nelson commemorative mug. £2,100. Feb 03.

Amersham Auction Rooms, Bucks. Moorcroft Macintyre Burslem pottery 3 piece tea set decorated with pansies, each with applied silver rims, London 1911. £2,100. Feb 02.

Woolley & Wallis, Salisbury. Pr R Crown Derby campana vases, signed 'Darlington', red factory marks, date code 1918, 20cm. £2,100. June 00.

Hamptons, Godalming. English part tea and coffee service, c1820, unmarked. (42) £2,100. Jan 00.

Andrew Hartley, Ilkley. Pair of 19thC French porcelain pot pourri vases, 12in high. £2,100. Aug 00.

Gorringes, Lewes. Early 19thC Coalport tea/coffee set. (43) £2,100. Mar 01.

Woolley & Wallis, Salisbury. English rectangular plaque, still life of fruit, signed E. Steele and dated 1881, 23 x 30.5cm. £2,100. June 00.

Rosebery's, London. Meissen dish with a scene depicting the Triumph of Venus after Boucher. £2,100. May 00.

Rupert Toovey, Washington, Sussex. William de Morgan ovoid vase, c1888-1897, 25.7cm high. £2,100. Dec 02.

Sample Analysis

What can we make of the porcelain on show in this section where there are more than 320 lots on display? Immediately on glancing at the page opposite one sees more than half a dozen Worcester and Royal Worcester lots with Stinton highland cattle or pheasants in abundance. Then they reappear on pages 27 and 28 in the £1,500-1,700 range before reappearing only once more at the end of the section with a Harry Stinton vase fetching a £1,000 hammer. Previous Stinton appearances in the £2,000-3,000 range are for either pairs of vases or more spectacular pieces. If one were to follow the Stinton theme into later Sections and throughout this volume using the *Index* then it is clearly possible to study the prices at auction in recent years.

Having suggested how a specific analysis might be pursued and in previous Sections followed various themes through the pages, let us now analyse a Section on a page-by-page basis. Assuming the Spode pearlware breakfast set is in perfect condition, see 349, then the £2,000 is to be expected, yet only the rarity of the MacIntyre vase at 350, with a registration number just into the early twentieth century, complete with rim chip can account for the same price. Ralph Wood figures, see 352, are always going to fetch good money as will Doulton Lambeth. The humourous George Tinworth mice groups at 353 and 366 give a clear indication of just how much this artist is valued. Later in this volume a pair of George Tinworth vases fetches £800. Also worthy of note on page 25 is a Clarice Cliff Isis vase at 359 and a Staffordshire slipware dish at 355. Note the comments made on Slipware in previous analyses.

Cats may be a theme in themselves and there is no doubt that they stimulate prices often well beyond any intrinsic worth. They represent truly, a very important collecting area. In whatever ceramic ware they appear, or from whatever factory, or even when they are unattributed, they are highly contested. In this section take note of the Royal Crown Derby Cheshire Cat paperweight at 363. This modern heavyweight cost the buyer a staggering £1,950. And see also 424 where a pair of Galle style seated cats fetched £1,600 and 504 where a single late nineteenth century Galle style cat with removable head fetched £1,300. Whilst on the subject of cats it is also worth mentioning that the bigger variety will always fetch big money. Do not miss the pair of Staffordshire lions at 367 which fetched £1,900.

Before leaving page 25 it is worth mentioning the Poole charger by Tony Morris which fetched £1,900. This Section is noteworthy for its Royal Doulton figures in the under £2,000 range. The Doulton theme is well documented throughout this volume. Also note a Worcester blue and white mug at 379 and a damaged Lowestoft ale beaker at 393 which again further makes the point about rarity. We are not given enough information as to why a Derby coffee can and saucer (389) with rubbing and restoration fetched over £2,000 but there can be no doubt that those who specialise in this subject will know the answer.

A great deal of time was taken examining minutely, the substantial damage to the Kangxi vase at 392 when editing this Section. This is a very clear example of the great respect now being paid for items of quality regardless of condition. Note that this is a very substantial vase at 32in high. It is also worth noting the Mason's ironstone service at 394, the Royal Dux group at 400 and how bidders got fired up over a high-fired Ruskin vase at 395.

On page 27, a Ruskin vase (413) in the same sale and a further Ruskin ginger jar (411) are pointers to the high values which are often placed on this art pottery. The reader can follow up the Ruskin theme through the *Index*. Fieldings Crown Devon (418) makes its first appearance for £1,650 and Hannah Barlow her first 'incisive' showing for Doulton at 405 and again at 431. There are about a dozen lots in this volume if the reader wishes to follow them up through the *Index*.

It is always pleasurable to see humour in ceramics. We have already mentioned the George Tinworth mice but readers should note the Wemyss pig by Plichta at 438 and the Clarice Cliff teddy bear book ends at 441, both about the £1,500 mark. Seeking humour in ceramics could be a theme in itself. Living ceramics artists are also following up this theme, some with considerable success. These may well be the antiques of the future. Cockerels are early birds and early cockerels do well at 442 and 474. Do also check out the Liverpool Delft char pot at 469. This inconspicuous and inauspicious dish is likely to be passed up by many of us in a boot fair or fleamarket, if the price were low and the item unidentified. Such a modest piece, yet such a massive price at £1,400. But remember, this is English Delft! Knowledge is a wonderful thing and in the world of antiques book study is probably more important than hands-on activities unless you are prepared to spend more time in and around the better quality antiques environments where you are likely to come across the rare and unusual. Anecdote is often educational. The blue and white skimming bowl at 495 was offered by an elderly person to a daughter-in-law as a gift. However it was turned down as it simply didn't appeal! The bowl subsequently fetched £1,350 at Amersham Auction Rooms in 2002. And be aware of turning down old bricks! The ones at 503 and 544 are worth £2,500 between them!

Let us now herald the first appearance of Sunderland lustre at 505, which can be an expensive interest. There are about another ten items to follow up if you have a particular interest in this category. And also the cracked ballooning Delft plate (526) which fetched £1,250. Larger pieces of early Mason's always fetch considerable sums, see 507, and follow the Mason's trail through the *Index*. So do large famille rose dishes. See 531. Belatedly one might suggest we have at last our first Rockingham at 551. Rockingham will be discussed at much greater length in subsequent analyses but if you wish to follow up now, check out the *Index*. And a big personal welcome also to the only piece of St Anthony's Pottery from Newcastle-on-Tyne, a superb pearlware horse at £1,100. See 608. This pottery was just down the road from where I was born in Wallsend, literally where the Roman Wall ended. This is why we have named our offices in Kent, *Wallsend House*.

There are many, many themes that may be followed from this Section alone. Royal Doulton, Clarice Cliff, Delft, Moorcroft, Staffordshire, to name but a few. Beswick and Beatrix Potter make their first appearance at 591, weighing in at an astonishing £1,100. And the first of three Royal Doulton Beefeaters makes his first appearance at 620 and again at 653 for around about a £1,000. The specialist dealers and collectors certainly know their market. To conclude, the terracotta figure of Pandora at 646 and the buff stoneware belamine at 645, along with the Ralph Wood creamware thinman, all rubbing shoulders with Moorcroft, Clarice Cliff, Derby and Crown Devon etc. open a fascinating window of almost a 100 lots which can be bought for a £1,000 or thereabouts.

348

Andrew Hartley, Ilkley. Pair R. Worcester vases, H Stinton, 5.75in. £2,000. Oct 99.

349

Woolley & Wallis, Salisbury. Spode pearlware blue/white breakfast set, 'Greek' pattern, early 19thC. £2,000. Mar 00.

350

Canterbury Auc. Galleries, Kent. MacIntyre Co Ltd Florian Ware vase, 8.5in, rare Butterfly pattern, printed mk. to base Rd No 326688, u/g green sig., W Moorcroft Des, rim chip. £2,000. Aug 00.

351

Bonham's, Bath. Hans Coper, 'Digswell' form. A stoneware vase, c1962, impressed HC seal to base, (r to rim), 21cm high. £2,000. Nov 01.

352

Gorringes, Lewes. Ralph Wood figure of shepherd, Gollancz Collection label below, 8.5in. £2,000. June 00.

353

Canterbury Auc. Galleries, Kent. Doulton Lambeth Tea Time Scandal, group of mice, 3.5in, damaged, George Tinworth. £2,000. Oct 00.

354

Rosebery's, London. Majolica teapot, Minton. £2,000. Jan 00.

355

Mellors & Kirk, Nottingham. Staffs slipware dish, base incised by the thrower with a marking out X, late 17thC, 44cms dia. £2,000. Apr 03.

356

Richard Winterton, Burton on Trent. Pr Minton art pottery plaques, c1870, in manner of W. S. Coleman, (unsigned) one impressed 'Minton' and Goode, retailer label, 23 x 60cm. £2,000. Jan 02.

357

Gorringes, Lewes. Kerr & Binns Worcester chess set, 1858, one side in parian with gilded mouldings, the other in plain white biscuit, Kings 3.5/3.25in. £2,000. June 03.

358

Gorringes, Lewes. Pair of Worcester blue and white cornucopia wall pockets, root and flower pattern, c1760, 8.75in. £2,000. Mar 01.

359

Gorringes, Lewes. Clarice Cliff Fantasque Isis vase, Umbrellas and Rain pattern, 9.5in. £2,000. Jan 03.

360

Sworders, Stansted Mount-fitchet. Montelupo Maiolica dish, painted with a mounted soldier, 17thC, 30cm. (slight rim flakes) £1,950. July 03.

361

Andrew Hartley, Ilkley. Pair R. Worcester vases, shape no. 42/G, with highland cattle in landscapes, signed H Stinton, 6in high. £1,950. Feb 01.

362

Maxwells, Wilmslow. Moorcroft vase 'Eventide', impressed and signed in blue, 6.5in high. £1,950. Sep 02.

363

Eastbourne Auction Rooms, Sussex. Royal Crown Derby Cheshire Cat paperweight. £1,950. Mar 02.

Hammer Prices £2,000-£1,850

364

Louis Taylor, Stoke on Trent. Set of four Royal Worcester vases/covers. £1,950. Dec 00.

365

Bearne's, Exeter. Group of 12 Camm Brothers (Smethwick) pottery nursery tiles, each tile 20cm square and framed as three sets of four, c1875, 2 tiles chipped. £1,950. July 03.

366

Hamptons, Godalming. Doulton Lambeth stoneware group, 'Playgoers', 12.5cm, incised J B and 1886, George Tinworth. £1,950. May 02.

367

Sotheby's, Billingshurst. Pair of Staffordshire porcelain lions, possibly Lloyd, Shelton, c1840. £1,900. Feb 00.

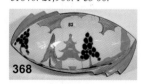

368

Thos Mawer & Son, Lincoln. Clarice Cliff, 'Kew', Bizarre 475 bowl, printed marks, 32cm wide. £1,900. Apr 02.

369

Rosebery's, London. Poole charger by Tony Morris, 42cm dia. £1,900. Feb 00.

370

Ambrose, Loughton. 19thC Minton pottery plaque, hand coloured, 'Sympathy' after Briton Riviere. £1,900. Dec 99.

371

Gorringes, Lewes. Pair of Moorcroft MacIntyre '18thC pattern' baluster vases, gilt bands & foot rim, Macintyre, green script signature and Jas. Shoolbred & Co marks, M2648, 8in. £1,900. Apr 01.

372

Wintertons, Lichfield. Pair of Royal Worcester vases by James Stinton, signed, wear to gilded base, rim, Grainger shape no 923, date code 1921, 22.5cm. £1,850. Mar 00.

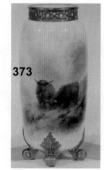

373

Andrew Hartley, Ilkley. Royal Worcester vase by H Stinton, shape no. G42, painted with highland cattle in landscapes, 9in high. £1,850. Oct 99.

374

A. Hartley, Ilkley. George Jones majolica cheese dish and cover, painted mark 5253 /80, 7.5in. £1,850. Aug 00.

Hammer Prices £1,850-£1,700

375

Gorringes, Lewes. Pr. Derby figures Shepherd/Shepherdess, c1768, 8.5in. £1,850. Dec 00.

376

Louis Taylor, Stoke on Trent. Royal Doulton pilot figure Mothers Day. £1,850. Dec 00.

377

Andrew Hartley, Ilkley. Royal Worcester porcelain tea set for nine settings, signed E Phillips. (31) £1,850. Apr 02.

378

Louis Taylor, Stoke on Trent. Royal Doulton Captain Cook loving cup, 9.75in high. £1,800. Sep 03.

379

Gorringes, Lewes. Worcester baluster mug, blue underglaze with Chinese figures within leaf shaped reserves, 3.5in. £1,800. July 00.

380

Sotheby's, Billingshurst. Mandarin, c1918, bone china Doulton figure, by Charles Noke, in a bronze glaze, 9.75in. £1,800. June 01.

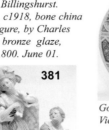

381

Gorringes, Lewes. Late 19thC Meissen group, 12.5in. £1,800. Dec 01.

382

Andrew Hartley, Ilkley. Set of 24 Royal Doulton porcelain figures of Dickens characters, 4in. £1,800. Dec 02.

383

Gorringes, Lewes. Meissen plate, central panel, lovers in a landscape, 10in. (minor chips) £1,800. Oct 00.

384

Dee, Atkinson & Harrison, Driffield. Hispano-Moresque 16thC plate, floral decoration in pink lustre and blue, 12.5in dia. £1800. Sep 02.

385

Canterbury Auc. Galleries, Kent. Pair of 19thC Meissen porcelain groups, 8.5in high. (2) £1,800. May 01.

386

Gorringes, Lewes. 19thC Vienna charger, painted with a scene from Belshazzars Feast, 21.5in. £1,800. Sep 00.

387

Cheffins, Cambridge. Wm de Morgan, Fulham bowl by Joe Juster, marks painted in black, 26cm. £1,800. Feb 02.

388

Gorringes, Lewes. 18thC Ralph Wood style ram, horns, ears repaired, 7in. £1,800. Mar 01.

389

Wintertons Ltd, Lichfield. Derby coffee can, stand, c1794, puce crown cross batons and no. 233, rubbing, restoration. £1,800. May 03.

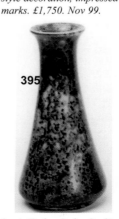

390

Louis Taylor, Stoke. Royal Doulton flambe buddha, 7in. (damage) £1,800. Dec 02.

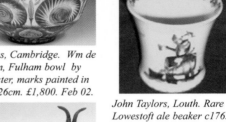

391

Gorringes, Lewes. Set of 12 early 19thC Mandarin plates with figure centres, 8.75in. £1,800. Apr 01.

392

Amersham Auction, Bucks. Late 17thC Kangxi porcelain vase, 32in, substantially riveted. £1,750. Sep 02.

393

John Taylors, Louth. Rare Lowestoft ale beaker c1765-1770, painted mark '5' poss. by Robert Allen, 7.5cm. (damaged) £1,750. June 01.

394

Wintertons, Lichfield. Mid 19thC Masons Ironstone china dinner service, printed and painted with Oriental style decoration, impressed marks. £1,750. Nov 99.

395

Louis Taylor, Stoke. Ruskin high-fired vase. £1,750. Mar 01.

396

Louis Taylor, Stoke. Royal Doulton, Mephisto, HN 723. (restoration) £1,750. Dec 02.

397

Henry Adams, Chichester. Pr. of Chamberlain's Worcester double-walled reticulated two-handled cups, stands and one cover, c1840, script mark in red. £1,750. Sep 2002.

398

John Taylors, Louth. Royal Doulton figurine 'Dolly'. £1,720. Oct 99.

399

Eastbourne Auction Rooms, Sussex. George Jones part majolica tea set. (some damage) £1,700. Dec 01.

400

Andrew Hartley, Ilkley. Royal Dux porcelain group, gilt embellishment, 23in, pink triangle mk. £1,700. June 01.

401

Gorringes, Lewes. Pair of Victorian Staffordshire pottery dog groups, 5.5in. £1,700. Oct 2002.

402

Canterbury Auc. Galleries, Kent. A pair of 19thC Berlin porcelain oval plaques, 7 x 5in and impressed with the KPM mark. £1,700. Oct 99.

403

Rosebery's, London. A pair of Grangers Worcester vases, painted with cattle scenes by John Stinton. £1,700. May 00.

404

Gorringes, Lewes. Minton majolica lily bowl on naturalistic base, surmounted by three green frogs, date code 1866, 4.5in. £1,700. Feb 01.

The numbering system aids the editorial analysis at the beginning of each section as well as providing a reader reference.

405

Sworders, Stansted Mountfitchet, Essex. Pair Doulton Hannah Barlow vases. £1,700. May 2000.

406

Hamptons, Godalming. Staffs cream ware jug, c1812, txfr. printed with 3 engravings, Admiral Nelson's ship, a lady and 2 children in a garden & 'The World in Planisphere', the name J H Holt 1812 to the spout and 2 verses, 26.5cm high. £1,700. Nov 01.

407

Phillips, London. Doulton. Prototype 2nd WW aviator. (1942) £1,700. Nov 99.

408

Stride & Son, Chichester. Pair Moorcroft Persian patt. vases, 8in high, chipped and cracked. £1,700. Mar 2003.

409

Dee, Atkinson & Harrison, Driffield. Victorian ironstone part dinner service with gilt and flo-blue scroll work and cartouche of floral sprigs to border. (52) £1,700. Aug 01.

410

Sworders, Stansted Mountfitchet. Montelupo Maiolica dish, 17thC, 30cm, chipped, short hairline. £1,700. July 03.

411

Eastbourne Auction Rooms, Sussex. Ruskin ginger jar, 10cm high. £1,700. Mar 2002.

412

Potteries Specialist Auctions, Stoke. R. Worcester Alexander the Great. £1,700. Mar 2003.

413

Louis Taylor, Stoke on Trent, Staffs. A Ruskin high-fired vase. £1,700. Mar 01.

414

Gorringes, Lewes. Minton majolica bowl of barrel form, 7in. £1,650. Apr 00.

415

Andrew Hartley, Ilkley. Pair of 19thC Imari porcelain vases, 24.25in high. £1,650. June 00.

416

Andrew Hartley, Ilkley. Minton Majolica game pie tureen with rabbit, 2 birds, date mk. 1864, 13in. £1,650. June 03.

417

Andrew Hartley, Ilkley. Pair Royal Worcester vases by H Stinton, Shape 302/H, 7in. £1,650. Oct 02.

Hammer Prices £1,700-£1,600

418

Gorringes, Lewes. Crown Devon figure of lady in floral and parcel gilt flapper dress, No 2280, 13.5in, inner base rim chip. £1,650. Oct 00.

419

Richard Winterton, Burton on Trent. Ironstone waste pail & cover, early 19thC, 40cm high. £1,650. Apr 03.

420

Gorringes, Lewes. Set of 8 Royal Worcester figures from the Nations of the World Series, 7in. £1,600. Sep 00.

421

Stride & Son, Chichester. George Jones Victorian majolica strawberry dish, 28cm. £1,600. Mar 02.

422

Hamptons, Godalming. Wedgwood Liverpool printed creamware punch bowl, c1780, inscribed 'Success to the Greyhound, 34cm, damaged. £1,600. Mar 02.

423

Andrew Hartley, Ilkley. Royal Worcester loving cup pheasants in a landscape by Jas. Stinton, 6.25in high. £1,600. Apr 02.

424

Gorringes, Lewes. Pair Galle style seated cats, initialled and monogrammed, 12.5in. £1,600. Mar 02.

425

Stride & Son, Chichester. Chinese famille rose tureen, painted cranes, pair doghead handles and pomegranate knob, 35cm. £1,600. July 03.

426

Gorringes, Lewes. Ralph Wood, pottery model of St George and the dragon, impressed mark Ra Wood, Burslem, c1785, 10.75in. £1,600. Dec 00.

427

Woolley & Wallis, Salisbury. Coalport vase/cover, green factory mark, pattern V.6043/ 121 S/S in red, W133 in green and Tiffany & Co. New York printed mk. c1900, 25cm. (restoration) £1,600. June 00.

27

428

Wintertons Ltd, Lichfield. Dresden porcelain pot pourri, c1890-1910, blue X swords mark and inscribed, no. 2745, 24in high. £1,600. July 02.

429

Gorringes, Lewes. Royal Doulton figure, A Spook HN625. £1,600. Oct 00.

430

Gorringes, Lewes. 18thC Meissen figure Scaramouche, c1744, blue X swords mark, 5.5in high. £1,600. Feb 01.

431

W & H Peacock, Bedford. Doulton Lambeth tankard, incised rabbits by Hannah Barlow. £1,600. Dec 02.

432

Amersham Auction Rooms, Bucks. Late 18thC Chinese Export porcelain covered bowl, 9in. £1,600. June 02.

433

Wintertons Ltd, Lichfield. Moorcroft Dawn pattern vase, c1930, impressed Moorcroft, Made in England, signature, 18.5cm. £1,600. July 02.

434

Louis Taylor, Stoke on Trent. Ruskin high-fired vase. £1,600. Mar 01.

435

Gorringes, Lewes. Clarice Cliff Sunrise pattern lotus jug, 9.75in. £1,600. Sep 02.

436

Wintertons Ltd, Lichfield. Berlin porcelain plaque, 19thC, impressed KPM sceptre mark, 25 x 17cm. £1,600. Nov 02.

437

Gorringes, Lewes. Clarice Cliff orange house pattern ribbed squat vase, 4in high. £1,550. Feb 01.

438

Andrew Hartley, Ilkley. Wemyss pottery figure by Plichta, modelled seated and painted with red roses, 15in wide. £1,550. Aug 00.

439

Sworders, Stansted Mount-fitchet. 19thC Meissen oval porcelain plaque 'The Chocolate Girl', after Jean-Etienne Liotard, u/g blue X swords mark, paper label for Sir Edward Reid, 15.5 x 11cm. £1,550. July 03.

440

Hamptons, Godalming. Copeland parian bust of 'The Mother', 1872-5, after model by R. Monti, (slight firing faults) impressed 'Ceramic and Crystal Palace Art Union', 38cm. £1,550. Jan 02.

441

Gorringes, Lewes. Pair of Clarice Cliff teddy bear bookends. £1,500. July 99.

442

Gorringes, Lewes. Ralph Wood, a pottery model of a cockerel, detachable head, c1800/20, 8.75in high. (restorations) £1,500. Dec 00.

443

Gorringes, Lewes. Minton majolica wine cooler, year mark for 1867, 15.5in. AF. £1,500. Sep 2000.

444

Sworders, Stansted Mount-fitchet. Royal Doulton figure, Odds and Ends, HN 1844, 7.75in high. £1,500. May 01.

445

Hamptons, Godalming. A fine satsuma vase, Meiji, in gilt 'Meizan', 12.5cm. £1,500. Mar 02.

446

Cheffins, Cambridge. 1930s pomegranate pattern vase, 30.5cm high. £1,500. Sep 01.

447

Andrew Hartley, Ilkley. Pair Royal Worcester vases, shape no G702, signed Jas. Stinton, 5.75in high. £1,500. Aug 00.

448

Louis Taylor, Stoke on Trent. Wedgwood basalt plaque, 'The Choice of Hercules', 8 x 11in. £1,500. Dec 02.

449

Rosebery's, London. Meissen twin handled soup tureen, 36cm wide. £1,500. June 03.

450

Gorringes, Lewes. Pair of majolica basketware straw-berry servers (lacks 1 sugar, 2 creamers) PODR marks for 1868, prob. George Jones, 9in. (1 damaged) £1,500. Apr 01.

451

Gorringes, Bexhill. New Hall porcelain 23 piece part tea service, gilt swags and green foliage. £1,500. May 02.

452

Henry Adams, Chichester. Chinese dish, Kangxi (1662-1722) with equestrian figures, 6 character Chenghua mark in u/g blue, small frit and crack to rim. £1,500. Sep 02.

453

Mellors & Kirk, Nottingham. Royal Crown Derby vase. £1,500. Feb 03.

454

Gorringes, Lewes. An 18thC Meissen figure of Harlequin c1744, blue X swords mark, 5.75in high. £1,500. Oct 01.

455

Wintertons Ltd, Lichfield. Life-size terracotta figure of a black schoolboy, c1900, prob. Goldscheider, 120cm, poss. by Haniroff. £1,500. Mar 02.

456

Wintertons Ltd, Lichfield. Derby ice pail, c1815, painted by Richard Dodson, red enamelled crown/cross batons mark, gilders number 40, two slight stress cracks, 25.5cm high. £1,500. Mar 02.

457

Peter Wilson, Nantwich. 19thC Spode tureen, transfer printed with 'Hog hunters meeting by surprise a tigress and her cubs', impressed mk., 5in high, hairline crack, crazing. £1,450. Nov 00.

458

Gorringes, Lewes. Large Minton parian group Amazon on horseback. £1,450. July 99.

459

Hamptons, Godalming. Late 17thC Frankfurt type Delft jar. £1,450. Mar 01.

460

Andrew Hartley, Ilkley. 19thC Meissen group 'Evening', 13.75in. £1,450. Sep 99.

> The illustrations in these pages are in descending price order. The price range is indicated at the top of each page.

461

Louis Taylor, Stoke on Trent. Royal Doulton, Bo Peep, HN 1328. £1,450. Sep 02.

462

Gorringes, Lewes. 19thC Meissen Wagner inspired group, incised L149, 10in. £1,450. Dec 00.

463

Hamptons, Godalming. English porcelain dessert service, c1796-1800, late Caughley or early Coalport? rustic figural scenes, gilder's No. 120. (21) £1,450. Sep 01.

464

Sworders, Stansted Mount-fitchet. Moorcroft Macintyre florianware vase, printed and signed marks, c1907, 20cm high. £1,450. Oct 02.

465

Louis Taylor, Stoke on Trent. Birks & Co., Pâte-sur-Pâte plaque. £1,450. Dec 02.

466

Rupert Toovey, Washington, Sussex. Pair of Mintons Renaissance-style jardinieres, c1878, 30cm. £1,400. July 03.

467

Mellors & Kirk, Nottingham. Coalport vase, St Guilio, Lake of Orta, 49cm, printed, impressed, mks. gilt script title, c1890. £1,400. June 03.

468

Wintertons Ltd, Lichfield. Cypriot biscuit earthenware amphora, with authentication certificate verifying 700 BC, 33cm high. £1,400. May 99.

Hammer Prices £1,500-£1,400

469

Dreweatt Neate, Newbury. Liverpool delft char-pot, manner of Zachariah Barnes, 23cm dia., 3rd qtr 18thC. (rim chips) £1,400. June 02.

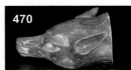

470

Sworders, Stansted Mount-fitchet. Ralph Wood fox head stirrup cup, 5.5in. (repair to ear and rim) £1,400. May 01.

471

Andrew Hartley, Ilkley. Pair 19thC Meissen figures of a shepherd and shepherdess, 10in high. £1,400. Aug 00.

472

Gorringes, Lewes. Clarice Cliff red autumn Stamford teapot, pair of cups, saucers and a plate. £1,400. June 00.

473

Sworders, Stansted Mount-fitchet. R. Doulton 'Sunshine Girl', HN 1348, 5.5in high. (restored) £1,400. Feb 02.

474

Gorringes, Lewes. 18thC cockerel 7.5in. £1,400. Apr 01.

475

Gorringes, Lewes. Art Deco Shelley 8 piece tête à tête, sugar bowl cracked. £1,400. Feb 01.

476

Gorringes, Lewes. Pair 19thC Meissen figures, 13in. £1,400. Feb 00.

477

Gorringes, Lewes. Moorcroft vase with fish swimming amongst pond weed, 14.5in. (restored) £1,400. Sep 00.

478

Lots Road Auctions, Chelsea. Art Deco Goldscheider figure of a seated young boy, 104cm high, af. £1,400. Oct 02.

479

Ambrose, Loughton. Royal Doulton figure, 'Mamselle' c1924-38, HN series 659, artist's monogram 'W', 14cm high. £1,400. Sep 00.

Hammer Prices £1,400-£1,300

480

Woolley & Wallis, Salisbury. Ralph Wood pearlware figure of Benjamin Franklin, c1790, 33cm. £1,400. Mar 00.

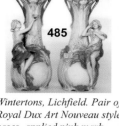

485

Wintertons, Lichfield. Pair of Royal Dux Art Nouveau style vases, applied pink mark, impressed marks 824 & 825, 43cm. £1,400. May 02.

481

Wintertons, Lichfield. Matt glaze Moorcroft Fish pattern vase, c1930, imp'd Moorcroft, Made in England, signature, 19cm. £1,400. July 02.

486

Phillips, London. Doulton. Prototype figure of a Harbour Master (1967) attributed to Mary Nicoll. £1,400. Nov 99.

482

Gorringes, Lewes. Set of 10 early 19thC Mandarin plates with figure centres, 8.75in. £1,400. Mar 02.

487

Cheffins, Cambridge. Pair of 18thC Stahn Paris porcelain ice pails, 'Angouleme' sprigs, crowned CP marks in red, 20cm dia. £1,400. Dec 00.

483

Gorringes, Lewes. Minton majolica bowl, date code 1871, 6in £1,400. June 03.

488

Tring Market Auctions, Herts. Royal Dux figural centrepiece bowl. £1,380. Jan 02.

484

Amersham Auction Rooms, Bucks. 18thC Meissen group, 7.75in high. £1,400. Oct 02.

489

Louis Taylor, Stoke on Trent. Set of eight W. Moorcroft Macintyre plates, 7.5in. £1,350. Sep 03.

490

Dockree's, Manchester, Set 12 Dresden monkey musicians after Meissen originals, 6in high approx. £1,350. Sep 99.

491

Andrew Hartley, Ilkley. Canton Famille rose bowl with ormolu mounts, 17.5in wide. £1,350. Sep 99.

492

Sworders, Stansted Mount-fitchet. 1920s majolica figure, 2 squirrels. £1,350. May 00.

493

Hamptons, Godalming. Pair 19thC Coalport vases, green printed marks, red titles, No. V5377, 35cm. £1,350. Sep 01.

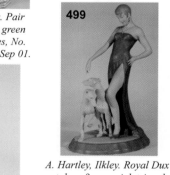

494

Gorringes, Lewes. Bow figure of a Huntsman, c1755, 7in. £1,350. Dec 00.

495

Amersham Auction Rooms, Bucks. Early 19thC Spode earthenware skimming bowl, 16in dia. £1,350. Sep 02.

496

Canterbury Auc. Galleries, Kent. Nantgarw plate, centre enamelled in colours, 8.5in. (discoloured, scratched and rubbed) £1,350. Aug 03.

497

Gorringes, Lewes. Royal Dux figure of a nude bather, No. 2996, 14.25in. £1,350. Feb 01.

498

Sworders, Stansted Mount-fitchet. R. Doulton ltd. edn. 'Jack Point', HN 3295, no. 46/85. £1,350. Mar 03.

499

A. Hartley, Ilkley. Royal Dux art deco figure, pink triangle mark. 15in. £1,300. Feb 00.

500

Gorringes, Lewes. R. Doulton Chang vase, larva glaze, Noke, 7in. £1,300. June 00.

501

Gorringes, Lewes. 17thC Arita dish, deer in landscape, 16.25in. £1,300. Sep 00.

502

Woolley & Wallis, Salisbury. Pr. of Meissen figural dishes, X swords mks. 2858 and 2863 incised, c1880, 31.5cm. (some damage) £1,300. June 00.

503

Gorringes, Lewes. 18thC English Delft chinoiserie decorated flower brick, 7in. £1,300. June 00.

504

Gorringes, Lewes. Late 19thC Galle style cat, removable head, monogram GR on back foot, 13in. £1,300. July 01.

505

Gorringes, Lewes.19thC Sunderland lustre mariners puzzle jug with rhymes and compass, 8in. £1,300. Oct 00.

506

Biddle & Webb, Birmingham. George Jones majolica pot with cover. £1,300. June 02.

507

Dreweatt Neate, Newbury. Mason's Ironstone footbath jug, dragon head handle beneath spout, 30.6cm, blue crown & drape mark, c1820-40. (faults) £1,300. June 02.

508

Gorringes, Lewes. Bow figure of a seated male drummer, c1756, 7in. £1,300. Dec 00.

Prices quoted are hammer prices which excluded the buyer's premium. Adding 15% will give an approximation to the buying price.

509

Stride & Son, Chichester. 19thC transfer printed foot-bath, by Pountney and Allies, Bristol. £1,300. May 02.

510

Clevedon Salerooms, Bristol. 19thC Staffs meat dish txfr. decoration, Night Sea Battle with 'Blanche' & 'La Pique', 20in wide. £1,300. Feb 02.

511

Mellors & Kirk, Nottingham. Royal Doulton bone china figure of The Wandering Minstrel. £1,300. Feb 2003.

512

Woolley & Wallis, Salisbury. Maiolica albarello, probably Caltagirone, 17thC, 37cm. £1,300. Mar 00.

513

Gorringes, Lewes. 18thC Meissen figure of Scapin from the Commedia Dell'Art, c1744, blue X swords mark, 5.75in. £1,300. Feb 01.

514

Wintertons Ltd, Lichfield. Derby teapot, c1765, Chinese figures, 14cm. £1,300. May 03.

515

Gorringes, Lewes. Pair of Moorcroft MacIntyre vases, Florian Ware mark, green WM monogram, Rd 347807 & M1057, 7in. £1,300. Apr 01.

516

Dreweatt Neate, Newbury. Copeland parian 'Night', after Raphaelle Monti, 66cm, impressed/incised mks., c1862, damage. £1,300. June 02.

517

Mellors & Kirk, Nottingham. 2 Derby vases, probably by Daniel Lucas, 53cm, circular 'Bloor Derby' or banner mks. c1825. £1,300. June 03.

518

W & H Peacock, Bedford. 19thC Wedgwood majolica strawberries and cream set, (some restoration) 43cm wide. £1,300. July 02.

519

Peter Wilson, Nantwich. 7 Shorter and Son toby jugs of D'Oyly Carte Opera Co. (crazing) £1,300. July 02.

520

Gorringes, Lewes. Chinese Kangxi period porcelain vase, 13in overall. £1,300. Sep 02.

521

Louis Taylor, Stoke on Trent. Pr. salt glazed sauceboats, 3 x 8in. (damage/restoration) £1,300. June 03.

522

Woolley & Wallis, Salisbury. 18thC Japanese Kakiemon dish raised on 3 feet, 14cm. £1,250. Sep 00.

Hammer Prices £1,300-£1,250

523

Phillips, Bath. Set 3 triple pearlware flower vases, 21cm high. £1,250. May 00.

524

A. Hartley, Ilkley. Ashworth Ironstone part dinner service. (45 piece) £1,250. Aug 00.

525

Amersham Auction Rooms, Bucks. Early 20thC Mintons majolica tureen, in low relief, 7in high. £1,250. Mar 01.

526

Gorringes, Lewes. 18thC Delft ballooning plate, leaf swag border, 9in. (2in crack and fritting) £1,250. July 02.

527

Louis Taylor, Stoke. R. Doulton character jug, Cavalier with goatee beard. £1,250. Dec 02.

528

Canterbury Auc. Galleries, Kent. Pr. Macintyre Moorcroft Florian ware vases, 8.75in high. £1,250. Dec 01.

529

Dockree's, Manchester. Mintons ewer, signed F. N. Sutton, 11.5in. £1,250. Sep 99.

530

Woolley & Wallis, Salisbury. Worcester dolphin ewer creamboat, c1765, 8.5cm. £1,250. Sep 00.

531

Tring Market Auctions, Herts. 18thC Famille Rose meat dish, 13in. £1,250. Sep 02.

532

Amersham Auction Rooms, Bucks. Royal Doulton china Sketch Girl, No N444, date 5-24, 7.5in. £1,250. June 01.

533

Sworders, Stansted Mount-fitchet. Montelupo Maiolica dish, 17thC, 29.7cm. (flaked and cracked) £1,250. July 03.

31

Hammer Prices £1,250-£1,200

534

Louis Taylor, Stoke. Royal Doulton, Mamselle, HN 724. (restored) £1,250. Sep 02.

535

Andrew Hartley, Ilkley. Pair of Royal Worcester porcelain vases, 11.25in. £1,250. Apr 02.

536

Sworders, Stansted Mountfitchet. Early 19thC tea/coffee set, c1800-1810, patt. no. 612. (38) £1,250. Dec 02.

537

Eastbourne Auction Rooms, Sussex. Royal Crown Derby, Ashbourne Hedgehog paperweight. £1,250. Mar 02.

538

Louis Taylor, Stoke on Trent. Royal Doulton 'Pierrette'. £1,220. Sep 01.

539

Hyperion Auctions, St Ives, Huntingdon. Clarice Cliff Lotus Jug. £1,200. July 99.

540

Woolley & Wallis, Salisbury. Staffs King Charles spaniel, 19thC, 21cm. £1,200. Mar 00.

541

Lots Road Auctions, Chelsea. Pr. 19thC Meissen chocolate cups/covers. £1,200. Oct 99.

542

Woolley & Wallis, Salisbury. English 19thC pottery foot-bath, 49cm. £1,200. Sep 00.

543

Gorringes, Lewes. Minton majolica jardiniere, date code 1883 (rim chip), 14.25in. £1,200. Feb 01.

544

Gorringes, Lewes. 18thC English (?) Delft flower brick with flowers and birds, 8in. £1,200. June 00.

545

Woolley & Wallis, Salisbury. Derby models of a ram and ewe, incised X mark, c1760, 13cm across. £1,200. Mar 00.

546

Woolley & Wallis, Salisbury. Goldscheider bronzed terra-cotta figure of a boy, incised & impressed marks, numerals, rectangular pad inscribed 'Frederick Goldscheider Wien', 84cm. £1,200. Sep 00.

547

Gorringes, Lewes. Moorcroft anemone pattern vase, dated 1953, 14.5in. £1,200. Dec 00.

548

Gorringes, Lewes. Moorcroft florian bowl, 'W Moorcroft des' painted mark, 9in. £1,200. Dec 00.

549

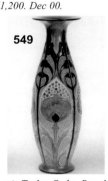

Louis Taylor, Stoke. Royal Doulton. Mark V. Marshall stoneware vase. £1,200. Dec 01.

550

Woolley & Wallis, Salisbury. Pr. Meissen models Bustards, X swords in blue, '2020' & '2015' incised, 19thC, 37cm, restorations. £1,200. Sep 00.

551

Dee, Atkinson & Harrison, Driffield. Rockingham dessert service. (14) £1,200. Apr 01.

552

Gorringes, Lewes. Royal Worcester ltd. edn. Wellington by Bernard Winskill, No 357 of 750, rosewood base, 15in wide. £1,200. June 00.

553

Gorringes, Lewes. Linthorpe. Christopher Dresser pottery vase, shape 168, by Henry Tooth, 18in. £1,200. June 01.

554

Gorringes, Lewes. Doulton Lambeth bloater fish jar and cover with fin knop, scaled body, 5.75in. £1,200. Mar 01.

555

Louis Taylor, Stoke on Trent. Royal Doulton, Dulcinea, HN 1419. £1,200. Sep 02.

556

Sworders, Stansted Mount-fitchet. Wedgwood lustre ginger jar/cover, no 25486, 8.5in dia. £1,200. Ju.ly 01.

557

Hamptons, Godalming. Meissen group of Count von Bruhl's Tailor, late 19thC, u/g blue X swords mark, incised No 171, impressed No 6, 21.3cm high. £1,200. Sep 01.

558

Eastbourne Auctions. George Jones Majolica sweetmeat, damage. £1,200. Mar 02.

559

Mervyn Carey, Tenterden. Early 19thC Mason's ironstone part dessert service. £1,200. Dec 01.

560

Hyperion Auctions, St Ives, Huntingdon. Early 19thC basket on stand, 'Beemaster' pattern. £1,200. Feb 01.

561

Andrew Hartley, Ilkley. Doulton Lambeth stoneware jardiniere by Hannah Barlow, impressed and incised marks, 16in wide. £1,200. Feb 02.

562

Louis Taylor, Stoke. Royal Doulton, Australian Digger, prob. HN322. £1,200. Sep 02.

563

Louis Taylor, Stoke. R. Doulton 'The Sketch Girl'. (slight damage) £1,200. Dec 02.

The numbering system aids the editorial analysis at the beginning of each section as well as providing a reader reference.

564

Clarke Gammon, Guildford. Tin glaze charger, prob. 18thC Bristol, 13.5in. £1,200. Feb 03.

565

Louis Taylor, Stoke on Trent. Royal Doulton, Pierette, HN 43. £1,200. Sep 02.

566

Gorringes, Lewes. Moorcroft flambe vase, impressed marks, 11in, £1,200. Mar 03.

567

Maxwells, Wilmslow. Clarice Cliff Bizarre lotus vase, txfr. mk., inscribed 'Inspiration Caprice' 10in. £1,200. Sep 02.

568

Louis Taylor, Stoke. Royal Doulton, Jester, HN 71. £1,200, Dec 02.

569

Canterbury Auc. Galleries. Clarice Cliff Fantasque Lotus pattern jug, Orange Chintz pattern, 11.5in high. (scratching) £1,150. Aug 03.

570

Louis Taylor, Stoke on Trent. Royal Doulton bull terrier. £1,150. Sep 01.

571

Andrew Hartley, Ilkley. Pair Grainger Worcester pot pourri vases, date mark 1897, 8.25in high. £1,150. Aug 03.

572

Academy Auctioneers, Ealing. Pair R. Crown Derby vases, Rd. 1902, 13in. £1,150. Aug 99.

573

Ambrose, Loughton. Ironstone dinner service, Copeland Spode 19thC. (50) £1,150. Dec 99.

574

Sworders, Stansted Mount-fitchet. Moorcroft Macintyre vase, no. 2862. £1,150. May 01.

575

Woolley & Wallis, Salisbury. Derby biscuit gp. of 2 virgins waking Cupid, after Pierre Stephan, incised 195, c1780, 31.5cm. £1,150. June 00.

576

Sworders, Stansted Mount-fitchet. 2 Alcock drug jars, Tamarinds and Honey, 12in., restored lids. £1,150. Feb 02.

577

Louis Taylor, Stoke. Royal Doulton, Blighty, should be HN 323. £1,150. Sep 02.

578

Canterbury Auc. Galleries, Kent. Moorcroft Florian ware vase, Revived Cornflower/ Brown Chrysanthemum patt., 5.75in. £1,150. Dec 01.

579

Louis Taylor, Stoke. Royal Doulton, The Little Mother, HN 1399. af. £1,150. Sep 02.

580

Amersham Auctions, Bucks. Moorcroft vase, c1916, Pansy design, impressed backstamps, incl. Burslem mark & painted William Moorcroft signature, 12.5in high. £1,150. Mar 02.

581

D M Nesbit, Southsea. 49 Beswick Beatrix Potter figures, with brown Beswick stamps. Includes scarce cat 'Simpkin'. £1,150. Feb 03.

582

Amersham Auctions, Bucks. Pair 19thC Minton majolica vases as a cluster of three graduated bamboo shoots, 6.5in high. £1,150. June 02.

583

Peter Wilson, Nantwich. 19thC pearlware jug, transfer/hand coloured 'The Tythe Pig', verse, m'gram 'WV', 10in. (firing crack) £1,150. Apr 00.

584

Louis Taylor, Stoke. Masons Ironstone dinner service. (damage). £1,150. Dec 02.

585

Andrew Hartley, Ilkley. Pair R. Worcester figures, signed Handley, shape no. 1388, 11in high. £1,150. Apr 02.

586

Phillips, Scotland. Pr Staffs greyhounds, of Disraeli type, 27cm. £1,100. Nov 99.

587

Mellors & Kirk, Nottingham. Porcelain plaque, probably Worcester, by R F Perling, signed, after Myles Birket Foster, 30.5 x 46cm, c1870. £1,100. June 03.

588

Sworders, Stansted Mount-fitchet. Montelupo Maiolica dish, with a musketeer and another of a Halberdier, 17thC, 30.7cm and 30.2cm. damage. (2) £1,100. July 03.

Hammer Prices £1,100-£1,050

589

Andrew Hartley, Ilkley. Pair George Jones porcelain vases, with pâte-sur-pâte bird panels 8in high. £1,100. Oct 99.

590

Sworders, Stansted Mount-fitchet. Montelupo Maiolica dish, soldier carrying axe, 17thC, 31.5cm. (chipped and cracked) £1,100. July 03.

591

Woolley & Wallis, Salisbury. Beswick Beatrix Potter figure of Duchess with flowers, gilt marks, 9.5cm. £1,100. Mar 00.

592

Ambrose, Loughton. Royal Doulton, 'Scotties' c1928-38, HN series, 1281 'E.H.' 14cm. £1,100. Sep 00.

593

Woolley & Wallis, Salisbury. Vienna dish, a young wood nymph on rocks beside a lake, signed 'Dittrich', inscribed 'Mimphe am Meere', c1870, 24cm. £1,100. Mar 00.

594

Gorringes, Lewes. Moorcroft Claremont, pattern ovoid vase, 7in. £1,100. June 00.

595

Woolley & Wallis, Salisbury. Chinese tureen/underdish, Qianlong, 1736-95, 37cm. (chip to knop) £1,100. June 00.

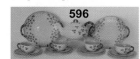

596

Dee, Atkinson & Harrison, Driffield. Belleek part tea set. (25 pieces) £1,100, Mar 00.

597

Gorringes, Lewes. Ralph Wood, a pottery sauceboat as a fox head with swan handle, c1785, 6.5in. £1,100. Dec 00.

598

Dreweatt Neate, Newbury. Lambeth delft wet drug jar, O:LAURIN, 20cm, c1780. (chips) £1,100. June 03.

599

Andrew Hartley, Ilkley. Pair Royal Worcester vases, shape 1654, 9.5in. £1,100. Apr 00.

600

Hamptons, Godalming. Royal Worcester blush ivory pot pourri, puce printed mark, shape No. 2048, date code 1909, 34cm. £1,100. Jan 02.

601

Gorringes, Lewes. Royal Doulton red haired clown character jug. £1,100. Apr 00.

602

Ambrose, Loughton. Pair of Burmantofts faience vases, incised peacock decoration, 23cm, impressed No. 2202. £1,100. Mar 02.

603

Gorringes, Lewes. William Staite Murray, studio pottery stoneware vase, pale grey glaze, impressed mark, 12in. £1,100. Apr 01.

604

Gorringes, Lewes. Royal Doulton seated jester, signed Noke. (af) £1,100. Apr 01.

605

Amersham Auctions, Bucks. 19thC Doulton Lambeth stone ware table lamp by Mark V Marshall. £1,100. June 01.

606

Hamptons, Godalming. Pair Royal Crown Derby vases, patt. no. 1131, green printed mark and date code1898, 21cm high. £1,100. May 02.

607

Canterbury Auc. Galleries, Kent. Bloor Derby porcelain dessert service, c1830, stains, repairs. (33) £1,100. Feb 02.

608

Cheffins, Cambridge. Early 19thC Pearlware horse, 15cm. poss. St Anthony's Pottery of Newcastle. £1,100. Apr 03.

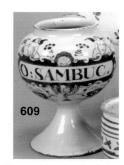

609

Dreweatt Neate, Newbury. Lambeth delft blue and white wet drug jar O:SAMBUC, 20cm, c1780. (chips and glaze flakes) £1,100. June 03.

610

Gorringes, Lewes. Theodore Deck majolica jardiniere with dragons in a turquoise glaze, 15.5in. £1,100. Apr 01.

611

Gorringes, Lewes. Clarice Cliff 'Rudyard' vase, shape 6028, 7in. £1,100. Apr 02.

612

Rupert Toovey, Washington, Sussex. Chinese famille rose Qianlong armorial porcelain part service, pieces with faults. £1,100. Feb 03.

613

Louis Taylor, Stoke on Trent. Wedgwood charger by Alfred Powell, mono-grammed, 18.5in. £1,100. Mar 03.

614

David Duggleby, Scarborough. R. Worcester Ariosto inkwell, printed marks and date code 1862, 14.5cm. £1,050. June 03.

615

Bristol Auctions, Bristol. Staffordshire Prattware pipe as a monkey, tail forming the mouthpiece, c1800, 11.2cm. £1,050. May 03.

616

Gorringes, Lewes. R. Doulton Chang vase, larva glaze. Noke, 7in. £1,050. June 00.

617

Dockree's, Manchester. Pair Vienna vases, 12.75in, c1890, damage. £1,050. Nov 00.

618

Gorringes, Bexhill. Clarice Cliff Fantasque Isis jug blue chintz patt. £1,050. Oct 99.

The illustrations in these pages are in descending price order. The price range is indicated at the top of each page.

619

Gorringes, Lewes. Pair 19thC Staffs mastiffs, spill vases, 6.5in. £1,050. Oct 00.

620

Sworders, Stansted Mountfitchet. R. Doulton Beefeater holding an illustrated London news sheet, bears green lion over circular 'Royal Doulton' mark (1922-27) initials NLW in red, 7.75in. £1,050. May 01.

621

Amersham Auctions, Bucks. Pair 19thC Meissen porcelain salts, of reclining figures in 18thC costume, 4.5in & 5in. £1,050. Feb 02.

622

Louis Taylor, Stoke. Pair of Staffs elephants, 7.75in, 19thC. (damage) £1,050. Dec 01.

623

Louis Taylor, Stoke on Trent. Royal Doulton, Pierette, HN 1749. £1,050. Sep 02.

624

Potteries Specialist Auctions, Stoke. R. Doulton, Spring HN1774, by Richard Garbe, RA. Restored. £1,050. Feb 03.

625

Potteries Specialist Auctions, Stoke. Beswick Aberdeen Angus calf, gloss. (special commission) £1,050. Feb 03.

626

Gorringes, Lewes. 19thC Meissen gp. cherubs as architects with rulers, plans, book, 8.5in, restored. £1,050. Dec 00.

627

Woolley & Wallis, Salisbury. Mason's Ironstone pt. dinner service, some impressed, c1820. (23) £1,050. Sep 00.

628

Canterbury Auc. Galleries. 19th/20thC Limoges pâte sur pâte porcelain panel, indistinct 'Marchal' incised Limoges, 7.25 x 5.25in. £1,050. Oct 02.

629

Richard Winterton, Burton on Trent. Series of 6 Susie Cooper 'seagull' plates, 17cm dia and matching larger plate, 22cm dia. (7) £1,050. Apr 03.

630

Bristol Auctions, Bristol. Clarice Cliff Biarritz dinner service, Orange Taormina pattern. (34) £1,050. May 03.

631

Locke & England, Leamington Spa. Pair of Martin Brothers stoneware wall pockets. £1,050. Nov 02.

632

Louis Taylor, Stoke on Trent. Royal Doulton, Reflections, HN 1848. £1,050. Sep 02.

633

Dee, Atkinson & Harrison, Driffield. Fielding's Crown Devon musical jug 'Sally', from the film 'Sally in Our Alley', 9in. £1,050. July 99.

634

John Taylors, Louth. Large Japanese Sumida ware vase with climbing monkeys, 47cm high. £1,040. July 01.

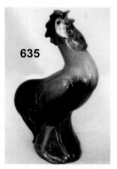

635

Sworders, Stansted Mountfitchet. A rare Royal Doulton cockerel, 8in. £1,040. Sep 01.

636

Tring Market Auctions, Herts. Early 19thC meat dish made for export to America, txfr. printed with The Boston State House pattern, impressed Rogers and 18 to base, 18.75in long. £1,020. Nov 02.

Hammer Prices £1,050-£1,000

637

Wintertons, Lichfield. Porcelain tea set, c1815, probrably Coalport, patt. no. 1009, teapot 16.5cm. (30) £1,000. July 03.

638

Gorringes, Lewes. Moorcroft Tudric bowl in Moonlit Blue patt., hammered pewter foot, 1311, 10.25in. £1,000. Feb 00.

639

Gorringes, Lewes. Doulton Lambeth studio decorated charger, after Birkett Foster by Lizzie Arnold, Sept 1881, 15.5in. £1,000. Apr 00.

640

Woolley & Wallis, Salisbury. 6 Derby trios, matching milk jug/sugar bowl, red painted marks, pattern no 753, early 19thC. £1,000. June 00.

641

Woolley & Wallis, Salisbury. French porcelain set of the Four Seasons, as maidens, X swords marks, late 19thC, 32cm. £1,000. June 00.

642

Woolley & Wallis, Salisbury. English Delft puzzle jug, mid 18thC, 18cm. (crack around base of handle and small glaze chips) £1,000. June 00.

Hammer Price £1,000

643

Canterbury Auc. Galleries, Kent. Moorcroft Florian peacock vase, brown printed mark for McIntyre & Co, green sig. mark, c1902, 5in high. £1,000. Aug 03.

644

Wintertons Ltd, Lichfield. Goldscheider exotic dancer, restored, 18in. £1,000. Nov 00.

645

Crows, Dorking. Buff stone-ware belamine jug. £1,000. June 03.

646

Gorringes, Lewes. Gold-scheider cold painted terra-cotta figure with Pandoras box, with electric light, sig. E Tell, 27in. £1,000. June 00.

647

Rosebery's, London. Dessert service, c1840, poss. Derby, (7). £1,000. Sep 02.

648

Gorringes, Lewes. 13 piece Grimwades Peter Rabbit childs teaset. £1,000. June 00.

649

Gorringes, Lewes. Doulton Burslem Tudor umbrella stand, original paper label below, 23in. (base cracks) £1,000. June 00.

650

Amersham Auctions, Bucks. Pair 19thC Japanese Imari porcelain vases 14in on gilt brass stands. £1,000. July 02.

651

Gorringes, Lewes. Beswick Beatrix Potter figure of Duchess with Flowers. (gold mark) £1,000. July 00.

652

R. Wintertons. Burton on Trent. Reissner & Kessel art nouveau vase, c1900, printed mark and impressed '740,7' 55cm, damage. £1,000. Sep 01.

653

Amersham Auctions, Bucks. R. Doulton china Beefeater, impressed 500 and date 9-20, 8in. £1,000. June 01.

654

Sworders, Stansted Mount-fitchet. Royal Worcester vase, by H Davis, cover and finial damage, 11in. £1,000. Sep 01.

655

Rosebery's, London. Moorcroft 'Frilled Orchid' pattern vase. £1,000. Oct 01.

656

Gorringes, Lewes. Moorcroft pomegranate waisted vase, 10.75in. £1,000. Feb 01.

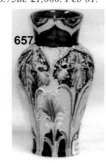

657

Louis Taylor, Stoke. William Moorcroft MacIntyre vase, 4.25in. £1,000. Sep 02.

658

Peter Wilson, Nantwich. R. Doulton bone china coffee set H4927, 'Reynard the Fox'. (18 incl lids) £1,000. Nov 01.

659

Louis Taylor, Stoke. Clarice Cliff Isis vase. £1,000. Dec 01.

660

Louis Taylor, Stoke. Pair of Doulton Hannah Barlow vases. (2) £1,000. Sep 01.

661

Gorringes, Lewes. 5 Meissen /Dresden monkey band figs., largest 5.5in. £1,000. Feb 01.

662

Gorringes, Bexhill. Moorcroft vase, impressed marks, signed, 7.25in. £1,000. Feb 03.

663

Woolley & Wallis, Salisbury. Pair of Minton porcelain figures, no marks, c1830-40, 14cm. £1,000. June 00.

664

R. Winterton, Burton on Trent. Pair creamware bough pots/stands, c1790. £1,000. Apr 01.

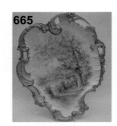

665

R. Winterton, Burton on Trent. Fieldings Crown Devon wall plaque. £1,000. Aug 02.

666

Wintertons Ltd, Lichfield. Royal Crown Derby Imari tea for two set, pattern 2451. £1,000. May 02.

667

Gorringes, Lewes. Ralph Wood creamware thinman toby jug, 9.25in. (restored) £1,000. Apr 00.

668

Sotheby's, Billingshurst. Staffordshire figure of George Washington, possibly John Parr or Kent & Parr, 1870s. £1,000. June 00.

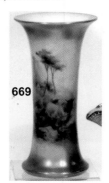

669

Andrew Hartley, Ilkley. Royal Worcester porcelain vase, shape no. G923, signed H Stinton, 7.5in. £1,000. Feb 03.

Section 4

Sample Analysis

Section Four is extensive offering almost 500 lots representing hammer prices between a £1,000 and £500. From our reckoning over the last several years there are over fifty per cent more ceramics lots sold at auction in this price range than is sold at between £1,000 and £2,000, the price range covered in Section Three. This is therefore a very fertile price range which will be well perused by dealers as well as collectors. And the larger number of lots sold means that it is now possible to compare dozens of lots representing a huge ceramic variety and yet occupying the same price, or near price range.

We can expect that everything that has gone before will be present in this Section, including British, European and Asian porcelain and a full complement of the various pottery bodies. We can also now expect that the novice reader studying the ceramics market for the first time, should be well prepared to notice some of the important lots and some of the more important issues in this Section. These may not, and perhaps should not always be the same lots or the same issues selected by the Editor as worthy of comment. Remember, every individual, be they dealer or collector will construct their own analyses around their own experiences. We intend that the sample analysis will provide a stepping stone or an example to aid the analyses of readers.

Image 672 offers some extremely badly damaged items of Sevres hard-paste porcelain from c1820 and this lot is certainly worthy of further discussion. It is my opinion that the new century has brought a sea change in our attitude to damage and in this case the over-riding factor must have been the sheer quality or the rarity of the pieces concerned. If someone is prepared to spend well over a £1,000, with added premium, to acquire this lot then we must anticipate that these pieces have some importance. One is prompted therefore to consider how much this part coffee service would have fetched if perfect? Under £5,000? Or over £5,000? In which case it would have boosted the appearance of French porcelain amongst the crème de la crème in Section One.

If Goldscheider is your forte there are many examples to go on and 680 may be your spur to search out at least twenty examples throughout this volume. Remember our first example fetched £10,000 in Section One. Never underestimate Goldscheider.

Image 691 illustrates a pair of pugs. Unfortunately, it isn't a theme which can be pursued through the *Index* but there are many easy-to-spot examples of pugs (and many other dogs) throughout this volume. Even in this Section there are at least seven to check out. Examples may be unattributed, or they could be Royal Worcester, or they may be Austrian earthenware, or Meissen, or Staffordshire, or terracotta. See images 733, 942, 945, 949, 986 and 1090. Pugs are never cheap.

The last time we encountered Pilkingtons Lancastrian was image 68, when a Richard Joyce vase fetched £7,600 in 2003. Now at 694, 833, 875 and 994, we can check out the prices of further pieces and note their price range is £950 to £620, all pieces selling in 2002. Pilkingtons does not reappear until three small bowls fetch £60 on page 120.

The Editor has spotted a Phillip's Longport blue and white meat dish, (704) which fetched £920 back in 2000 in Salisbury at Woolley and Wallis. Experts in blue and white will no doubt consider whether this dish is the Edward and George Phillips partnership of c1822-1834 or the continuation of the Longport factory under George Phillips from 1834-1848, who it is believed added the Staffordshire knot to the mark although we are lacking this detail in the caption. I will opt for the earlier partnership based on feel and style. In any event this dish was well worth its price and should have proved a sound investment. Remember, it is always wise to buy the very best you can afford within your budget. With a little bit of luck this should improve the chances of your purchase increasing in value in years to come.

Whether or not you call a pig a pig, or a swine, the language seems to sound sensual or earthy! However we must use the term pig as in our next example the 'Rye' versions are famous. No reader, not even a novice should miss the humour implicit in, or expect the twentieth century Rye pig at 731 to sell for less than the £880 hammer price shown. Never underestimate pigs in general. Be prepared to browse these pages for as many as you can find right down to the Yorkshire pig money-box on page 112. They are nearly always worth putting your money into!

The London saltglaze mug at 757 is worthy of comment. Nineteenth and twentieth century pots are as common as can be and have only limited value. However go back into the first half of the eighteenth century and then find a dated example like this one and you can forget about the large rim chips! £850 is a fair price. They do not appear that often and you may have to dig into the Thames mud to find another. I should imagine your chances of finding one through the trade or in the Thames mud are about evens either way!

Readers may like to consider Burmantofts at this point, another factory which rarely comes cheap. The last appearance in this volume was image 602 where a pair of unspectacular 8in vases fetched £1,100. There are examples at 783, 858, and 1144 and there are further examples to find via the *Index*, if readers wish to make themselves acquainted with values.

Searching through other potential lines of enquiry, Pendelfin makes its first appearance at 882. Once again wonderful, but this time cartoon humour. And humour as well as collectability has resulted in a very healthy £705 hammer price despite Daisy Duck not being in the healthiest of conditions. Check out other hammer prices via the *Index*. Wilkinson, Royal Staffordshire last appeared at 147 when a set of ten Toby jugs of allied commanders in the First World War sold for £4,500 at Halls Fine Art in Shrewsbury. In this Section at 899 is a Wilkinson Louis Wain 'The Laughing Cat' which fetched £700 three years ago at Gorringes in Lewes. I must admit to having absolutely no expertise in this particular area of collecting and I have no idea whether it is rare or not. However the price is the price and it's not cheap. So why? May I suggest some possibilities. It *is* by a well-known factory, it *is* full of humour, it *is* a cat and it *is* highly collectable and the magic name Louis Wain *is* present. However, has it been a good investment or not?

Belleek has already appeared twice before but there are a dozen items to choose from in these pages. In this Section pages 45, 46, 47 and 50 show typical Belleek prices in this range.

Royal Copenhagen makes a first appearance at 953 and £600 for Snowy Owl. There are more to choose from in the remaining Sections. Check out the *Index* for Royal Copenhagen prices right down to £25 on the final picture page of this volume. Readers should also notice that Beswick bulls and cows are beginning to appear from page 48 onwards. The Beswick trail is quite extensive and may be followed through the *Index* where there are nearly forty lots from which to choose.

Hammer Prices £980-£950

Hogbens, Folkestone. Moorcroft Anemone Flambe vase, 13in. £980. Mar 00.

Dockree's, Manchester. Pair of late 19thC Vienna vases, 9.5in overall, chipped, £980. Nov 00.

Dreweatt Neate, Newbury. Sèvres (hardpaste) part coffee service, c1820: sucrier/cover (gilder's mark FB.20), 4 coffee cans/saucers. interlaced 'L's' cypher for Louis XVIII, incised marks, (Much damage and repairs) £980. June 02.

Sworders, Stansted Mount-fitchet. Late 19th/early 20thC Coalport porcelain jewelled cabaret set, patt. No. T 2334, printed mks. £980. Mar 03.

Bristol Auctions, Bristol. 1st period Worcester vase, c1770, overglaze 'dry blue' enamel painted with floral bouquets, 24cm. £980. July 03.

Lambert & Foster, Tenterden. 5 R. Worcester cups, 6 saucers, date code 1929. £960. Aug 99.

Gorringes, Bexhill. Meissen group. £960. July 99.

Hamptons, Marlborough. Whieldon type tea caddy, 18thC. £960. Nov 99.

D M Nesbit & Co, Southsea. English Delft wet drug jar, inscribed 'O:Momord', 14cm high. £960. Oct 03.

Cheffins, Cambridge. 18th/early 19thC Dutch Delft plaque, shaped oval blue marble frame, 58cm high. £950. Dec 00.

Andrew Hartley, Ilkley. Goldscheider pottery figure of a young woman, 18in high. £950. Dec 00.

Clarke Gammon, Guildford. Pair Royal Dux candlesticks, 17in. £950. Nov 99.

Gorringes, Lewes. Clarice Cliff orange roof cottage sifter, 5.5in. £950. June 00.

Richard Wintertons, Burton on Trent. Dresden pot pourri, c1860. £950. May 01.

Andrew Hartley, Ilkley. 19thC Japanese imari porcelain charger, with Geisha girl, signed, 17.5in. £950. Apr 01.

Gorringes, Lewes. Royal Worcester pedestal oval dish signed T. Lockyer, 12.25in. £950. Dec 00.

Gorringes, Bexhill. Pr. 18thC Caughley blue & white small tureens, covers and dishes in Chinese style, 8.25in. (some faults) £950. Dec 01.

Andrew Hartley, Ilkley. Majolica cheese dish with rustic loop handle, as a tree trunk with trailing bramble, 10in high. £950. Dec 01.

Gorringes, Bexhill. Minton majolica wall pocket, No 1690, 10.5in. £950. Dec 01.

Gorringes, Lewes. Pair of Moorcroft pomegranate vases, 6.5in. £950. Mar 01.

Henry Adams, Chichester. Royal Crown Derby porcelain 'Japan' dessert service, c1895, red printed factory marks, date code, red painted pattern number 4591. £950. Sep 02.

Tring Market Auctions, Herts. Pair of white glazed Pug dogs. £950. Jan 02.

Richard Wintertons, Burton on Trent. Royal Doulton. Mephistopheles D5757, verse to base. (large) £950. Aug 01.

Gorringes, Bexhill. Linthorpe pottery Christopher Dresser sea urchin jug no. 312. £950. Feb 01.

Gorringes, Lewes. Pilkington R. Lancastrian lustre vase, No. 3027, 7.25in. £950. Oct 02.

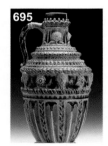

Mellors & Kirk, Nottingham. Doulton Lambeth ewer by Arthur Barlow. £950. Dec 02.

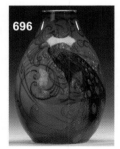

Mellors & Kirk, Nottingham. Royal Doulton Sung vase. £950. Feb 03.

Mellors & Kirk, Nottingham. Derby figure of Diana with a Hunting Dog, 'Pale Family' period, c1756-59, 30cm, dealer's label. £950. Apr 03.

698

Potteries Specialist Auctions, Stoke. Royal Worcester Pat Eddery on Grundy. £950. Mar 03.

699

Andrew Hartley, Ilkley. Royal Worcester porcelain vase by Jas Stinton, model no. G702, 5.5in high. £950. Aug 03.

700

Louis Taylor, Stoke on Trent. Ruskin high fired vase, red flambe glazes. £940. Dec 00.

701

Louis Taylor, Stoke on Trent. Royal Doulton, Toinette, HN 1940. £940. Sep 02.

702

Sworders, Stansted Mountfitchet. Sicilian alberello, 11in. (cracks/chips) 17thC. £940. Feb 02.

703

Sworder & Sons, Stansted Mountfitchet. Ruskin bowl. £920. May 00.

704

Woolley & Wallis, Salisbury. English meat plate, 'Pastoral Scene' pattern, impressed for Phillip's Longport, early 19thC, 43cm. £920. Sep 00.

705

Louis Taylor, Stoke on Trent. Royal Doulton prototype figure. £920. Dec 01.

Prices quoted are hammer prices which excluded the buyer's premium. Adding 15% will give an approximation to the buying price.

706

Gorringes, Lewes. Bow figure of a grape gatherer wearing a tricorn hat, scalloped floral sprigged base, c1762, 6.25in. £920. Dec 00.

707

Amersham Auction Rooms, Bucks. Late 18thC Chinese Export porcelain pedestal cup and cover with a kylin finial, 10.5in. £920. June 02.

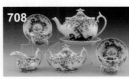

708

Hamptons, Godalming. Spode stone china tea/coffee service, c1815. (29) £920. Mar 02.

709

D M Nesbit & Co, Southsea. Italian Maiolica Albarelli drug jar, painted acanthus, inscribed 'V.Otvzia', 19cm. £920. Oct 03.

710

Hogbens, Folkestone. Moorcroft Pomegranate vase, 14in high. £900. Mar 00.

711

Woolley & Wallis, Salisbury. Staffordshire pearlware group of Romulus and Remus, first half 19thC, 23cm. (damage, restoration). £900. June 00.

712

Great Western Auctions, Glasgow. Wedgwood basalt coffee pot, sugar and creamer (chip to lid). £900. May 00.

713

Gorringes, Lewes. Caughley masonic cormorant and fisherman cabbage leaf jug, set square/compass motif, mask spout, 7.25in. £900. Apr 00.

Hammer Prices £950-£900

714

Gorringes, Lewes. Copeland majolica jar surmounted with a fish on top of a fishing net, 6.5in. £900. Apr 00.

715

Gorringes, Lewes. Late 19thC Japanese satsuma hexagonal vase decorated with samurai, 20.5in. £900. Sep 00.

716

Cheffins, Cambridge. Japanese satsuma Kogo, signed Raizan, 9cm. £900. Sep 01.

717

Gorringes, Lewes. Royal Worcester coffee pot, signed E. Townsend, date code 1929, 7in. £900. Dec 00.

718

Gorringes, Lewes. Meissen monkey band figure of harpsichord player seated on a monkey's back, N.19, 5in and another holding sheet music. £900. Oct 00.

719

Wintertons Ltd, Lichfield. 12 Royal Doulton figures. Gandalf, Aragon, Samwise, Gimli, Gollum, Bilbo, Frodo, Baromir, Legolas, Barliman Butterbur, Galadriel and Tom Bombadil. £900. Mar 00.

720

Woolley & Wallis, Salisbury. Chelsea dish, no mark, c1750-55, 22.2cm. £900. Sep 00.

721

Gorringes, Lewes. Pr. of early 19thC Sunderland lustre marriage or christening jugs, inscribed 'Mary Crobes 1831' and 'Mercy Crobes 1831' and each decorated with a ship portrait of the William IV and a rhyme, 6in. £900. Feb 01.

722

Gorringes, Lewes. Royal Worcester vase, pierced cover and knop, by Jas Stinton, No 474, 7.25in. £900. June 00.

723

Rosebery's, London. Paris porcelain part coffee service. £900. Sep 01.

Hammer Prices £900-£850

Gorringes, Lewes. Bow group of 'Summer' and 'Autumn' as a boy and girl, on scroll base, 10in. £900. Mar 01.

Gorringes. Lewes. Bow candlestick bird group with floral bocage and dog at the base, 9in. £900. Mar 01.

Mellors & Kirk, Nottingham. Pair of James McIntyre & Co Florian Ware vases, by William Moorcroft. £900. Dec 02.

Dreweatt Neate, Newbury. Pair of ormolu and Samson porcelain candelabra, 35cm high. (damage/restoration) £900. Nov 02.

D M Nesbit & Co, Southsea. White glazed Troika pottery vase, 23cm. £900. Sep 03.

Gorringes, Lewes. Royal Worcester teapot, signed H. Ayrton. £900. Dec 00.

Peter Wilson, Nantwich. Wedgwood 'Florentine' part dinner/coffee service, pattern no W4170. (95) £890. Nov 00.

Rupert Toovey, Washington, Sussex. Early 20thC Rye pig with detachable head, incised 'Won't be drove', 24cm long. £880. Dec 02.

D. Duggleby, Scarborough. Mintons majolica game dish, impressed marks, No. 668/10, 34cm. (base crack, tip of duck wing lacking) £880. June 03.

Andrew Hartley, Ilkley. Royal Worcester pug dog, 14.75in, impressed. £880. June 00.

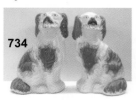

Gorringes, Lewes. Pair of Staffordshire spaniels with baskets of flowers in their mouths, 8in. £880. Apr 01.

Sotheby's, Billingshurst. Blighty, R. Doulton Titanian figure, 1918-1939, by E W Light, printed mark, 11.5in. £880. June 01.

Tring Market Auctions, Herts. Derby Biscuit group 'Poetry', incised crown, X batons mark, 216, mk. of Isaac Farnsworth, 10.25in high. £880. Nov 02.

Andrew Hartley, Ilkley. Pair of Derby porcelain Mansion House dwarf figures, with inscriptions, late 19thC, 6.5in. £875. Aug 01.

Sworders, Stansted Mount-fitchet. Aynsley Edward VII coronation cup, 7in high. £860. July 01.

Andrew Hartley, Ilkley. Pair Royal Worcester vases, Shape No. 2298, signed F. Parker, 9in. £860. Apr 02.

Peter Wilson, Nantwich. Pair Royal Dux figures as female and male water carriers, pink triangle and impressed marks to base, 21in. £850. Nov 99.

Gorringes, Lewes. Victorian porcelain dessert service: a pair of oval, pair of square dishes, 4 circular dishes and 16 plates. £850. Apr 00.

Amersham Auction Rooms, Bucks. Pair of late Victorian Staffs china models of two seated King Charles spaniels, 7.5in high. £850. Apr 01.

Rosebery's, London. Italian faience lamp base, 31cm high. £850. Mar 02.

Gorringes, Lewes. Two identical Austrian earthenware seated pug dogs with glass eyes, 8in. £850. Dec 00.

Rosebery's, London. Satsuma coffee service, c1900. £850. Oct 01.

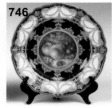

Phillips, Leeds. R. Worcester cabinet plate painted by R. Sebright. £850. Mar 00.

Woolley & Wallis, Salisbury. Chinese ewer. Transitional, c1640-50 (frits to handle, rim and spout, cover re-glued) 15cm. (2) £850. June 00.

Andrew Hartley, Ilkley. Blush Worcester porcelain urn, shape No. 1518, 14.5in. £850. Dec 00.

Gorringes, Lewes. Pr. 19thC Meissen floral encrusted 2-branch candelabrum, 10.5in. £850. June 00.

Gorringes, Lewes. Near pair of Royal Doulton Florence Barlow vases, 10.25in and 10.5in. £850. June 00.

R. Winterton, Burton on Trent. R. Crown Derby. Set 'element' figures. (4) £850. Dec 02.

752

A. Hartley, Ilkley. Pr. French porcelain/gilt metal fruit comports, 10in. £850. Apr 02.

753

Gorringes, Lewes. Late 18thC English tin glazed earthenware jar, incised verse, dated 1775, 9in. af. £850. Apr 01.

The numbering system aids the editorial analysis at the beginning of each section as well as providing a reader reference.

754

Gorringes, Lewes. Pair of R. Worcester vases printed and painted with cottages entitled Harvington and Cropthorne, both signed Rushton, G923, 8in. £850. Apr 01.

755

Mellors & Kirk, Nottingham. 2 Dutch Delftware landscape plaques. £850. Dec 02.

756

Andrew Hartley, Ilkley. Pair of R. Doulton stoneware vases by Hannah Barlow, impressed marks, 15in. £850. Oct 00.

757

Dreweatt Neate, Newbury. London salt glazed stoneware commemorative mug, inscribed George Baverstock, dated 1731, 18.5cm. (large rim chips) £850. June 02.

758

Gorringes, Bexhill. Copeland Parian group, 'Go to Sleep', after J Durham for 'The Art Union', impressed marks to base, 17.5in. £850. Feb 03.

759

Louis Taylor, Stoke. William Moorcroft/Macintyre miniature florian ware vase, 2.75in. (slight damage) £850. Mar 03.

760

R. Winterton, Burton on Trent. Mintons Majolica butter dish, 1876. £850. Apr 03.

761

Cheffins, Cambridge. Late 18th/early 19thC Dutch Delft plaque bearing the date 1747 on the reverse, 57cm high. £850. Dec 00.

762

Woolley & Wallis, Salisbury. Wedgwood 3 coloured jasperware vase, 20thC, impressed, Wedgwood, England, 23.5cm. (knop re-glued and with a metal pin) £840. June 00.

763

Andrew Hartley, Ilkley. Pair of Royal Worcester vases, shape no. 2491, 4.25in. £840. Oct 00.

764

Woolley & Wallis, Salisbury. Staffs model of Wellington, 19thC, 29cm. £840. Sep 00.

765

Canterbury Auc. Galleries. 19thC Meissen group, 8.75in. (slight damage) £840. Dec 01.

766

Amersham Auction Rooms, Bucks. Early 20thC Vienna, porcelain plaque, 7 x 5in. £820. Mar 02.

Hammer Prices £850-£820

767

Woolley & Wallis, Salisbury. Garniture of 3 'Real Stone China' vases, printed marks, pattern no 222, c1830-40, largest 32cm. £820. June 00.

768

Canterbury Auc.Galleries, Kent. 19thC Sevres porcelain urn, cover and stand, thought to have been decorated by Jacques Sinsson, c1843, 6in high overall. £820. Apr 02.

769

Tring Market Auctions, Herts. 18thC Bristol Delft punch bowl, interior inscribed 'One More Bowl and Then', 10.5in dia. af. £820. May 02.

770

Gorringes, Lewes. 19thC Continental majolica ewer and bowl, restored handle, impressed anchor mark, both 11in. £820. Mar 01.

771

Phillips, Leeds. R. Worcester cabinet plate painted by R. Sebright. £820. Mar 00.

772

Hamptons, Godalming. Pair of satsuma vases, c1900, in the manner of Kinkozan, 15.3cm. £820. Mar 02.

773

Louis Taylor, Stoke. Royal Doulton, The Mask Seller, HN 1361. £820. Sep 02.

774

Lots Road Auctions, Chelsea. Meissen, figure of a classical maiden, X swords in u/g blue, impressed and incised marks, 27cm high. £820. Mar 03.

775

Kivell & Sons, Bude. Moorcroft Florian vase, 12in high. £820. Mar 03.

776

Louis Taylor, Stoke. Royal Doulton prototype, woman with cat on a chair. (slightly chipped) £820. June 03.

777

Louis Taylor, Stoke. Leslie Johnson porcelain plaque, hand painted and signed, 9.5 x 7in. £820. Dec 02.

41

Hammer Prices £805-£800

Phillips, London. R. Doulton. HM The Queen Mother, colour trial figure by Eric Griffiths, version of HN2882 in yellow, c1980. £805. Nov 99.

Gorringes, Bexhill. Meissen group. £800. July 99.

Finn & Sons, Canterbury. Early 20thC Japanese cat. £800. Sep 99.

Sworders, Stansted Mountfitchet. Sevres portrait tea service, incl. Mme Dubary, Mme Pompadour & Marie Antoinette. Titles on bases, 1852-56 (1 cup a/f). £800. Sep 99.

Hamptons, Marlborough. 19thC Meissen parrot. £800. Nov 99.

Andrew Hartley, Ilkley. Burmantofts Faience plaque, fishing boats approaching the coast, green glazes, impressed mark, 17.75in. £800. Dec 99.

Woolley & Wallis, Salisbury. Pair of Staffs models of Neptune and Venus, 1st half 19thC, 28cm. (Venus with minor chips) £800. June 00.

Woolley & Wallis, Salisbury. English porcelain plate, by Edwin Steele, signed, raised gilt Greek key border, 23.5cm. £800. June 00.

Woolley & Wallis, Salisbury. Near pair R. Worcester vases, signed 'Ayrton', black printed factory marks, Shape 2701, mid 20thC, 20.5cm. (tip to one knop restored) £800. Sep 00.

Amersham Auction Rooms, Bucks. 1930s Goldscheider painted terracotta wall mask, 13.75in. £800. Apr 01.

Clevedon Salerooms, Bristol. 19thC Meissen part tea and coffee service. (37 pieces in all) £800. Mar 01.

Gorringes, Lewes. Minton majolica jardiniere, impressed and 1023, much damage to base, 10.75in with a majolica circular stand, 11in. £800. July 00.

Gorringes, Lewes. Clarice Cliff Bonjour dinner service with silver and black banded decoration, monogrammed RH. (60) £800. July 00.

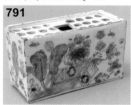

Gorringes, Bexhill. Early 18thC Delft flower brick. £800. Sep 01.

Dockree's, Manchester. Five Victorian pastille burners and cottages. £800. Nov 99.

Woolley & Wallis, Salisbury. Pair of Bloor Derby figures of a Scotsman and his Lass, attributed to William Coffee, she with N378 incised, 30cm. £800. June 00.

Cheffins, Cambridge. Crown Derby cabaret set, date codes c1887, pattern 495, Imari. (27) £800. Dec 01.

Gorringes, Lewes. Doulton Lambeth vase by Ernest Bishop, decorated by Hannah Barlow, 17in. £800. Dec 00.

Gorringes, Lewes. Two 19thC Meissen figures of ladies emblematic of touch and sight and a later figure for smell, 5.5in. £800. Feb 01.

Gorringes, Lewes. Mid 19thC Derby 19 piece dessert service, pattern No. 609. £800. Feb 01.

Thos Mawer & Son, Lincoln. George Jones & Son Ltd majolica strawberry plate, 37cm long. £800. Apr 02.

Wintertons Ltd, Lichfield. Pair of Wood & Sons 'Persian' vases, probably to a design by Charlotte Rhead, shape no. 19, pattern 775, printed, painted and impressed marks, 13in. £800. Sep 02.

Gorringes, Lewes. 19thC Sevres dish, painted figures beside a carriage against a gilded bleu celeste ground in ormolu frame with dragon handles and dolphin legs, 16in. £800. Apr 01.

Gorringes, Lewes. Chelsea Derby figure of a fishergirl with net, underside incised No. 43. £800. Apr 01.

Gorringes, Lewes. William Staite Murray, studio pottery stoneware vase, impressed mark, 9.25in. £800. Apr 01.

Eastbourne Auction Rooms, Sussex. Royal Crown Derby Buxton Badger paperweight. £800. Mar 02.

Peter Wilson, Nantwich. R. Doulton 'fox hunt' coffee service. (15) £800. July 02.

Andrew Hartley, Ilkley. Porcelain sparrow beak jug in polychrome, 18thC, poss. Liverpool, 3in. £800. Aug 02.

806

Rosebery's, London. Meissen figure group, father seated on a couch with 3 children, 19thC, 19cm. £800. Sep 02.

807

Louis Taylor, Stoke. Royal Doulton, The Old Lavender Seller, HN 1492. £800. Sep 02.

The illustrations in these pages are in descending price order. The price range is indicated at the top of each page.

808

Louis Taylor, Stoke on Trent. Royal Doulton character jug, Pearly boy. £800. Dec 02.

809

Wintertons Ltd, Lichfield. Pearlware chestnut basket on stand, c1820, grazing rabbits pattern, 11.5in. £800. Nov 02.

810

Tring Market Auctions, Herts. Biscuit figure 'Romantic Boy', incised 26, (possibly a Rockingham mould number?) 5.5in high. £800. Nov 02.

811

Lots Road Auctions, Chelsea. Pr. of candlesticks, Royal Worcester Porcelain modelled as robed classical maidens, 29cm, £800. Nov 02.

812

Gorringes, Bexhill. Clarice Cliff crocus pattern 15 piece coffee service. £800. Oct 02.

813

Wintertons Ltd, Lichfield. Coalport vase, signed H Chivers, c1910, pattern no. 7540, M?S 325, chip to foot, 36cm. £800. Jan 03.

814

Sworder & Sons, Stansted Mountfitchet. 18thC Dutch Delft butter tub in Kakiemon style, painted mark, 12.5cm long. (damage) £800. Feb 03.

815

Tring Market Auctions, Herts. Early 20thC W. Moorcroft pottery vase, impressed and painted marks, paper label, c1919, 5.5in. £800. Jan 03.

816

Gorringes, Lewes. Pair of George Tinworth Doulton vases, incised artist monogram and impressed factory marks, 7.5in. £800. Jan 03.

817

Clarke Gammon, Guildford. Tin glazed pottery charger with stylized star and floral decoration, 18thC, 13.5in. £800. Feb 03.

818

Lots Road Auctions, Chelsea. Meissen porcelain, centre-piece depicting Flora seated upon a lion and attended by cherubs, 25cm. £800. Mar 03.

819

Mellors & Kirk, Nottingham. David Leach stoneware vase, 42cm high, impressed seals, c1970. £800. Apr 03.

820

Gorringes, Lewes. Pair of Longton Hall leaf dishes, c1770, 9in. £800. June 03.

821

Mellors & Kirk, Nottingham. Doulton butter dish, Hannah B Barlow, EPNS cover/stand, dish 13cm, impressed mark, incised artist's monogram, 198 and initials of assistant, B N, dated 1885. (3) £800. June 03.

Hammer Prices £800-£780

822

Stride & Son, Chichester. Pair of Spode royal blue and gilt fish scale vases, no 1166, 13cm. £800. July 03.

823

Hogbens, Folkestone. Rockingham 1830s part dinner service, hand painted panels. £800. July 03.

824

Clevedon Salerooms, Bristol. 19thC Meissen porcelain table centre, incised F.117 and impressed numbers, 8.5in high. £790. Nov 00.

825

Ambrose, Loughton. Pair of Carltonware lustre vases and covers. £780. Feb 00.

826

Richard Wintertons, Burton on Trent. R. Doulton. 'Smuts' D6198 (large) £780. Aug 01.

827

Gorringes, Lewes. Seven 19thC Passau porcelain figures 'A Band of Cherubs', 9in. £780. Feb 01.

828

Great Western Auctions, Glasgow. Royal Doulton figure group 'Scotties' HN 1287. £780. Apr 00.

829

Woolley & Wallis, Salisbury. Royal Worcester pot pourri vase, shape 1720, puce mark 1907, 20cm. £780. June 00.

830

Andrew Hartley, Ilkley. 19thC Meissen figure 'Chocolate Girl', 15.25in. £780. June 00.

831

Gorringes, Lewes. Royal Doulton Eliza Simmance vase, 14in. £780. June 00.

832

Sworder & Sons, Stansted Mountfitchet. 18thC pottery toby jug, 10in. £780. May 01.

Hammer Prices £780-£750

833

Richard Wintertons, Burton on Trent. Art pottery charger, Pilkingtons R. Lancastrian, £780. Dec 02.

834

Tring Market Auctions, Herts. R. Dux figure of shepherdess, pink triangle mk., stamp 1101, c1890, 24.5in. £780. Nov 02.

835

Potteries Specialist Auctions. Stoke. R. Worcester Princess Ann on Dublet. £780. Mar 03.

836

Mellors & Kirk, Nottingham. 2 Meissen tea caddies, 12cms, X swords in u/g blue or unmarked, c1750. £780. Apr 03.

837

Canterbury Auc. Galleries. R. Doulton porcelain figure, Standing Beefeater, model 505, 7.5in, green printed mk., black initials 'BC', impressed date code for June 1926, chip to newspaper. £780. Aug 03.

838

Louis Taylor, Stoke. Royal Doulton figure, Marion, HN 1582. £760. Sep 02.

839

Fellows & Sons, Hockley, B'ham. Royal Doulton figure 'Damaris', HN 2079, printed marks, painted no. & initials 'RH', 7.5in. £760. July 03.

840

Wintertons Ltd, Lichfield. Moorcroft Macintyre vase of green/gold Florian design 404017, 21cm. £750. Jan 99.

841

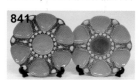

Gorringes, Lewes. 2 Minton majolica oyster plates, date mark 1875, 9in. £750. Sep 00.

842

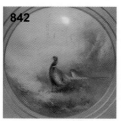

Andrew Hartley, Ilkley. Royal Worcester porcelain plaque painted with pheasants in a landscape by Jas Stinton, 4.25in wide. £750. Apr 00.

843

Mervyn Carey, Tenterden. Victorian parian (possibly Copeland) bust of Lord Nelson, 9.5in. £750. Dec 99.

844

Rosebery's, London. Royal Doulton figure Mephistopholes and Marguerite. £750. June 00.

845

Bruton Knowles, Gloucester. Lustre ginger jar by Richard Joyce with shying horses and trees, yellow lustre on an opalescent ground, 7in high. £750. May 00.

846

Golding Young, Grantham. 19thC majolica cheese dish, probably Wedgwood. £750. June 00.

847

Gorringes, Lewes. Moorcroft cylindrical vase, 8.25in. £750. Sep 00.

848

Wintertons Ltd, Lichfield. Pair Royal Worcester vases, signed James Stinton, 14,5cm, Grainger's shape no 923, date code 1919. £750. July 00.

849

Mellors & Kirk, Nottingham. Royal Doulton Cabaret service. £750. Dec 02.

850

Andrew Hartley, Ilkley. Pair of Meissen porcelain figural candlesticks, 19thC, 11.25in high. £750. Apr 02.

851

Gorringes, Lewes. Bow figure of 'Fire' holding a brazier & standing by a phoenix, 10.5in, restored. £750. Mar 01.

852

Gorringes, Lewes. Clarice Cliff spire pattern conical sifter, 5.5in. £750. June 00.

853

Gorringes, Lewes. Victorian George Jones majolica nut dish with squirrel handle and moulded with cob nuts and ferns, 10.25in. £750. June 01.

854

Wintertons Ltd, Lichfield. Moorcroft Macintyre vase, honesty pattern, printed mark, painted WM initials, c1903, 7.7cm. (two slight chips to footrim) £750. Dec 01.

855

Gorringes, Lewes. Royal Dux group of a lady. No. 597, 11.5in. £750. Feb 01.

856

Sworder & Sons, Stansted Mountfitchet. Pair of Chinese famille rose dishes, 28.5cm. £750. June 03.

857

Gorringes, Lewes. Royal Dux Art Nouveau centrepiece as two scantily dressed maidens, No. 694, 13in. £750. Feb 01.

858

Andrew Hartley, Ilkley. Pair of Burmantofts, faience tiles, relief moulded, 11.75in wide, unsigned, impressed marks to reverse. £750. Feb 01.

859

Gorringes, Lewes. Bow figure of 'Earth', 9.5in. (af) £750. Mar 01.

860

Andrew Hartley, Ilkley. Bloor Derby vase, exotic birds in a landscape, reverse depicting fruit, 11.5in. £750. Apr 02.

861

Andrew Hartley, Ilkley. Pair of Vienna porcelain vases, 19thC, 18in. £750. June 02.

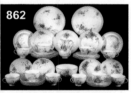

862

Wintertons Ltd, Lichfield. Royal Worcester blush ivory ground part tea set, gilt rims, printed puce & brown marks, date cyphers for 1897, 1898 and 1905. (35) £740. Feb 02.

863

Gorringes, Lewes. Clarice Cliff aurea pattern part breakfast set. (10) £740. Oct 00.

864

Canterbury Auc. Galleries. Pair 19thC Derby 'Mansion House' dwarfs, 6.75in & 7in. (slight damage) £740. Dec 01.

865

Hamptons, Godalming. c1895, Coalport 'jewelled' vase, gilt mark 'Chicago Exhibition', 21.2cm. £740. Sep 01.

866

Hamptons, Godalming. Crown Derby dessert service in 'Japan' palette, some impressed 'Derby' patt. 495 with an oval dish and muffin dish. (21) £740. Sep 01.

Prices quoted are hammer prices which excluded the buyer's premium. Adding 15% will give an approximation to the buying price.

867

Louis Taylor, Stoke. Large R. Doulton jug, 'Ard of Earing', D6588. £740. June 03.

868

A. Hartley, Ilkley. Doulton Lambeth stoneware jug by Hannah Barlow. £740. Aug 03.

869

Woolley & Wallis, Salisbury. Staffs watch stand, 19thC, 19.5cm. (chips) £730. Sep 00.

870

Andrew Hartley, Ilkley. Belleek porcelain part tea set, Shamrock pattern, 2nd black mark. (10) £730. June 01.

871

Rosebery's, London. Royal Doulton stoneware figure by John Broad. £720. June 00.

872

Gorringes, Lewes. Pair late 19thC Continental jardinieres in the aesthetic taste, marked LL below, 13in. £720. Sep 00.

873

Hamptons, Godalming. 19thC Meissen courting couple in 18thC dress, incised N 104, impressed No 50, decorators No 68, 27cm. £720. Sep 01.

874

Woolley & Wallis, Salisbury. Pair of Meissen sweetmeats, X swords marks, '2782' & '2875' incised, 2nd half 19thC, 17.5cm. £720. Sep 00.

875

Maxwells, Wilmslow. Royal Lancastrian pottery vase by Gordon Forsyth, impressed and painted marks, No 3034 X11, 6in. £720. Sep 02.

Hammer Prices £750-£700

876

Sworders, Stansted Mount-fitchet. 18thC Whieldon style pottery toby jug, 10in. (slight damage) £720. May 01.

877

Potteries Specialist Auctions, Stoke. Royal Crown Derby paperweight Ltd. Edn. 100 years RCD. £720. Mar 03.

878

Louis Taylor, Stoke. Royal Doulton, The New Bonnet, HN1728. £720. Dec 02.

879

Richard Wintertons, Burton on Trent. R. Doulton Tango pattern teaset. £720. May 02.

880

Louis Taylor, Stoke on Trent. Royal Doulton, Frangcon, HN 1720. £720. Mar 03.

881

Gorringes, Lewes. Doulton Burslem vase decorated with figures playing golf, 7.5in. (neck af) £720. Oct 02.

882

P.S.A., Stoke. Pendelfin rare Daisy Duck, out of production. (slight repair to back and minor wears) £705. Apr 03.

883

Hamptons, Marlborough. Wedgwood Fairyland lustre bowl, 11in, Daisy Makeig Jones, c1920, restorations. £700. Sep 99.

884

Locke & England, Leamington Spa. R. Doulton 'Guy Fawkes' HN98, printed and script marks, 26.5cm. £700. May 03.

885

Clacton Auctions, Essex. William Moorcroft flambe leaf berries vase, 9in. £700. Nov 99.

886

John Taylors, Louth. Goldscheider figurine by Lorenzl. £700. Nov 99.

887

Mervyn Carey, Tenterden. 19thC Meissen figure of an itinerant tailor, 8.25in, damaged. £700. Dec 99.

888

Gorringes, Lewes. Coalport jewelled cushion form trinket box with central lake scene, No V7246, 4in £700. Apr 00.

889

Bruton Knowles, Gloucester. Lustre vase by Richard Joyce (2123), decorated carp in reeds on a multi-coloured opaque ground, monogram, 7.75in high. £700. May 00.

890

Amersham Auction Rooms, Bucks. Pair of late 19thC unmarked Parian figures, approx. 11.5in. £700. Aug 02.

891

Gorringes, Lewes. Pair of early 19thC Mason's Patent Ironstone jugs with panels of oriental vases against gilded royal blue grounds, 8in. (one spout chipped) £700. Apr 00.

892

Gorringes, Lewes. Clarice Cliff Honolulu pattern clog, 5.5in. £700. June 00.

893

Gorringes, Lewes. Dr Wall Worcester blue and white trefoil shell hors d'oeuvres dish, 8in. £700. June 00.

894

Gorringes, Lewes. Meissen figure of a boy playing a flute, 4in, another of a girl dancing and another of a cherub, 4in. £700. Jan 02.

895

Hamptons, Godalming. Pair flatbacks/spill vases in form of lion and lioness with cubs, 29cm. £700. May 02.

896

Gorringes, Lewes. 18thC Delft charger, probably Bristol, 14in. £700. June 03.

897

Gorringes. Lewes. Chamberlain Worcester Japan pattern mug, No. 240, 4.5in. £700. Oct 00.

898

Gorringes, Lewes. Royal Worcester blush porcelain pot pourri, No. 1286, date code 1889, 12in. £700. Dec 00.

899

Gorringes, Lewes. Wilkinson Louis Wain 'The Laughing Cat', 7in. £700. Dec 00.

900

Gorringes, Lewes. Mintons vase, exotic bird vignettes, rose swags, mkd. As O.A.1301, 11in. £700. June 00.

901

Gorringes, Bexhill. Zsolnay iridescent lustre vase. £700. Sep 01.

902

Andrew Hartley, Ilkley. Clarice Cliff Newport pottery bizarre tea for two, Stamford shape, printed and painted with the Solomon's Seal pattern. (8) £700. Feb 02.

903

Gorringes, Lewes. 19thC Berlin vase (no knop) with finely painted classical panels, 16.5in. £700. Apr 01.

904

Crows, Dorking. Royal Worcester vase, Harry Stinton, date mark 1918, shape no. 2491, 10cm. £700. Jan 03.

905

Locke & England, Leamington Spa. Pair of Canton famille rose vases, early 19thC, 45cm. (one cracked) £700. May 03.

906

Louis Taylor, Stoke on Trent. Royal Doulton, Miss Fortune, HN 1879. £700. Mar 03.

907

Gorringes, Lewes. Two early 20thC German bisque Bathing Belles, with hair wigs, 2.5in. £700. Jan 03.

908

Gorringes, Bexhill. Cantagalli bowl, c1895, after design by Wm. De Morgan, underside marked with a cockerel, 11in. £700. Feb 03.

909

Potteries Specialist Auctions, Stoke. Set of Royal Doulton Beatles jugs to include the limited edition John Lennon colourway. £700. Feb 03.

910

Locke & England, Leamington Spa. 19thC stone china footbath, Claremont pattern, 50cm wide. (minor chipping to handles) £700. May 03.

911

912

Gorringes, Bexhill. Pair of Vienna cabinet plates, central panels painted with figures, underglaze blue beehive mark to base. £700. June 03.

Dee, Atkinson & Harrison, Driffield. Belleek part tea set and tray, 2nd period. (10) £680. July 99.

913

John Taylors, Louth. Clarice Cliff bizarre jug. £680. Feb 00.

914

Phillips, Bath. 18thC English Delft drug jar, E:LENITIVUM on a winged angel and scroll label, 20cm. £680. May 00.

915

Woolley & Wallis, Salisbury. Mason's Ironstone part dinner service, printed marks, mid 19thC. (3 pieces damaged) (18) £680. Sep 00.

> The numbering system aids the editorial analysis at the beginning of each section as well as providing a reader reference.

916

Hamptons, Godalming. Early Qianlong famille rose teaset, c1740-50. (7) £680. Mar 02.

917

Dreweatt Neate, Newbury. Creamware Liverpool printed dated commemorative jug, names for John Hearn Esqr. Prospect, dated 1802, 35.5cm. (large hole through base, cracks) £680. June 02.

918

Richard Wintertons, Burton on Trent. Set of Royal Doulton Dickens figures. £680. Aug 02.

919

Canterbury Auc. Galleries. Pair Royal Worcester cream glazed porcelain figures of women, 10in, green painted mark to base, around mark 'Worcester Shot Enamels' and No. 2/57. £680. Aug 02.

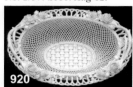

920

Wintertons Ltd, Lichfield. Belleek basket, (4th period) BS. 044, four strands, single pad, 12.25in. £680. Nov 02.

921

Sworders, Stansted Mount-fitchet. 7 19thC Sunderland lustre items. £680. Feb 03.

922

Potteries Specialist Auctions, Stoke. Rare Royal Doulton Old Charley wall pocket D6110. £680. Feb 03.

923

Sworders, Stansted Mount-fitchet. William de Morgan Persian style guglet shaped bottle vase by James Hersey, Fulham period (1888-1897), impressed mark J. H. and 7 1/2, 22cm. £680. June 03.

924

Louis Taylor, Stoke. Susie Cooper part nursery ware set, 'Skier' design. £680. Dec 02.

925

Louis Taylor, Stoke on Trent. Goldscheider terracotta bust of young woman, signature to reverse, 23in. £680. June 03.

926

Fellows & Sons, Hockley, B'ham. Composite Crown Devon Fieldings coffee set, all painted with ducks, dogs or game birds, gilded interiors, each signed either R. Hinton, J. Coleman or W. Lamonby. (8) £680. July 03.

927

Phillips, Scotland. Blue and white dog dish, 27cm. £660. Nov 99.

928

Louis Taylor, Stoke. William Moorcroft vase, signed to base, 8.5in. £660. June 03.

929

Crows, Dorking. Davenport Ironstone Dessert Service, 4 shell shaped dishes, 3 rectangular, 3 oval dishes and 12 dessert plates. £660. Jan 03.

930

Hamptons, Godalming. Derby biscuit group of two virgins awakening cupid, c1780, William Duesbury & Co, incised N195, 34cm. £660. July 00.

931

Sworders, Stansted Mount-fitchet. 19thC English porcelain part dinner service, 29 pieces incl. 2 tureens and covers. £660. Nov 01.

932

Bristol Auctions, Bristol. Staffordshire Prattware pipe as an ochre monkey wearing a yellow bicorn hat smoking a pipe, tail as mouthpiece, c1800, 13.7cm. £660. May 03.

933

Dee, Atkinson & Harrison, Driffield. Shelley coffee set, patt. no. 11778/9, reg. no. 756535. (15) £650. Feb 00.

934

Andrew Hartley, Ilkley. Pair Minton Secessionist pottery vases, 12.75in. £650. Oct 00.

Hammer Prices £680-£650

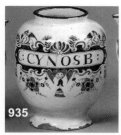

935

Phillips, Bath. 18thC English Delft drug jar, C:CYNOSB on a winged angel and scroll label, 21cm. £650. May 00.

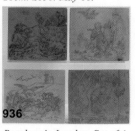

936

Rosebery's, London. Set of 4 early Doulton stoneware tiles, incised decoration depicting scenes of foxes from fables by Goethe. £650. June 00.

937

Gorringes, Lewes. Minton majolica strawberry dish, year mark for 1873, reg. mark for 1876, 10.25in. (some damage) £650. July 00.

938

Gorringes, Lewes. Royal Worcester coffee cup/saucer painted with white doves on a parcel gilt sky blue ground, signed Johnson. £650. Apr 00.

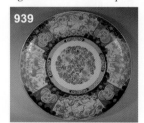

939

Woolley & Wallis, Salisbury. Japanese Imari charger, 19thC, 56cm. £650. June 00.

940

Gorringes, Lewes. Royal Worcester oval dish, gilt gadrooned border, signed T. Lockyer, 12.25in. £650. Dec 00.

Hammer Prices £650-£640

Clevedon Salerooms, Bristol. Clarice Cliff preserve pot in 'Sunray'. 4in. £650. Nov 00.

Woolley & Wallis, Salisbury. Meissen pug dog, X swords mark, 2nd half 19thC, 24cm. (restorations) £650. Sep 00.

Clevedon Salerooms, Bristol. Thomas Forester majolica jardinière. £650. Mar 01.

Wintertons Ltd, Lichfield. Beswick Shorthorn bull, 'CH Gwersylt, Lord Oxford 74th'. £650. Nov 00.

Gorringes, Lewes. 2 identical Austrian earthenware pug dogs, glass eyes, 6.5in. £650. Dec 00.

Gorringes, Lewes. Royal Worcester cleft top jug with pheasants, sig. Jas. Stinton, No. 1438. £650. Dec 00.

Hamptons, Godalming. Pair of Coalport 'jewelled' vases, c1900, gilt No V1291, 26cm. £650. Sep 01.

Gorringes, Lewes. 19thC Continental porcelain plaque, a lady holding a Roman oil lamp in jewelled brass easel frame, 12in. £650. Oct 00.

Gorringes, Lewes. Austrian earthenware pug dog, glass eyes, 13.5in. £650. Dec 00.

Gorringes, Lewes. Royal Worcester cabinet cup/saucer painted with sheep, date code 1931, and a similar pair painted with a ram and ewe, both signed E. Barker, date code 1931. £650. Dec 00.

Louis Taylor, Stoke on Trent. Royal Doulton fox in hunting dress. £650. Mar 02.

Woolley & Wallis, Salisbury. English porcelain New Hall type sparrow beak jug, no mark, late 18thC, 11.5cm. £650. June 00.

Gorringes, Lewes. Royal Copenhagen figure, Snowy Owl, 1829. £650. Feb 01.

Gorringes, Lewes. Moorcroft shallow bowl, pomegranate and grape pattern, 10.5in. £650. Jan 02.

Thos Mawer & Son, Lincoln. Majolica game tureen, 27cm. (lid repaired) £650. Apr 02.

Gorringes, Lewes. 18thC Worcester 'Queen Charlotte' pattern teapot 5.5in, and stand, 5in. £650. Mar 01.

Dreweatt Neate, Newbury. London delft gallipot, 9cm, first quarter 18thC. (minor rim chips) £650. June 03.

Gorringes, Lewes. Minton style majolica bowl, 19thC, 5.5in dia. £650. Mar 01.

Gorringes, Lewes. 18thC Chinese group of 2 immortals holding sceptres and fruit. £650. Apr 01.

Gorringes, Lewes. Moorcroft pomegranate pattern vase, green script signature & Made for Liberty & Co stamp, 6in. (2 chips) £650. Apr 01.

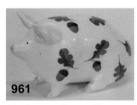

Eastbourne Auction Rooms, Sussex. Wemyss style pottery pig, 17cm. £650. July 02.

Woolley & Wallis, Salisbury. Chinese famille verte vase, 19thC, 74cm. £650. Sep 00.

Gorringes, Bexhill. Pair of German porcelain figures, 16.5in. £650. Oct 02.

Wintertons Ltd, Lichfield. Coalport ewer, signed H Chivers, c1910, patt. no. 7450 M/S, 149, 36cm. £650. Jan 03.

Mellors & Kirk, Nottingham. Pinxton cup and saucer. £650. Feb 03.

Rupert Toovey, Washington, Sussex. Minton majolica jug, c1876, 14cm high. (chip to base) £650. May 03.

Andrew Hartley, Ilkley. Goldscheider terracotta wall mask, stamped mks., incised 6625, 8.5in. £640. Dec 99.

968

Andrew Hartley, Ilkley. Goldscheider terracotta wall mask, stamped and incised marks, 13.25in. £640. Dec 99.

969

Andrew Hartley, Ilkley. 18thC Dutch Delft charger with chinoiserie scene of a lady on terrace, 13.5in. £640. Apr 00.

970

Woolley & Wallis, Salisbury. Creamware jug, probably Melbourne, one side portrait of a lady, the reverse with a building & butterfly, no mark, c1770, 16cm. £640. June 00.

971

Sworders, Stansted Mount-fitchet. 3 Minton Majolica oyster dishes, marked to base Minton/323 /lozenge mk. for 1868, 23cm. £640. Oct 02.

972

Clevedon Salerooms, Bristol. Elton crackle glaze vase. £640. Mar 01.

973

Sworders, Stansted Mount-fitchet. Royal Worcester vase, signed Spilsbury, 11in. (puce no. H247) £640. May 01.

974

Gorringes, Lewes. Bow figure from the Comedia del Arte series with floral bocage, 7in., one hand and one finger missing. £640. Oct 00.

> The illustrations in these pages are in descending price order. The price range is indicated at the top of each page.

975

Sworders, Stansted Mount-fitchet. Pilkingtons Lancas-trian lustre vase by Richard Joyce, impressed marks, painted monogram, 6.75in high. £640. Dec 01.

976

Andrew Hartley, Ilkley. Meissen allegorical group of classical maiden playing lute, 19thC, 11.5in. £640. Apr 02.

977

Louis Taylor, Stoke on Trent. Royal Doulton Flambe Sung vase, 7in. £640. June 03.

978

Gorringes, Lewes. Victorian Langley stoneware salad bowl and servers with landscape decoration, 8in. £640. Apr 01.

979

Phillips, London. Doulton. Lady Diana Spencer, HN2885, by Eric Griffiths, 1982, No 1 of 1500. £630. Nov 99.

980

Peter Wilson, Nantwich. Shelley bone china coffee service for six. 15 pieces. £630. Nov 00.

981

Cheffins, Cambridge. Pair of 19thC George Jones majolica dishes, impressed registration diamond, painted pattern No 2515, 26cm. £630. Sep 01.

982

Amersham Auction Rooms, Bucks. Late 18thC Wedgwood yellow and blue stoneware vase, 7in. £620. Mar 01.

Hammer Prices £640-£620

983

Ambrose, Loughton. 69 piece Midwinter pt. dinner service, 'Zambesi'. £620. Sep 99,

984

Clarke Gammon, Guildford. Pair of Continental tinglazed tobacco jars, 19thC stamped 'Stevens, Brussells', 12in. £620. Feb 00.

985

Gorringes, Bexhill. Early Charlotte Rhead charger. £620. Feb 00.

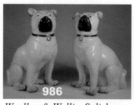

986

Woolley & Wallis, Salisbury. Pair of Staffordshire pugs, c1900, 28cm. (one with front leg re-glued) £620. June 00

987

Woolley & Wallis, Salisbury. Royal Worcester vase, signed R Sebright, puce mark, 2510, c1932, 10.5cm. £620. June 00.

988

Rosebery's, London. Pair of R. Dux figures. £620. Dec 00.

989

Gorringes, Lewes. Pair of Nankin oval tureens and covers, 6in. £620. July 00.

990

Hamptons, Godalming. Pair of 19thC Chinese Export ware vases. £620. Jan 01.

991

Woolley & Wallis, Salisbury. 18 Royal Worcester models of birds together with a Royal Crown Derby model of a long tailed tit. (19) £620. Sep 00.

992

Woolley & Wallis, Salisbury. Set 6 Wedgwood pearlware plates of botanical specimens, 19thC, impressed 'Wedgwood' 24.5cm. £620. Sep 00.

993

Woolley & Wallis, Salisbury. Set 6 R. Worcester teacups/ saucers, with waterlilies, signed 'R Austin', puce marks, c1916. (damage) £620. Sep 00.

994

Louis Taylor, Stoke on Trent. Pilkington's R. Lancastrian lustre vase. £620. Sep 02.

Hammer Prices £620-£600

995

Wintertons Ltd, Lichfield. Late 19thC porcelain plaque, reverse signed J. Lesage and titled 'Phyllida'. Exhibition label, 11.75in. £620. Sep 01.

996

Amersham Auction Rooms, Bucks. Victorian Doulton Lambeth glazed stoneware jug, by Mark V Marshall, as a cockerel, textured body, 5.75in high. £620. Sep 01.

997

Cheffins, Cambridge. 18thC Chinese famille rose dish, the cavetto sides trellis pierced, 30cm. £620. Dec 01.

998

Gorringes, Lewes. Bow figure Autumn from the seated rustic seasons being a Vendageur, c1755, 5.25in. £620. Dec 00.

999

Andrew Hartley, Ilkley. Royal Dux porcelain group, donkey and foal, pink triangle mark, 13in wide. £620. June 02.

1000

Cheffins, Cambridge. 18thC Chinese blue and white soup tureen and cover, 35cm across the handles £620. Dec 01.

1001

Hamptons, Godalming. Qianlong famille rose armorial dish, c1760, with feathered cartouche surmounted by a bat and motto 'Prudentia' for Wakefield impaling Christie, 28cm. £620. Nov 01.

1002

Gorringes, Lewes. Art Deco Gray's pottery water jug with enamel painted geometric design, 8in. £620. Mar 01.

1003

Eastbourne Auction Rooms, Sussex. Royal Crown Derby Rowsley Rabbit paperweight. £620. Mar 02.

1004

Bristol Auctions, Bristol. A c19thC Meissen porcelain figure group, of Bacchus on a barrel with three companions, mould no. C35, press no. 121, 33cm. (af) £620. July 03.

1005

Bristol Auction, Bristol. Martin Bros vase, incised floral decoration, incised R W Martin & Bros, London & Southall, dated 4.1889, 23cm. £610. Apr 02.

1006

Wintertons Ltd, Lichfield. 19thC Berlin style porcelain plaque, title in pencil verso 'Antigone', impressed no 808, 25.5 x 17.5cm. £600. July 00.

1007

Andrew Hartley, Ilkley. Belleek porcelain basket, open trellis work, impressed mark Belleek Co Fermagh Ireland, 13in wide. £600. Dec 99.

1008

Woolley & Wallis, Salisbury. R. Worcester vase, shape 1937, signed 'Chivers', date code 1899, (knop restored), 24cm. £600. Mar 00.

1009

Wintertons Ltd, Lichfield. Hannah Barlow Doulton Lambeth stoneware tapering jug, 9.5in. £600. Nov 00.

1010

Woolley & Wallis, Salisbury. Chantilly box/cover, painted in the Kakiemon style, 1735-45, 10.5cm. (2) £600. June 00.

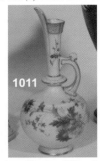

1011

Andrew Hartley, Ilkley. Pair of Royal Worcester blue blush ewers, shape no. 783, painted roses, 7.25in. £600. Apr 00.

1012

Gorringes, Lewes. Carltonware Guinness is Good For You sealion lamp, revolving shade, 15in. £600. Dec 00.

1013

Gorringes, Lewes. Clarice Cliff Circus plate, by Laura Knight with three trapeze artists, 9in. £600. Feb 01.

1014

Woolley & Wallis, Salisbury. Staffordshire model of Sir Charles Napier, 19thC, 40.5cm. £600. Sep 00.

1015

Andrew Hartley, Ilkley. 19thC Copeland porcelain plaque by William Yale of Balmoral Castle, signed, 12.25 x 16in. £600. Aug 00.

1016

Gorringes, Lewes. Early 19thC 17-piece part dinner service, printed with seashells (af) £600. Apr 00.

1017

Gorringes, Lewes. Royal Doulton buddha, in Sung and lustre glazes, incised below 210, 6.25in. £600. Sep 00.

1018

Woolley & Wallis, Salisbury. Pair of Meissen vases and covers, X swords marks, 2nd half 19thC, 29.5cm. (damaged) £600. Sep 00.

1019

Gorringes, Lewes. 18thC Ralph Wood style figure of a sailor and anchor, 8in. £600. June 00.

1020

Woolley & Wallis, Salisbury. Pr. R. Worcester vases, gilt rims, green marks, shape 405, date codes 1909, 12cm. (one restored) £600. Sep 00.

50

1021

Gorringes, Lewes. 18thC Prattware teapoy moulded on both sides with figures, poss. George III and Queen Caroline, 5in. £600. July 00.

1022

Gorringes, Lewes. Linthorpe pottery tray by Christopher Dresser, impressed with green glazed japonaiserie motifs, modelled by Henry Tooth, 13.5in. £600. June 01.

Prices quoted are hammer prices which excluded the buyer's premium. Adding 15% will give an approximation to the buying price.

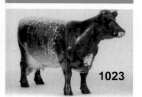

1023

Wintertons, Lichfield. Beswick Shorthorn cow, 'CH Eaton, Wild Eyes 91st'. £600. Nov 00.

1024

Gorringes, Lewes. Clarice Cliff Circus plate by Laura Knight, animal trainer and bear, 9in. £600. Feb 01.

1025

Eastbourne Auction Rooms, Sussex. Royal Crown Derby Stony Middleton Mouse paperweight. £600. Mar 02.

1026

Hamptons, Godalming. 19thC Meissen part dinner service, (2 plates chipped to foot rim) 25.5cm, u/g blue X swords mark, impressed numbers and painted decorators numbers. (19) £600. Nov 01.

1027

Gorringes, Lewes. Pair of Royal Worcester vases, No. 2249, date code 1909, 9.5in. £600. Dec 00.

1028

Sworders, Stansted Mount-fitchet. Copeland and Garrett 'New Blanche' polychrome foot bath, serial no. B.N: 547, 17in wide, (af) £600. Apr 01.

1029

Gorringes, Lewes. Clarice Cliff Circus plate by Laura Knight, 3 sea lions balancing balls, 9in. £600. Feb 01.

1030

Sworders, Stansted Mount-fitchet. Wemyss tyg with pink tulips and green foliage, impressed marks, 19cm. £600. Oct 01.

1031

Gorringes, Lewes. 18thC Leeds (?) creamware sauceboat, moulded with a heron and fox, the handle formed as a classical bust, 8in. £600. Mar 01.

1032

Gorringes, Lewes. Clarice Cliff Circus plate by Laura Knight, lion tamer, reclining lion, 9in. £600. Feb 01.

1033

Gorringes, Lewes. Clarice Cliff ribbed lotus table lamp, orange chintz pattern, 12in. (believed drilled for a lamp at the factory) £600. Dec 00.

1034

Biddle & Webb, Birmingham. Large Lladro centre piece, a lady with a dog. £600. Jan 02.

1035

Gorringes, Bexhill. Moorcroft florian ware vase, 10in., 2in x half inch rim piece chipped, broken, re-stuck. £600. Oct 02.

1036

Gorringes, Lewes. Minton majolica 'pineapple' jug with leaf handle, 8in. £600. Jan 02.

Hammer Price £600

1037

Wintertons Ltd, Lichfield. Derby Porter mug, c1815, 'View in Switzerland', John Brewer, 5in. £600. Mar 02.

1038

Gorringes, Lewes. Prattware pattern medallion moulded with a cherub riding a dolphin, 4.5in. £600. Mar 01.

1039

Gorringes, Lewes. Royal Worcester blush gilt figure of a negro from the Countries of the World series, No 840, 6.75in. £600. Mar 01.

1040

Gorringes, Lewes. Clarice Cliff Circus plate by Laura Knight with a high wire acrobat, 9in. £600. Feb 01.

1041

Wintertons Ltd, Lichfield. Minton pottery charger, sgd. W. Hubpill, impressed marks, date cipher February 1877, 58cm. £600. May 02.

1042

Rosebery's, London. Pair of Paris porcelain vases, early 20thC, with twin ring mask handles, 28cm. £600. Mar 02.

1043

Gorringes, Lewes. 18thC Daois immortal holding a fruit and sceptre, 7in. £600. Apr 01.

1044

R. Wintertons, Burton on Trent. Bust of Washington Irving, A.W H. Goss. £600. Sep 02.

1045

Tring Market Auctions, Herts. Pair 19thC Rockingham scent bottles, af, 5in. £600. Nov 02.

1046

Andrew Hartley, Ilkley. Royal Dux porcelain group, lovers embracing, pink triangle mark, 18.5in. £600. Oct 02.

Hammer Prices £600-£580

R. Wintertons, Burton on Trent. James Macintyre Moorcroft cracker jar, c1890. (2cm chip to base rim) £600. Jan 03.

Mellors & Kirk, Nottingham. R. Crown Derby miniature Witches pattern flat iron and trivet. £600. Feb 03.

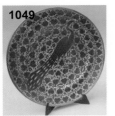

Gorringes, Bexhill. Cantagalli charger, c1895, after William De Morgan, marked to underside with u/g blue cockerel, 12.75in. £600. Feb 03.

Cheffins, Cambridge. English porcelain, 'The Angler's Delight', early 19thC fish head stirrup cup, 10.25in. £600. Apr 03.

Wintertons Ltd, Lichfield. Royal Crown Derby Imari dessert service, date code 1914, patt. no. 4493, printed marks. (18) £600. Mar 03.

Gorringes, Bexhill. Three Clarice Cliff bonjour shaped milk jugs, pt. cruet set, salt, toast rack, teapot, large mug and other items, orange roof house and green banding. £600. Mar 03.

Gorringes, Lewes. Early Carter, Stabler Adams, Poole pottery figure, impressed mk., c1921-25, 8in. £600. Mar 03.

Amersham Auction Rooms, Bucks. Late Victorian Doulton Lambeth stoneware oil lamp, impressed factory stamp, 17in. £600. Mar 03.

Tring Market Auctions, Herts. Derby Biscuit group 'Two Virgins Awakening Cupid', crown and X batons mark in blue, 10in. £600. Nov 02.

R. Winterton, Burton on Trent. George Jones majolica sardine dish, c1870, impressed marks and 1831 in script, length 22cm. £600. Apr 03.

Sworders, Stansted Mountfitchet. Sicilian Maiolica wet drug jar, dated 1708, 'Violt. Semp. CE.', 21cm., chip to rim & flaking. £600. July 03.

Rosebery's, London. Swansea Royal commemorative plate for the coronation of Queen Victoria, 15cm. £600. June 03.

Locke & England, Leamington Spa. Royal Dux donkey group, pink triangle. £600. July 03.

Louis Taylor. Stoke on Trent. Beswick dairy shorthorn cow 'CL - Eaton Wild Eyes'. £590. June 01.

Andrew Hartley, Ilkley. 19thC Doulton Lambeth pottery oil lamp, 24.75in. £590. Apr 01.

Gorringes, Lewes. Copeland parian figure of a seated hound, 12in. £580. Apr 01.

Louis Taylor, Stoke. Royal Doulton, Old Charley, wall pocket, 7.25in. £580. Mar 03.

Rosebery's, London. Masons Ironstone soup tureen. £580. Nov 99.

Andrew Hartley, Ilkley. Royal Dux porcelain art nouveau vase, with a reclining maiden, 14.5in wide. £580. Feb 00.

Gorringes, Lewes. Royal Worcester vase, date code 1957, pattern 2363, 8.25in. £580. Dec 00.

A. Hartley, Ilkley. Creamware cow creamer with milk maid, sponge decorated, late 18th/19thC, 6.5in. £580. Apr 02.

Richard Winterton, Burton on Trent. Imari cabaret set, c1895. £580. Aug 01.

Tring Market Auctions, Herts. Meissen bust of a girl child, incised no. 2764, impressed 121, 6in. £580. Nov 02.

Woolley & Wallis, Salisbury. Moorcroft ovoid vase, 'Moorcroft, Potter to H.M. The Queen' and 'Made in England' impressed, 23.5cm. £580. Sep 00.

Potteries Specialist Auctions, Stoke. Rare Royal Doulton Jester wall pocket D6111. £580. Feb 03.

Tring Market Auctions, Herts. Pr. 19thC Staffs spill figure groups of ponies, foals, both spills cut, 6in. £580. Mar 03.

Gorringes, Lewes. Doulton Lambeth stoneware bottle base, floral bosses and acanthus leaves by Frank Butler 1883, 10.5in. £580. Apr 00.

A. Hartley, Ilkley. Graingers Worcester porcelain reticulated vase. £580. Apr 00.

1075

Lambert & Foster, Tenterden. R. Doulton, Jester, C J Noke, issued 1928-1949, HN1295 EJE, 10in., hat damage, both sides glued. £580. June 03.

1076

Louis Taylor, Stoke on Trent. Pair of English porcelain plaques, prob. Spode, by A. Connelly, signed, dated 1939, 6 x 7.5in. £580. July 03.

1077

Wallis and Wallis, Lewes. Georgian Masonic lustre mug printed 'Masons Arms', 4in high. £575. May 02.

1078

Rosebery's, London. Meissen cherub group. £570. May 00.

1079

John Taylors, Louth. Parian Copeland figure, 'Musidora' by W Theed, published 1867, 44cm. £570. July 01.

1080

Cheffins, Cambridge. 19thC Qajar (Persian) pottery tile, 30.5cm. £560. Sep 99.

1081

Mervyn Carey, Tenterden. Hochst porcelain figure of a Turk, 7.75in. £560. Dec 99.

The numbering system aids the editorial analysis at the beginning of each section as well as providing a reader reference.

1082

Andrew Hartley, Ilkley. 19thC Meissen porcelain figure of a lady, 7.25in. £560. Feb 00.

1083

Locke & England, Leamington Spa. Imari charger, figures in garden, 46cm. £560. May 03.

1084

Louis Taylor, Stoke. Pair of Wm Moorcroft Pomegranate vases. £560. June 01.

1085

Woolley & Wallis, Salisbury. Pr. Staffs models of a ram and ewe, with a flowering tree, 1st half 19thC, 12cm. (few chips) £560. June 00.

1086

Morphets, Harrogate. Doulton Titanian vase by F Henri, signed, printed mark, impressed for c1920, 8in. £560. Mar 01.

1087

Gorringes, Lewes. Pair of Meissen child figures (af) 5in. £560. June 00.

1088

Gorringes, Lewes. 19thC French porcelain and ormolu inkwell, 8in. £560. July 00.

1089

Sworders, Stansted Mountfitchet. Hadley's Worcester teapot, 8in. £560. July 01.

1090

Canterbury Auc. Galleries, Kent. Austrian painted terracotta figure of a pug, 7.75in. (some repairs) £560. Oct 01.

Hammer Prices £580-£550

1091

Andrew Hartley, Ilkley. Pair of Derby porcelain figures, a youth, maiden as musicians, 18thC, 8.25in. £560. Apr 02.

1092

Wintertons Ltd, Lichfield. Staffordshire pottery jug, c1835, inscribed 'I wish I was in Dixey land Sally is the girl for me', 20cm. £560. Jan 03.

1093

Andrew Hartley, Ilkley. Royal Worcester porcelain vase by Harry Stinton, 5.75in, date mark 1919. £560. Aug 03.

1094

Fellows & Sons, Hockley, Birmingham. Late 19th/early 20thC Royal Doulton vase, painted with a young maiden, printed factory mark, painted initials and numbers 'RA 7183', 8.25in. £560. July 03.

1095

Clacton Auctions, Essex. Clarice Cliff Bonjour preserve pot 'Lorna' patt. £550. Nov 99.

1096

Ambrose, Loughton. First period early 19thC W. H. Goss vase. £550. Dec 99.

1097

Dee, Atkinson & Harrison, Driffield. Pr. 19thC saltglaze spaniels on a shaped base, 3in. £550. Apr 01.

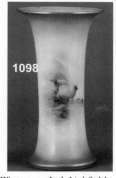

1098

Wintertons Ltd, Lichfield. Royal Worcester vase, signed E Barker, Grainger's shape no 923, date code 1919, 18cm high. £550. July 00.

1099

Andrew Hartley, Ilkley. Persian Qajar tile of a hunter on horseback, 7.5 x 5in, 19thC. £550. Feb 01.

1100

Gorringes, Lewes. Moorcroft vase with hibiscus on a pale ground, 12in. £550. June 00.

Hammer Prices £550-£540

1101

Gorringes, Lewes. Pr. Derby figures of a lady with flowers and a gentleman with fruit, 8in. (restored) £550. June 00.

1102

Gorringes, Lewes. Royal Doulton Tony Weller teapot, 6.5in. £550. June 00.

1103

Cheffins, Cambridge. Mintons majolica jardiniere, date code for 1884, impressed marks 40cm dia. £550. June 01.

1104

Gorringes, Lewes. Late 19thC R. Copenhagen, Europa and the Bull, no. 12130, restored neck, 10.25in. £550. Sep 00.

1105

Gorringes, Lewes. Pair 18thC Chinese plates, Rockefeller pattern, 8in. £550. Sep 00.

1106

Richard Wintertons, Burton on Trent. Set of six Coalport cabinet plates, c1860, marked 6/2521. £550. Jan 02.

1107

Clevedon Salerooms, Bristol. R. Doulton Kingsware spirit barrel, 7in. £550. Sep 01.

1108

R. Wintertons, Burton on Trent. Crown Devon vase with a grouse & pheasant, signed 'Coleman' £550. Nov 01.

1109

Gorringes, Lewes. Set of seven German monkey band figures, largest 5.5in, smallest 4.5in. £550. Feb 01.

1110

Wintertons, Lichfield. Five Coalport porcelain plates, c1860-70, with named British birds, red bird inscriptions, wear, 9.5in. £550. Feb 02.

1111

Gorringes, Lewes. Clarice Cliff gay day vase, shape 370, 5.75in. £550. Apr 01.

1112

Gorringes, Lewes. Moorcroft MacIntyre florian vase, green script signature, M2105, 3.5in. (restored) £550. Oct 02.

1113

Gorringes, Lewes. Walton spill vase group with tree and bocage back with a ram and a lamb, 7.5in. £550. Mar 01.

1114

Gorringes, Lewes. 18thC Leeds creamware jug, painted in puce with floral bouquets, 4.5in. £550. Mar 01.

1115

Hamptons, Godalming. Copeland & Garrett ice cream pail, c1840, original liner, (decoration worn) 30cm, printed mark. £550. May 02.

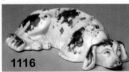

1116

Amersham Auction Rooms, Bucks. Pair of late 19thC Staffordshire pottery models of hounds, printed labels from the Doris Keane Collection, 9in long. £550. Aug 02.

1117

Mellors & Kirk, Nottingham. Derby tea and coffee service. £550. Dec 02.

1118

Sworders, Stansted Mountfitchet. 14 piece early 19thC Wedgwood creamware, gilt and blue cornflower type decoration, uppercase with impressed mark, impressed 'B' and 'P'. £550. Oct 03.

1119

Amersham Auction Rooms, Bucks. Late 19thC Japanese Imari porcelain bowl, 13 x 10in. £550. Sep 02.

1120

Richard Wintertons, Burton on Tren. Extensive Mintons dinner service. £550. Feb 03.

1121

Mellors & Kirk, Nottingham. Royal Crown Derby retailer's plaque, 14.5cm, printed marks, date code 1932. £550. Apr 03.

1122

Sworders, Stansted Mountfitchet. Set 8 19thC Majolica scallop shaped plates, one with impressed heart, six '11', one unmarked. (one chipped) each 22.5cm. £550. June 03.

1123

Dockree's, Manchester. Pair of Staffs sheep. £540. Nov 99.

1124

Clevedon Salerooms, Bristol. Royal Doulton series ware 'Golf' pattern jug, painted no D5716, 9.5in. £540. Nov 00.

1125

Finn & Sons, Canterbury. Pair 19thC Meissen figures. £540. Mar 00.

1126

Woolley & Wallis, Salisbury. MacIntyre 'Aurelian ware' vase, printed marks, Rd. no. 314901, c1900, 31cm. £540. Sep 00.

1127

Clevedon Salerooms, Bristol. Elton crackle glaze vase. £540. Mar 01.

1128

Gorringes, Lewes. Victorian Staffordshire group of 2 ladies fishing, 15in. £540. June 00.

1129

Gorringes, Lewes. Ruskin bowl with speckled pink glaze, c1900, crossed swords mark, 8.5in. £540. Feb 01.

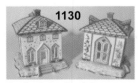

1130

Locke & England, Leamington Spa. Pair early 19thC Minton pastille burners in the form of Gothic lodges. £540. Sep 02.

1131

Hamptons, Godalming. 19thC Coalport 'jewelled' trinket box, heart shaped, green mark, No. V2712, retailers mark A. B. Daniell and Son, London, 10cm. £540. Sep 01.

1132

Gorringes, Lewes. 18thC Derby figure of Shakespeare wearing a pink cloak, 11.5in. £540. Mar 01.

The illustrations in these pages are in descending price order. The price range is indicated at the top of each page.

1133

Gorringes, Lewes. Worcester Mansfield pattern coffee pot, c1770, 9in. £540. Mar 01.

1134

Bristol Auction Rooms, Bristol. Martin Bros tobacco jar, incised scroll and griffin decoration, incised Martin Brothers, London & Southall, dated 11.1892, 12cm dia., chip to rim. £540. Apr 02.

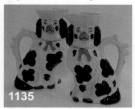

1135

Richard Wintertons, Burton on Trent. Pair Staffs flat back pitchers, c1890 in the form of seated spaniels. £540. Sep 02.

1136

A. Hartley, Ilkley. Meissen porcelain group of children in 18thC dress with a bird cage, 19thC, 5.5in. £540. Aug 02.

1137

Mellors & Kirk, Nottingham. Minton & Co 'Poonah' dessert service. £540. Dec 02.

1138

Locke & England, Leamington Spa. Clarice Cliff pottery, Red Roof pattern vase of goblet form, 15cm. £540. Sep 02.

1139

Bristol Auction Rooms. Pair of Staffs pottery figures of chimney seeps on muleback, 24.5cm. £530. Oct 02.

1140

Mervyn Carey, Tenterden. Pair of Worcester porcelain plates with landscapes by Harry Davis, 10.75in. £525. Dec 99.

1141

Phillips, Leeds. Royal Worcester teapot and cover. £520. Dec 99.

1142

Andrew Hartley, Ilkley. Pair of Chelsea Derby porcelain candlesticks, seated musicians, 7.5in. £520. Feb 00.

1143

Potteries Specialist Auctions, Stoke. Royal Worcester Hereford bull. £520. Mar 03.

1144

Andrew Hartley, Ilkley. Burmantofts faience pottery vase, shape no 2046, colour no 34, 13.25in. £520. Aug 00.

1145

Clevedon Salerooms, Bristol. George Jones game dish. £520. Mar 01.

1146

Ambrose, Loughton. Pair of 19thC continental porcelain candelabrum. £520. Sep 99.

1147

Richard Wintertons, Burton on Trent. Pair of sleeve vases signed 'Hinton' and painted with spaniels. £520. Nov 01.

Hammer Prices £540-£520

1148

Andrew Hartley, Ilkley. Royal Worcester porcelain vase, shape no 2268, signed Jas. Stinton, 4.25in. £520. Aug 00.

1149

Peter Wilson, Nantwich. Late 19thC Samsonite figures of a lady & gentleman, restoration to gentleman's hat, firing crack around neck, 7.5in. £520. Nov 01.

1150

W & H Peacock, Bedford. Susie Cooper caramel ground floral decorated tea service. £520. July 03.

1151

Wintertons Ltd, Lichfield. Pair of Minton Hollins & Co, 8in tiles in manner of John Moyr Smith, titled 'Mechanics' and 'Botany', moulded marks, s.d. 8in high. £520. May 01.

1152

Gorringes, Lewes. Chamberlains Worcester campana shape sauce tureen, floral knop, painted on both sides with horse crest, motto 'Be Trew', 8in. £520. Mar 01.

1153

Gorringes, Lewes. 18thC Derby figure of Neptune and dolphin, 8.25in. £520. Mar 01.

1154

Gorringes, Lewes. Worcester mug, bamboo, fence & pagoda patt, c1765, 6in. £520. Mar 01.

1155

Louis Taylor, Stoke on Trent. Royal Doulton Reynard the Fox coffee set. £520. Dec 02.

1156

Gorringes, Lewes. Art Deco Keramos Vienna earthenware wall plaque of lady harlequin, 10in. £520. Mar 02.

1157

Rosebery's, London. Royal Worcester blush ivory spill vase, painted by Jas. Stinton, 16cm high. £520. June 03.

Section 5

Sample Analysis

The price range from £500 down to £250 is even more prolific than the previous Section. Almost 30% more lots on average sell in this price range than in the previous range. The reader is tactfully reminded at this point that it is very important to read the *Introduction* and check out the *Analyses* in previous Sections. This will assist in analysing this Section as well as providing a more informed perspective on the market overall. Whilst the analysis presented here is frequently prompted by the lots appearing in this Section, the themed analysis may still range across the whole volume. For example, *cats* may again be considered in this Section as may *Goldscheider* but this must also be viewed within the context of previous discussion. None of the individual section analyses are independent of the volume as a whole, much as a chapter in a book lacks meaning when isolated from the context of the work as a whole. However the reader will have noticed that the Editor in each Section always concentrates on introducing new themes as well as expanding on earlier discussion. In addition it is always useful to use specific examples within each Section to make interesting market points.

Section 5 for the first time introduces William J Mycock. There are relatively few examples - only four - but they only occur in Section 5 in the price range £500-£400. See pages 57, 63 and 64. Is this enough to gauge prices in general considering these lots all sold in 2000? Probably not, but now that there is a price range for Mycock in our possession, albeit for three years ago, we now possess some useful information on Mycock in the market place. One thing worth mentioning about this factory is that it doesn't appear very often and this may explain the relatively high prices, although it is obvious the lots shown have quality. Perhaps a reader has further information as it is disappointing that we have been unable to develop more analysis on this factory's output.

There are several dozen items of parian in these pages. We started with £3,000 for T*he Veiled Bride* on page 20 and will end up with a small £60 item of parian on page 120. Parian, a vitrified porcelain, introduced by Copeland & Garrett (see Glossary), first appeared in 1842. Probably the most well-known figure is Miranda, the daughter of Prospero in what was probably Shakespeare's greatest play, *The Tempest*. Miranda has come to symbolise innocence and charity. She may be seen on page 65. This Minton version fetched only £400 and prices of parian have seemed fairly flat in recent years. It hardly seems right that a Minton Miranda should fetch the same as a modern Royal Doulton bone china fox on the same page. I know which I would buy as an investment! Miranda any day is preferable to a cross-looking fox which seems to lack any subtlety, charm or humour. Royal Doulton is an enigma. You either love it or you hate it or like the Editor you like some pieces and hate others, hardly surprising from such a vast output.

Early Wedgwood has already been discussed but there are four modern Keith Murray items here, the first a basalt bowl at £500. Use the *Index* to check further lots. Brannam also appears for the first time. See the first image at 1158. This type of art pottery and Brannam in particular has seriously increased in value in recent years. It is always worth looking out for the larger pieces of art pottery. Other Brannam examples are on pages 65 and 75. Or follow up further using the *Index*.

There are enough examples of Imari in these pages for the reader to get a serious feel for prices from the very top to the very bottom of the market. Prices of Asian ceramics at the lower end of the market in particular have declined in recent years, influenced by the huge amount of reproduction which will be the ruin of the industry if it continues to be displayed along with genuine old and antique goods in circumstances where the inexperienced or the unwary may be misled. However there are still some genuine and spectacular pieces around in the £300-£500 price range which deserve consideration. The name Imari stems from the port from which it was shipped, the porcelain generally being made in Arita. Some fine examples may be found on pages 58, 63, 65 and 73 although the whole range of Imari is extensive and can be checked out through the *Index*.

Although Goldscheider has appeared in previous discussion relating to their life-size figures which fetch a small fortune it is worthwhile in passing to show that this particular price range is where you can expect to find Goldscheider wall masks. Check out the previous Section at image 968 at £640. Check out also pages 61 to 63 and 78. Goldscheider wall masks therefore show up in the price range £640 down to £260.

The first showing of Tabernes (Spain), better known as Lladro occurred at £600 hammer on page 51. There are further examples on page 58 and 62 within this price range. The Lladro figures which were exported from the country, are of excellent quality. I believe the factory opened its doors in 1952 and although modern in the sense that they date from the second half of the twentieth century, Lladro is now highly collectable. Incidentally, eroticism in art is a theme we will not be following in this volume and this is not based on prudishness but rather on the lack of examples. However the Lladro figure of a dark-skinned beauty, image 1210 is erotic and will always fetch a good price, in this case £480 in 2000 suggests that this figure is worth a lot more today.

Even though pottery and porcelain pigs have already been discussed, don't miss the modern Moorcroft example which still brought £440 in 2002. See page 61. Also in passing you might consider doing some homework on the Wemyss prices in this Section, for example pages 62 and 63. However the Wemyss trail actually begins at £4,000 and doesn't end until an interesting lidless and chipped honey pot fetched £120 on page 105.

A trail which actually ends rather than begins in this Section is Wedgwood Fairyland Lustre where on page 64 a Daisy Makeig-Jones vase fetched £400 in July 2000. Wedgwood Fairyland Lustre is a trail which actually begins also at £4,000 in Section 2. You can check out Fairyland and Daisy Makeig-Jones through the *Index*. Another trail which makes a significant showing in this Section is Carltonware which incredibly began at £4,600 on page 16, and continues right through into the very lowest price range on page 124 where the trail goes cold at £45. One of the most interesting lots is image 825 on page 43. There are more than twenty Carltonware lots in this volume.

As a final summary here are some of the lots that the Editor feels were sensible purchases which could show investment potential. Of course, every reader will have their own ideas and particular favourites. From an investment and a pleasure point of view I suggest the Moorcroft pig at 1278, the Miranda at 1388, the Royal Worcester Bonzo, 1419, and the Staffordshire zebra pair at 1621. I would suggest also that Burmantofts majolica humourous animal figures have potential. There is an example for £260 at 1767 which is a sensible price but surely the crocodile at 2827 which fetched only £70 was an absolute snip.

1158

Ambrose Loughton. A. C. H. Brannam terracotta stick stand. £500. Sep 99.

1159

Dee, Atkinson & Harrison, Driffield. Late 19thC Royal Worcester pot pourri, RD No 142778, dated 1892, 15in, fault to base. £500. Feb 00.

Prices quoted are hammer prices which excluded the buyer's premium. Adding 15% will give an approximation to the buying price.

1160

Bruton Knowles, Gloucester. Lustre vase by William S Mycock, 1916, monogram, 9.75in high. £500. May 00.

1161

Sworders, Stansted, Mountfitchet. Shelley bone china part tea service, pattern no. 11724/6. (16) £500. Apr 01.

1162

Cheffins, Cambridge. 2 dated Chinese mugs, inscribed within a green oval 'Ed Pytts Middleton To His Niece Miss Mary Ford 1784', 15.5cm and 14cm. £500. Nov 01.

1163

Bruton Knowles Gloucester. Mycock Lustre vase, 1922, 8.5in. £500. May 00.

1164

Phillips, Bath. Japanese Arita charger. £500. May 00.

1165

Great Western, Glasgow. Keith Murray Wedgwood basalt bowl. £500. May 00.

1166

Woolley & Wallis, Salisbury. Chinese tureen, Qianlong, 1736-95 36cm. (extensive damage) £500. June 00.

1167

Cheffins, Cambridge. Pair of mid 19thC Dresden porcelain figures, printed, incised mks., 46.5cm high. £500. Dec 00.

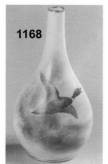

1168

Phillips, Bath. R. Worcester vase, mallard drake in flight, by James Stinton, Graingers shape 151, date code 1909, 14cm high. £500. May 00.

1169

Canterbury Auc. Galleries, Kent. Copeland Parianware bust of Clytie after Delpech, Art Union of London, 13.25in. £500. Aug 00.

1170

Gorringes, Lewes. Novelty Samson owl jar, 9.5in. £500. Apr 00.

1171

Gorringes, Lewes. Vienna porcelain charger, 'Rinaldo and Almida', after Kauffmann, 13.5in. £500. June 00.

1172

Amersham Auction Rooms Bucks. Victorian Staffordshire cream glazed pottery chicken, 12.5in high. £500. Dec 01.

1173

Woolley & Wallis, Salisbury. German porcelain plaque, gilt wood frame, 2nd half 19thC, 12.2cm. £500. Sep 00.

Hammer Price £500

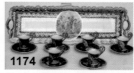

1174

Dockree's, Manchester. 19thC Dresden suite of six cabinet cups/saucers with tray, polychrome transfer scenes, one saucer cracked and stapled. £500. Feb 01.

1175

Gorringes, Lewes. Pr. 18thC Ralph Wood (?) pearlware groups, 6.25in. £500. Jul 00.

1176

Gorringes, Lewes. Pair of Davenport Japan pot pourri bowls with gilt knops and masks, 6in. (one cover restored). £500. Apr 00.

1177

Gorringes, Lewes. Early 20thC Austrian Goldscheider figure of a young peasant boy, 38in. £500. Feb 01.

1178

Gorringes Lewes. Clarice Cliff 'blue chintz' teapot, (spout chipped) and matching water jug. £500. Oct 00.

1179

Hogbens, Folkestone. Possibly Sevre lidded vase, c1850. £500. May 01.

1180

Gorringes, Lewes. Burmantofts faience vase, isnik style, monogrammed KL, 1902, 7in. £500. Sep 00.

1181

Woolley & Wallis, Salisbury. Set of 5 Chinese Wucai deep U-shaped cups, with stylized lotus flower and leaf scroll, c1670, 7.5cm. £500. June 00.

1182

Dee, Atkinson & Harrison, Driffield. 19thC Staffs spill vase, 6.5in. £500. Dec 00.

1183

Gorringes,Lewes. Clarice Cliff Circus oval dish, by Laura Knight with showgirls, clowns, a ring master and horses, 12.5in. £500. Feb 01.

1184

Wintertons, Lichfield. Chelsea Derby bough pot, c1770, fraction mark to base 76/2, 3.75in. £500. Mar 02.

1185

Sworders, Stansted Mountfitchet. R. Worcester pot pourri, date code c1911, 7.5in. £500. July 01.

Hammer Prices £500-£480

1186
W & H Peacock, Bedford. Doulton Lambeth tea service incised with grazing goats, by Hannah Barlow. £500. Dec 02.

1187
Rosebery's, London. Meissen allegorical figure group of Venus, 28cm. £500. Mar 02.

1188
Gorringes, Lewes. Caughley Fisherman pattern coffee pot, c1780, 8.5in. £500. Mar 01.

1189
Tring Market Auctions, Herts. 17thC Italian maiolica drug jar, 'Ollo Lavrino', 8.25in, some chips. £500. May 02.

1190
Louis Taylor, Stoke on Trent. Beswick standing shire mare. £500. Sep 02.

1191
Sworders, Stansted Mountfitchet. Coalport 'jewelled' vase, No. V5955/200 1st., 6.5in. £500. July 01.

1192
Andrew Hartley, Ilkley. Pair R. Dux figures, pink triangle marks, 16.5in. £500. June 02.

1193
Locke & England, Leamington Spa. Florian Moorcroft vase, 'Honesty'. £500. Sep 02.

1194
Locke & England, Leamington Spa. Meissen figure of a man raising the lid of an ewer, X swords mark in blue, 20cm. (slight chip) £500. June 03.

1195
Louis Taylor, Stoke. Pair Wm. Moorcroft candlesticks, Pomegranate. £490. Dec 02.

1196
Richard Wintertons, Burton on Trent. William Ridgway transfer printed footbath, c1840. (crack) £490. Aug 03.

1197
Hamptons, Marlborough. Late 19thC willow pattern tureen. £480. Sep 99.

1198
Dockree's, Manchester. Pair 19thC majolica ice pails, 21.5in. £480. Sep 00.

1199
Andrew Hartley, Ilkley. 19thC Imari porcelain charger in iron red, blue & green and gilt, 22in. £480. Sep 99.

1200
Clarke Gammon, Guildford. 19thC Spode pottery pill slab, 13.5 x 12in. £480. Feb 01.

1201
Woolley & Wallis, Salisbury. Pr. Staffs figures, Dick Turpin and Tom King, 19thC, 26.5cm. (flaking) £480. Sep 00.

1202
Gorringes, Lewes. Pair of early 19thC Derby vases, 7in. handle missing. £480. Oct 00.

1203
Richard Wintertons, Burton on Trent. Crown Devon vase signed 'Cox' painted with highland cattle. £480. Nov 01.

1204
Louis Taylor, Stoke. R. Crown Derby, Rowsley Rabbit, Ltd. Edn. of 500 for John Sinclair 1997. £480. Sep 03.

1205
Woolley & Wallis, Salisbury. Lowestoft dolphin ewer cream boat, no marks, c1775, 7.5cm. 5mm hair crack. £480. Sep 00.

1206
Andrew Hartley, Ilkley. 18thC Derby figure of Minerva, 15.5in. £480. Apr 01.

1207
Gorringes, Bexhill. Royal Doulton limited edition jug The Regency Coach, 158/500, 10.75in. £480. Oct 01.

1208
Clevedon Salerooms, Bristol. Elton crackle glaze vase. £480. Mar 01.

1209
Gorringes, Lewes. Early 19thC creamware jug, James and Jemima, Orme 1804, with 'The Spinning Jenny' and 'The Deserted Village', 7in. £480. July 00.

1210
Gorringes, Lewes. Lladro figure of a dark skinned beauty, 29in. £480. Sep 00.

1211
R. Wintertons, Burton on Trent. Pair of 18thC tea bowls/saucers painted with 'Lang Lizen' figures. £480. Aug 01.

1212
Richard Wintertons, Burton on Trent. Clarice Cliff Cottage bookend. £480. Aug 01.

1213
John Taylors, Louth. Victorian Staffordshire blue and white foot bath. £480. June 01.

1214
Hamptons, Godalming. Coalport 'jewelled' jar, late 19thC, green printed marks, 8.8cm high. £480. Sep 01.

1215

Gorringes, Lewes. Pair of R. Worcester bon bon dishes, one signed H. Ayrton, the other H. H. Price, date code 1929, 5.25in. £480. Dec 00.

1216

Andrew Hartley, Ilkley. Pair R. Dux figures, shepherd and shepherdess, both in green and pink dress, pink triangle marks, 9.75in. £480. Dec 01.

The numbering system aids the editorial analysis at the beginning of each section as well as providing a reader reference.

1217

Gorringes, Lewes. R. Doulton George VI & Elizabeth Coronation loving cup, No. 43 of 2000, certificate by Charles Noke, 10.5in. £480. Feb. 01.

1218

Rosebery's, London. Continental terracotta pug, glass eyes, 21cm. £480. Mar 02.

1219

Gorringes, Lewes. Royal Worcester coffee pot, 7.5in., by E. Townsend, badly scratched. £480. Feb 01.

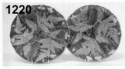

1220

Gorringes, Lewes. Set of six 19thC majolica dessert plates, 8.5in. £480. Mar 01.

1221

Gorringes, Lewes. Harlequin set of 9 German monkey band figures, 6.75in. £480. Feb 01.

1222

Tring Market Auctions, Herts. Early 19thC Ridgway part teaset. £480. Jan 02.

1223

Gorringes, Lewes. Set of six Berlin cabinet plates, 9in. £480. Feb.01.

1224

Wintertons Ltd, Lichfield. German saltglazed stoneware jug, c1800, lacking pewter cover, 26cm. £480. Nov 02.

1225

Andrew Hartley, Ilkley. Set of 4 Continental porcelain medallions, unsigned, labels verso, 19thC, 3.25 x 2.75in, unframed. £480. June 02.

1226

Louis Taylor, Stoke on Trent. Victorian Parian Ware group, 'Florence Nightingale' after Phyffers, 13in. £480. Dec 02.

1227

Locke & England, Leamington Spa. English porcelain 18thC wrythen moulded tea service, (23) £480. Jan 03.

1228

Gorringes, Lewes. Chelsea porcelain figure, emblematic of fire, 6.5in. £480. Apr 01.

1229

Eastbourne Auction Rooms, Sussex. Mintons Successionist vase, 48cm. £480. July 02.

1230

Gorringes, Bexhill. Royal Doulton stoneware vase by Hannah Barlow, stylised borders by F. C. Pope, 18.5in. (cracked) £480. July 02.

1231

Tring Market Auctions, Herts. Vienna porcelain portrait plate. £480. Jan 02.

1232

Locke & England, Leamington Spa. Pair of 1950s Midwinter pottery Jessie Tate vases, 10.5cm. £475. Sep 02.

1233

Louis Taylor, Stoke on Trent. Royal Crown Derby, Stoney Middleton Squirrel, Ltd. Edn. of 500 for John Sinclair no. 89. £470. Sep 03.

1234

Louis Taylor, Stoke on Trent. Wedgwood Keith Murray vase, 7.75in. £470. Mar 03.

1235

Gorringes, Lewes. 18thC figure of Priapus with a child, (old restoration), 6.75in. £460. Apr 00.

1236

Gorringes, Lewes. Wemyss Victorian diamond Jubilee commemorative goblet impressed Wemyss Ware R.H. & S. and oval T. Goode & Co mark, 5.5in. £460. Apr 00.

1237

Louis Taylor, Stoke on Trent. Royal Doulton, Farmers Boy, HN 2520. £460. Sep 02.

1238

Sworders, Stansted Mount-fitchet. Royal Worcester vase, by E. Barker, puce mark 1324, 10cm. £460. Apr 01.

1239

Gorringes, Lewes. 8 Beatrix Potter figures, R. Doulton Mr Apple and 3 Wade figures of Butcher, Baker and Candlestick Maker. £460. Feb 01.

1240

Woolley & Wallis, Salisbury. Liverpool porcelain teapot, no mark, c1760, 17cm long. (damage) £460. June 00.

1241

Locke & England, Leamington Spa. R. Dux lady by pool, pink triangle mark. £460. July 03.

1242

Andrew Hartley, Ilkley. R. Dux porcelain figure, milk maid beside a cow, pink triangle mark, 8.5in. £460. Dec 01.

1243

Louis Taylor, Stoke. One of a pair of W. Moorcroft Flambe vases, 4in. £460. Mar 03.

Hammer Prices £460-£440

1244

Gorringes, Lewes. William Moorcroft 'leaf and berry' vase, 8.75in. £460. June 00.

1245

Gorringes, Lewes. Royal Copenhagen figure, Potato woman, 1549. £460. Feb 01.

1246

Bristol Auction Rooms, Bristol. Pr. Doulton Lambeth Church Altar vases, incised IHS, 20cm. £460. Apr 02.

1247

Andrew Hartley, Ilkley. Royal Dux porcelain figure of a nude water nymph in a lily pad, printed and triangle marks, 6in. £460. Apr 02.

1248

Gorringes, Lewes. Samson armorial vase, 13in high. (cracked) £460. Apr 01.

1249

Thos Mawer & Son, Lincoln. Meissen service of 'Onion' lattice plates and an oval basket. (25) £460. Nov 02.

1250

Andrew Hartley, Ilkley. Doulton Lambeth stoneware ewer by Florence Barlow, dated 1874, impressed marks, 9.75in high. £460. June 02.

1251

Andrew Hartley, Ilkley. Pair porcelain tea bowls, saucers, in polychrome, 18thC, poss. Liverpool. £460. Aug 02.

1252

Louis Taylor, Stoke on Trent. Fairing 'Well! What are you looking at?' 4in. (restored hand) £460. June 03.

1253

Andrew Hartley, Ilkley. English porcelain tea bowl and saucer, late 18thC, poss. Liverpool. £460. Feb 03.

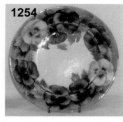

1254

Louis Taylor, Stoke on Trent. William Moorcroft plate. 7.25in dia. £460. June 03.

1255

Thos Mawer & Son, Lincoln. Beswick rearing huntsman with Jack Russell, fox and 6 hounds. £460. June 03.

1256

Richard Wintertons, Burton on Trent. Royal Doulton character jug, clown with white hair. £460. July 03.

1257

Dee, Atkinson & Harrison, Driffield. 2 Beswick mallards, one rising, one settling, 6.5in and 5.5in high. £450. Apr 01.

1258

Gorringes, Lewes. Victorian bargeware teapot, inscribed 'R Carter, Swadlincote 1885', 11in. £450. June 00.

1259

R. Wintertons, Burton on Trent. Alcock Imari pot pourri jar, c1840. £450. Apr 03.

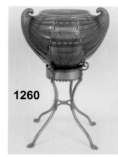

1260

Bonhams, Bath. Jardiniere and brass stand, impressed marks to base, attributed to Dr Christopher Dresser, for Bretby, 72cm. £450. Nov 01.

1261

Tring Market Auctions, Herts. Pair of Staffordshire spaniels, each with a basket of flowers, 7.5in high. £450. Sep 02.

1262

Tring Market Auctions, Herts. Pair of Derby biscuit figures, gardener, companion, bases incised numeral 7, incised mark for Isaac Farnsworth, size No 3, slightly af, 5.5in high. £450. Nov 02.

1263

Louis Taylor, Stoke on Trent. Royal Doulton figure 'The Fiddler', HN2171, designed by Mary Nicol. £450. Dec 02.

1264

Rosebery's, London. Derby porcelain named view in Perthshire, Scotland mug, c1810, 13cm. £450. Sep 02.

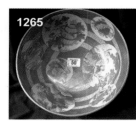

1265

Biddle & Webb, Birmingham. Late 19thC Japanese Kutani bowl. £450. Sep 01.

1266

Hamptons, Godalming. Crown Ducal Charlotte Rhead charger, painted and printed marks and pattern number 4954. £450. July 02.

1267

Clark Gammon, Guildford. 19thC Prattware part dessert service. (15) £450. Apr 02.

1268

Ambrose, Loughton. Pair of Doulton Lambeth Art Union stoneware vases, impressed and incised marks 3550, one mkd. Emily Partington, 8550, the other Eliza Simmance, 2204, 40.5cm. £450. Feb 02.

1269

Mellors & Kirk, Nottingham. 1st period Worcester polychrome coffee cup and saucer, crescent in underglaze blue, c1770. £450. Apr 03.

1270

Gorringes, Lewes. 18thC porcelain scallop shell pickle dish, 7.5in. £440. Oct 00.

Peter Wilson, Nantwich. One of a pair of 19thC Sevres sweet dishes, in polychrome enamels, marks to base, chips, 6.5 x 6.5in. £440. Nov 99.

Andrew Hartley, Ilkley. Goldscheider terracotta wall mask, stamped marks, 13in. £440. Dec 99.

Andrew Hartley, Ilkley. Goldscheider terracotta wall mask, stamped mks. impressed 7081, 11in. £440. Dec 99.

The illustrations in these pages are in descending price order. The price range is indicated at the top of each page.

Andrew Hartley, Ilkley. Early 19thC Famille rose porcelain jardiniere, with figures on a terrace. 7.5in. £440. Apr 00.

Gorringes, Lewes. Royal Worcester figure of Welshman in national costume, No. 1875, 7in. £440. Mar 01.

Dockree's, Manchester. Royal Worcester oil lamp, 15in, coded 1893. £440. May 00.

Woolley & Wallis, Salisbury. Staffs model of an elephant with hunter and dead tiger, late 19th/early 20thC, 22.5cm. (chips) £440. June 00.

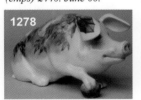

Amersham Auction Rooms, Bucks. Late 20thC Moorcroft pottery model of Peter the Pig, The Temptation design, impressed, incised, painted marks, 12in. £440. Oct 02.

Gorringes, Lewes. Galle style cat with glass eyes, dog medallion, 13.5in. (some damage) £440. Oct 00.

Amersham Auction Rooms, Bucks. Pair of late 18thC Worcester porcelain coffee cups/saucers. £440. June 01.

Canterbury Auc. Galleries, Kent. Copeland Parianware bust of 'Love' after R. Monti, 13.25in, impressed mark and impressed Crystal Palace Art Union. £440. June 01.

Dockree's, Manchester. Pair of Royal Worcester vases, date code 1897, 7.25in high. £440. Nov 00.

Andrew Hartley, Ilkley. Herculeneum pottery meat plate, 'Etruscan', early 19thC, 18in. £440. Aug 01.

Sworders, Stansted Mount-fitchet, Pr. Castle Hedingham jugs, inscribed 'Made at the Art Pottery, Castle Hedingham, by C. Bingham 1893', 8.5in. (damage) £440. Apr 01.

Woolley & Wallis, Salisbury. Rogers pearlware meat plate, impressed, c1820, 53.7cm. £440. Sep 00.

Gorringes, Lewes. Satsuma heart shaped trinket box and cover with chrysanthemum decoration, 4in. £440. Sep 00.

Louis Taylor, Stoke on Trent. Wm. Moorcroft vase, 'orchid', 8.75in. £440. Dec 02.

Canterbury Auc. Galleries, Kent. Pair of Derby porcelain figures representing two of the seasons, 8.75in, painted mark in red of crowned 'D', c1810. £440. Aug 03.

Tring Market Auctions, Herts. Dessert service, tall comport, 4 short comports, 12 plates, comports impressed 'Pearl', the plates 'Semi-China'. Some damage. £430. May 02.

Rosebery's, London. Pair of Carlton ware Handcraft vases. £430. Oct 01.

Thos Mawer & Son, Lincoln. 19thC Staffordshire meat plate 'Ruined Castle and Bridge', 53 x 41cm, maker unknown. £430. Nov 02.

Louis Taylor, Stoke on Trent. Royal Doulton, Fiona, HN 1933. af. £430. Sep 02.

Louis Taylor, Stoke. Royal Doulton, Primroses, HN1617, designer L.H., introduced 1934 and withdrawn 1949. £430. Sep 03.

Lambert & Foster, Tenterden. Maling ware Daisy pattern 6157 K, lustre bowl, c1949-63, 8.5in. £420. Aug 99.

Wintertons Ltd, Lichfield. Late 19thC stoneware stilton dish, 24.5cm. £420. Jan 00.

Hamptons, Marlborough. Pr. Minton vases. £420. Mar 00.

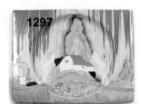

Gorringes, Lewes. Clarice Cliff Forest Glen pattern plate, 10.25in. £420. Apr 00.

Finns, Canterbury. Majolica sardine dish. £420. Sep 99.

61

Hammer Price £420

1299

Gorringes, Lewes. Minton majolica teapot as Japanese dwarf. £420. July 99.

1300

Gorringes, Lewes. Carlton-ware bowl decorated with birds amidst flowering trees, 8in. £420. July 00.

1301

A. Hartley, Ilkley. Victorian Staffs pottery advertising jug, brown printed with 'McNish's Doctors Special Whisky', 8in high. £420. Aug 00.

1302

Clevedon Salerooms, Bristol. 19thC Masons ironstone vase, 20in. £420. June 01.

1303

Gorringes, Lewes. Royal Doulton vase, stylised heart motifs, 6.25in. £420. June 00.

1304

Dee, Atkinson & Harrison, Driffield. R. Doulton Tommy Bulldog, Rd No 662746 in green, 6.5in. £420. Dec 00.

1305

Woolley & Wallis, Salisbury. New Hall part tea service, no marks, pattern No 89, late 18thC. (16) £420. Sep 00.

1306

Woolley & Wallis, Salisbury. Malcolm Pepper, 3 stoneware vases, 26cm, 24.5cm and 29in dia, impressed marks, c1970-80. £420. Sep 00.

1307

Clarke Gammon, Guildford. Lladro porcelain group of a huntsman being attacked by 3 geese, 13in. £420. Apr 01.

1308

Woolley & Wallis, Salisbury. Porcelain cream boat, Worcester or Caughley, c1775, 10.5cm. £420. Sep 00.

1309

Gorringes, Lewes. Egyptian Pre-Dynastic red ware vessel c4000-3000BC, 10in, 20thC iron stand. £420. July 00.

1310

Gorringes, Lewes. Pair of R. Doulton vases, monogrammed LB, 14in. £420. June 00.

1311

Gorringes, Lewes. German porcelain dish with pierced sides, 18.5in. £420. July 00.

1312

Woolley & Wallis, Salisbury. Pr. Staffs figures of gardener and companion, 1st half of 19thC, 13.5cm. £420. June 00.

1313

Gorringes, Lewes. 2 Wemyss biscuit barrels, sweet peas, 5in., one damaged. £420. July 00.

1314

Louis Taylor, Stoke on Trent. Beswick Barnacle Goose. £420. June 01.

1315

Gorringes, Lewes. Austrian earthenware pug dog with glass eyes, 9in. £420. Dec 00.

1316

Gorringes, Lewes. Goldscheider art deco mask, 9in. £420. Dec 00.

1317

Gorringes, Lewes. Minton majolica strawberry dish, registration mark for 1867, 9in. £420. Sep 00.

1318

Andrew Hartley, Ilkley. Clarice Cliff Bizarre Newport pottery flower basket, Autumn Crocus pattern. £420. Apr 01.

1319

Gorringes, Bexhill. First period Worcester 'Plantation' pattern mug. £420. July 01.

1320

Andrew Hartley, Ilkley. Pearlware puzzle jug, early 19thC, 8.25in. £420. Oct 01.

1321

Gorringes, Lewes. Moorcroft florian bowl, 'W. Moorcroft des' painted mark, 9in. (damaged) £420. Dec 00.

1322

Gorringes, Lewes. Sitzendorf centrepiece, 11.5in high. £420. Apr 01.

1323

Gorringes, Lewes. Clarice Cliff 5-piece 'Lydiat' table centre. £420. Sep 00.

1324

Sworders, Stansted Mount-fitchet. 4 English bone china mounted dog heads, 3.75in., Scottie damaged. £420. Apr 01.

1325

Sworders, Stansted Mount-fitchet. Japanese ginger jar, late 19thC, 14in. £420. Apr 01.

1326

Andrew Hartley, Ilkley. Creamware figure, late 18th/19thC, 6.75in. £420. Apr 02.

1327

Gorringes, Lewes. Chinese sang de bouef baluster vase, 16in. £420. Apr 01.

1328

Gorringes, Bexhill. Royal Doulton blue ground vase, by Eliza Simmance, inscribed 115, 15in. £420. Sep 02.

1329

Gorringes, Lewes. Pair of 18thC Derby figures of a lady and gentleman with dogs, 8.5in. £420. Apr 01.

1330

Peter Wilson, Nantwich. Doulton Burslem earthenware oviform vase, c1905, 31cm high. £420. July 02.

1331

Canterbury Auc. Galleries, Kent. Pair of 19thC French (Paris) faience plaques enamelled in colours after William Hogarth (1697-1764) 14.75 x 12.25in. £420. Aug 02.

Prices quoted are hammer prices which excluded the buyer's premium. Adding 15% will give an approximation to the buying price.

1332

Tring Market Auctions, Herts. 19thC waste pail, Laconia pattern, printed coat of arms mark to base with J.M.& S. in scroll, small glaze chip to rim, 13.5in. £420. Sep 02.

1333

Tring Market Auctions, Herts. Pair of smear glazed Derby Biscuit figures, incised crown and X batons mks., numerals 369, af, 10in. £420. Nov 02.

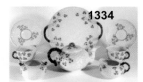

1334

A. Hartley, Ilkley. Belleek porcelain tea set for 6, green shamrock design, third black mark. (22) £420. Feb 03.

1335

Tring Market Auctions, Herts. Pair of Imari vases, 11in. £420. Mar 03.

1336

Locke & England, Leamington Spa. Clarice Cliff sugar dredger, 'house and garden', printed mark 'Clarice Cliff, Wilkinson Ltd, England', 14cm. £420. Jan 03.

1337

Amersham Auction Rooms, Bucks. Pair of late 19thC Japanese Imari porcelain chargers, 16in. £420. Mar 03.

1338

Louis Taylor, Stoke. Royal Doulton Flambe sung vase, fish swimming amongst weed, Fred Moore's monogram to base, 8in. £420. June 03.

1339

Amersham Auction Rooms, Bucks. Pair late 19thC Royal Worcester shot enamelled porcelain Bedouin figures, 8in and 7.75in. £420. Mar 03.

1340

Louis Taylor, Stoke. Carlton Ware claret jug, silver plate mounted, 10in. £420. Dec 02.

1341

Louis Taylor, Stoke on Trent. Poole Pottery vase, 10in. £420. June 03.

1342

Louis Taylor, Stoke. Royal Doulton stoneware jug 'Toby Philpott', 4in. £420. Mar 03.

1343

Gorringes, Bexhill. Delphin Massier-Vallauris stoneware majolica cockerel, marked, 13.5in. £420. Sep 03.

Hammer Prices £420-£400

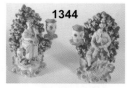

1344

Locke & England, Leamington Spa. Pair of 18thC Derby porcelain candle brackets as shepherd and shepherdess, 21cm. £410. Sep 02.

1345

John Taylors, Louth. Derby figurine cherub climbing on oak tree. 8in. £410. Mar 00.

1346

Louis Taylor, Stoke. William Moorcroft florian preserve pot, silver plate mounts, 3.75in. £410. June 03.

1347

Peter Wilson, Nantwich. Vienna vase, classical ladies, signed K. Webb, 19thC, 27cm. £410. July 02.

1348

Louis Taylor, Stoke on Trent. Clarice Cliff, Wilkinsons Ltd vase, 12in. £410. Sep 03.

1349

Gorringes, Lewes. Wemyss heart shaped inkwell with pink dog roses, impressed mark and oval T.Goode & Co mark, 7in. £400. Apr 00.

1350

Bruton Knowles, Gloucester. William S Mycock lustre vase, 1924, 5.5in. £400. May 00.

1351

Gorringes, Lewes. Pair of 19thC Staffs ram and sheep figures, 4.75in. £400. Oct 00.

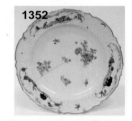

1352

Gorringes, Lewes. Chelsea red anchor plate, 11.25in. (cracked) £400. Apr 00.

1353

Louis Taylor, Stoke. Clarice Cliff, Newport Pottery inkwell, 'Berries', 3.25in. £400. Sep 03.

1354

Andrew Hartley, Ilkley. Goldscheider terracotta wall mask, stamped and incised 2549, 10.75in. £400. Dec 99.

Hammer Price £400

1355
Wintertons Ltd, Lichfield. Pr. of Moore's vases, as winged cherubs pushing floral 'vases', 17cm. £400. May 00.

1356
Gorringes, Lewes. 18thC Whieldon cream jug moulded with vines and a similar teapot. £400. Apr 00.

1357
Hamptons, Godalming. Wedgwood 'Fairyland' lustre vase, Firbolg pattern, c1918, Daisy Mackeig Jones, 20cm, patt. No. Z5200, printed urn mark, England. £400. July 00.

1358
Clevedon Salerooms, Bristol. 19thC Staffordshire meat dish dark blue transfer decoration, 16.5in wide. £400. Nov 00.

1359
Richard Wintertons, Burton on Trent. (Creamware?) Masonic jug, c1770, emblem and arms, 22cm. Restored. £400. Jan 01.

1360
Woolley & Wallis, Salisbury. Ludwigsburg bough pot, mid 18thC, incised and painted 'KP' mark, 21cm. (chips) £400. Sep 00.

1361
Bruton Knowles, Gloucester. Vase by William S Mycock, 1922, with gilt foliage on a mottled blue ground, 8.75in high. £400. May 00.

1362
Woolley & Wallis, Salisbury. Pair of Chinese saucer dishes, 6 character Yongzheng mark of the period 1723-35, 21.5cm. (rim frits) £400. Sep 00.

1363
Gorringes, Lewes. Two 18thC German salt glaze bellarmines with moulded coat of arms, 8in. £400. Oct 00.

1364
Bruton Knowles, Gloucester. Vase by William S Mycock, 1923, roses and foliage on an orange mottled ground, 7in high. £400. May 00.

1365
Woolley & Wallis, Salisbury. Porcelain scent flask with gilt metal stopper, small moulded wheel mark, 18thC, perhaps Hochst, 7cm. (three tiny flat chips to base) £400. Sep 00.

1366
Woolley & Wallis, Salisbury. Cauldon bone china dessert service, c1910-15. (18) £400. Sep 00.

1367
Gorringes, Lewes. Clarice Cliff orange secrets small jardiniere, 6in. £400. June 00.

1368
Woolley & Wallis, Salisbury. Pair of Ironstone sauce tureens, 1st half 19thC, 20.5cm wide. £400. Sep 00.

1369
Gorringes, Lewes. Moorcroft Flaminian ware dish, Liberty mark, 10.25in. £400. Sep 00.

1370
Louis Taylor, Stoke on Trent. Staffs pottery figure, Spaniel and 2 puppies £400. June 01.

1371
Gorringes, Lewes. Pair of Royal Dux fisherboy and fishergirl figures, No. 2291, 11.25in. £400. Feb 01.

1372
Gorringes, Lewes. 19thC Continental majolica water jug decorated with hanging game and greyhound handle, 8in. £400. Feb 01.

1373
Gorringes, Lewes. 19thC Paris porcelain vase and cover with floral and animal panels, 22in. £400. Oct 00.

1374
Rosebery's, London. Copeland Transvaal commemorative loving cup. £400. Sep 01.

1375
Hamptons, Godalming. Meissen Marcolini period figure group, u/g blue X swords and asterisk mark, incised model No. 2157, 32.5cm wide. £400. Jan 02.

1376
Gorringes, Lewes. Moorcroft flambe grape and leaf vase, 6.5in. £400. Dec 00.

1377
Tring Market Auctions, Herts. Pr. Staffs equestrian figures of the Prince and Princess of Wales. £400. Jan 02.

1378
Hamptons, Godalming. Japanese stoneware model of three terrapins, Meiji period, 2 character seal mark, 31.5cm long. £400. Sep 01.

1379
Gorringes, Lewes. Similar set of seven German monkey band figures. £400. Feb 01.

1380
Woolley & Wallis, Salisbury. New Hall late 18thC, pt. tea/ coffee service, patt. No. 318, (damage) (20) £400. Sep 00.

1381
Gorringes, Bexhill. Pair of Chien Lung famille rose dishes, 9in dia. £400. July 02.

1382
Locke & England, Leamington Spa. 1920s Carlton ware tray, rouge ground, 36 x 21cm. £400. Sep 02.

1383
Richard Wintertons, Burton on Trent. Pair campana vases after Palissy. £400. Apr 02.

1384

Peter Wilson, Nantwich. 19thC pair of earthenware grotesque Mansion House caricatures. 7in. £400. Nov 01.

1385

Gorringes, Lewes. 14 piece Rosenthal Elite part desert service. £400. Apr 01.

The numbering system aids the editorial analysis at the beginning of each section as well as providing a reader reference.

1386

Fellows & Sons, Hockley, Birmingham. Set of Wade Walt Disney figures, Snow White and the 7 Dwarves, printed mks., Snow White 4in, dwarves 3in. £400. July 03.

1387

Mellors & Kirk, Nottingham. Royal Doulton bone china model of a fox. £400. Feb 03.

1388

Tring Market Auctions, Herts. 19thC Minton parian figure of Miranda by John Bell, 15in. £400. Nov 02.

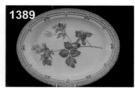

1389

Sworders, Stansted Mount-fitchet. Copenhagen oval meat dish, in the 'Flora Donica' pattern. £400. July 01.

1390

Potteries Specialist Auctions, Stoke. Pendelfin. Cyril Squirrel, in pink, out of production, (chips and wear) also Pooch, minor wears. (2) £400. Apr 03.

1391

Tring Market Auctions, Herts. 19thC Staffordshire porcelain part dessert service. (6) £400. May 02.

1392

Andrew Hartley, Ilkley. 18thC Worcester porcelain cream boat with loop handle, gilded rim, 4.5in. £400. Aug 03.

1393

Gorringes, Bexhill. Pair of Grainger Worcester wall brackets, each with a portrait bust flanked by wings, painted mark, 8in. £400. July 02.

1394

Tring Market Auctions, Herts. Pair of French porcelain figures in the Art Nouveau style, 16in. £400. Nov 02.

1395

Gorringes, Bexhill. Pair of Augustus Rex porcelain jars, underglaze mark to base, 11.25in high. £400. June 03.

1396

Rosebery's, London. A large Spode jardiniere, c1900 in Sevres style. £400. Sep 02.

1397

Locke & England, Leamington Spa. Imari 19thC charger, 43.5cm. £400. May 03.

1398

Wintertons Ltd, Lichfield. Royal Doulton Edward VIII loving cup, c1936, painted mark, No 594 of edition of 2000, 26cm. £400. May 03.

1399

Louis Taylor, Stoke. Porcelain plaque, Leslie Johnson, 7.5 x 6in, signed. £400. June 03.

1400

Gorringes, Lewes. 19thC porcelain water jug (possibly Newhall) 9in. £400. Apr 01.

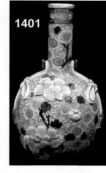

1401

Rosebery's, London. Imari bottle vase. £390. Jan 00.

1402

Wintertons, Bakewell. Border Fine Arts, 'Under the Hammer (Belgian Blue)', No. 1214 of 1750, certificate. £390. Feb 02.

1403

Great Western Auctions, Glasgow. Clarice Cliff sugar shaker. £390. May 00.

1404

Hyperion, St Ives, Huntingdon. Walter Moorcroft, Hibiscus pattern vase. £380. July 99.

1405

Hamptons, Godalming. Brannam Barum Litchdon pottery vase, dated 1909, 35cm. £380. Nov 99.

1406

Rosebery's, London, Clarice Cliff 'Autumn' pattern plate. £380. June 00.

1407

John Taylors, Louth. 19thC urn vase hand painted. £380.

1408

Dockree's, Manchester. Five Caughley tea bowls and four saucers, a similar cup, c1800. £380. Sep 00.

1409

Woolley & Wallis, Salisbury. Two rare Chinese ewers, Kangxi 1662-1722, 16.5cm. (damage). £380. June 00.

1410

Dee, Atkinson & Harrison, Driffield. 19thC Cauldon tea set, including a pair of vases. (24) £380. Dec 00.

1411

Gorringes, Lewes. Louis Wain earthenware jug with 2 black cats and motto 'Good gracious how you frightened me' The Bristol Cat and Dog Pottery, 6in. £380. June 00.

Hammer Prices £380-£375

1412

1413

Gorringes, Lewes. Pair of majolica shell dishes, 9.5in. £380. Sep 00.

Gorringes, Lewes. Moorcroft Macintyre milk jug, pewter lid, No. M339, 6in, similar teapot stand, No. M178W, 5.25in. (cracked) £380. Oct 00.

1414

Amersham Auction Rooms, Bucks. Royal Dux porcelain model of a dromedary, 18in. £380. July 02.

1415

Canterbury Auc. Galleries, Kent. Pair late 19thC Staffs pottery spill vases, 7.25in. £380. Aug 02.

1416

Woolley & Wallis, Salisbury. Nantgarw long oval pen tray, 'Nant-Garw C.W.' impressed, c1815, 24cm., pt. re-gilding to the rim. £380. Sep 00.

1417

Dee, Atkinson & Harrison, Driffield. Early 19thC Staffs pearlware figure entitled 'Salt', 6.5in. £380. Apr 01.

66

1418

Gorringes, Lewes. Royal Copenhagen Japan pattern vase, pattern no. 1286, 8in. £380. Apr 00.

1419

Gorringes, Lewes. Royal Worcester bonzo dog figure, No. 2855, date code 1932, 2.75in. £380. Dec 00.

1420

Gorringes, Bexhill. Johnson Bros. 'Old Britain Castles' dinner service. (112) £380. Oct 01.

1421

Woolley & Wallis, Salisbury. Royal Worcester vase, signed 'H Stinton', shape 2491, puce mark, c1919, 10cm. (two minute chips) £380. Sep 00.

1422

Hamptons, Godalming. Coalport 'jewelled' vase, late 19thC, green printed mark, gilt No. V2590, retailers mark indistinct, 15cm. £380. Sep 01.

1423

Gorringes, Lewes. Cow and milkmaid group, 7in and a small cow figure, 3in. Staffordshire. £380. Oct 00.

1424

Sworders, Stansted Mount-fitchet. Pair of R. Worcester figures of Victorian children holding baskets, no. 880, 10in high approx. (girl with detached head) £380. Apr 01.

1425

Gorringes, Lewes. 19thC Staffs seated cat with sponged decoration, 5.5in, similar smaller cat, 2in. £380. Jan 02.

1426

Gorringes, Lewes. Royal Worcester cup and saucer, highland cattle, both signed H. Stinton, and saucer with pheasant, signed Jns, Stinton, date code 1949. £380. Dec 00.

1427

Rosebery's, London. Masons ironstone jug, c1840, 21.5cm high with 2 other graduated in size of a similar pattern and later date. £380. Mar 02.

1428

Tring Market Auctions, Herts. 19thC Spode Armorial part tea/coffee service with some Copeland & Garrett replacements, black script mk., some damage. (30) £380. May 02.

1429

Gorringes, Lewes. Royal Worcester vase, signed H. Davis and floral spray panel signed E. Phillips, 2401 and date code 1906, 10.75in. (restoration) £380. Feb 01.

1430

Gorringes, Lewes. Bow figure of a man wearing a turquoise cloak, 9.5in. (head re-stuck, base repaired) £380. Apr 01.

1431

Locke & England, Leamington Spa. Matched set of Mason's ironstone jugs, printed marks in blue, smallest in black, 18cm to 9cm. £380. Feb 03.

1432

Gorringes, Lewes. Derby porcelain model of a cow and calf with bocage, 6in. £380. Apr 01.

1433

Canterbury Auc. Galleries, Kent. Copeland Parianware bust 'Miranda' after W C Marshall, impressed mark, socle impressed 'Crystal Palace Art Union', 11in. £380. Aug 03.

1434

Locke & England, Leamington Spa. Pair Worcester porcelain vases, 22.5cm. £380. Sep 02.

1435

Dee, Atkinson & Harrison, Driffield. 17thC Isnik pottery plate, 10.5in. (damaged) £380. Apr 02.

1436

Potteries Specialist Auctions, Stoke. Pendelfin. Pair rabbit bookends, dressed in lilac. (chips/wear) £380. Apr 03.

1437

Gorringes, Bexhill. Pair of Minton vases, A. Boullimies sig., painted mark to base, 14in. (one af) £380. June 03.

1438

Gorringes, Bexhill. Victorian Sunderland lustre box, with naval scene, inscribed 'The flag that's braved a thousand years, the battle and the breeze', 5in. £380. Dec 01.

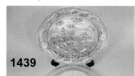

1439

Thos Mawer & Son, Lincoln. Spode. Pair Indian sporting series soup dishes, impressed mark Spode 44, 'Chase of the Wolf', 24cm. £375. Feb 03.

1440

Tring Market Auctions, Herts. 19thC Staffs lustre jug, with a 9-strong negro band, printed verse 'I wish I was in Dixy Land', and 'Sally is the girl for me'. £370. Nov 02.

1441

Andrew Hartley, Ilkley. Leeds Creamware fruit comport, 12.25in wide. £370. Apr 01.

1442

Wintertons Ltd, Lichfield. Parian figure, c1870, imp'd Maidenhood, reverse imp'd Published Sept 2 1868, Copeland, 57cm. £370. Dec 01.

1443

Louis Taylor, Stoke on Trent. 19thC Wedgwood Jasperware copy of the Portland vase, c1870s, 7.5in. £370. Mar 03.

1444

Tring Market Auctions, Herts. Royal Crown Derby Japan pattern vase, year marks for 1904, 11in. £370. Mar 03.

1445

Ambrose, Loughton. Minton Secessionist Jardiniere. £360. Dec 99.

1446

Dockree's, Manchester. Wade wolf jug (damaged) £360. Nov 1999.

The illustrations in these pages are in descending price order. The price range is indicated at the top of each page.

1447

David Duggleby, Scarborough. Victorian stoneware puzzle jug sprigged with a hunting scene, probably Derbyshire, c1840, 7.5in. £360. Apr 00.

1448

Wintertons Ltd, Lichfield. 19thC 'Semi China' soup tureen, blue and white transfer printed, 25cm high. with a ladle. £360. Mar 00.

1449

Hamptons, Godalming. Royal Worcester blush ivory vase, puce printed mark and shape No. 1445, date code for 1893, 28.4cm high. £360. Sep 01.

1450

John Taylors, Louth. Pair 18thC pistol grip knife and fork decorated with under glazed blue. £360. Mar 00.

1451

Wintertons Ltd, Lichfield. Pair of Read and Clementson 'Chantilian', pottery meat plates, 56cm. £360. Mar 00.

1452

Dee, Atkinson & Harrison, Driffield. R. Doulton figure of the year Amy 1991, HN 3316, 8.5in. £360. Feb 00.

1453

Dee, Atkinson & Harrison, Driffield. Garniture of three vases, by Thomas Forester & Sons, exotic blue flora on a gilt ground, 9.5in and 10.75in high. £360. Mar 00.

1454

Gorringes, Lewes. Large Wade porcelain figure of Jock and another of Tramp, 5.5in. £360. Oct 00.

1455

Gorringes, Lewes. Victorian majolica novelty jug as a seated bear with spoon handle, possibly by Gibbs and Carry, Amworth, 11in. (small crack) £360. July 00.

Hammer Prices £370-£360

1456

Gorringes, Lewes. Pair 19thC Delft vases, monogrammed TF, 16in. (chipped and cracked) £360. July 00.

1457

Dockree's, Manchester. Caughley blue/white jug with pagoda design, overall length 3.75in. £360. Sep 00.

1458

Gorringes, Lewes. 19thC Sevres chocolate cup, cover and saucer. £360. July 00.

1459

Amersham Auction Rooms, Bucks. Royal Doulton cream glazed china bulldog, printed black mark and Rd. 645658, 5.75in. £360. Oct 03.

1460

Gorringes, Lewes. Clarice Cliff buttercup pattern tête è tête. (6) £360. Sep 00.

1461

Gorringes, Lewes. Clarice Cliff autumn lotus jug, 8.25in. £360. June 00.

1462

Amersham Auction Rooms, Bucks. 19thC pearl ware jug, religiously inspired texts, John Stephens, born April 3rd 1825, 9in. £360. May 01.

1463

Cheffins, Cambridge. Late 17thC German saltglazed stoneware Bellarmine, 22cm. £360. Apr 01.

1464

Amersham Auction Rooms, Bucks. Late19th/early 20thC kutani porcelain vase, 19in. £360. June 01.

1465

Gorringes, Lewes. Royal Worcester cup and saucer, highland cattle, sgnd. Stinton, date code 1938. £360. Dec 00.

1466

Amersham Auction Rooms, Bucks. Late 19thC Meissen porcelain biblical figure of a man, 11.5in. £360. Sep 01.

1467

Lambert & Foster, Tenterden. Minton, H & Co. 'Scinde' dinnerware. (57) (some af) £360. Feb 02.

1468

Gorringes, Bexhill. Royal Dux porcelain shepherd boy with dog, 17in. (repairs) £360. May 02.

1469

Sworders, Stansted Mount-fitchet. 10 pieces of miniature pottery and porcelain, incl. 2 Worcester tankards and 2 Derby cups and saucers, (some damage) Worcester 1.5in high. £360. Apr 01.

1470

Hamptons, Godalming. Pair of 'Chantilly' vases, probably Samson, Kakiemon colours, with a leopard in foliage, 10in. £360. July 02.

1471

Wintertons Ltd, Lichfield. Pair of Staffs porcelain loving cups, c1870, printed and enamelled with The Farmers Arms, dogs collar marked T Lowe, 13in. £360. Jan 03.

1472

Rosebery's, London. Victorian Staffs figure group and a clock group. £360. Mar 02.

1473

W & H Peacock, Bedford. 19thC transfer printed, part dinner service. £360. Jan 03.

1474

Thos Mawer & Son, Lincoln. Royal Doulton 'Norfolk' part breakfast set. £360. June 03.

1475

Rosebery's, London. Pair of Crown Devon pottery vases, by J Coleman, unmarked, impressed no. 89? to base, 33cm high. £360. Sep 02.

1476

Locke & England, Leamington Spa. 19thC Italian pottery ecclesiastical vessel, red lustre finish, latin inscriptions, blue cockerel mark for Cantagalli, 45cm. (one handle finial repaired) £360. Sep 03.

1477

Canterbury Auc. Galleries, Kent. R. Doulton porcelain figure, The Cobbler, HN542, impressed date code 1929, 7.5in. £360. Aug 03.

1478

Tring Market Auctions, Herts. 19thC Imari bowl, 12in wide. £360. Jan 03.

1479

R. Wintertons, Burton on Trent. Shelley Late Foley Intarsio teapot of Lord Kitchener. (spout restored) £360. Aug 02.

1480

Gorringes, Lewes. Early 19thC Sunderland lustre frog mug printed with a view of the Sunderland Iron Bridge in black, 4.75in. £360. June 03.

1481

Wintertons Ltd, Lichfield. R. Winton Chintz 'Sweet Pea' breakfast set, replacement 'Somerset' egg cup, printed marks, s.d. £350. Nov 99.

1482

Lambert & Foster, Tenterden. Pair of Continental figures of a man and woman, blue X mark, 40cm. £350. Aug 03.

1483

Cheffins, Cambridge. Mid 20thC vase, partly labelled and impressed 'Moorcroft' and 'Made in England', 26cm. £350. Dec 00.

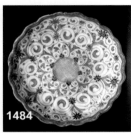

1484

Clarke Gammon, Guildford. Italian Deruta Maiolica Crespina of scalloped form, c1600, 10in. £350. Apr 01.

1485

Andrew Hartley, Ilkley. Chamberlains Worcester porcelain plate from the Yeo service, border No 298, 8.75in. £350. Feb 01.

1486

Tring Market Auctions, Herts. Flight Worcester part tea and coffee service, blue crescent mark. (13) £350. May 02.

1487

Hamptons, Godalming. Clarice Cliff wind bells bizarre pattern vase of Meiping form, black printed mark to base, 15.5cm. £350. Mar 02.

1488

Hamptons, Godalming. Meissen flower girl, late 19thC, u/g blue X swords with cancellation mark, incised No 11, impressed No 93, 14cm. £350. Sep 01.

1489

Gorringes, Lewes. Moorcroft Macintyre florian ware vase, 5in. (rim chip) £350. Oct 00.

1490

Rosebery's, London. Minton Secessionist vase. £350. Oct 01.

1491

Andrew Hartley, Ilkley. Pair of Caughley sauce boats, 18thC, 8.5in. £350. Oct 01.

1492

Louis Taylor, Stoke on Trent. Beswick standing shire mare. £350. Sep 02.

1493

Tring Market Auctions, Herts. Pair of candelabra figures by Samson after Meissen, cross swords and 'S' mark in u/g blue, 13in. af. £350. May 02.

1494

Richard Wintertons, Burton on Trent. Pearlware group, c1800, (of Walton type) St George & the Dragon, 25cm. (damages) £350. Jan 02.

Prices quoted are hammer prices which excluded the buyer's premium. Adding 15% will give an approximation to the buying price.

1495

Louis Taylor, Stoke on Trent. Beswick elephant and tiger, 12in. £350. Mar 03.

1496

Louis Taylor, Stoke on Trent. Royal Doulton smooth haired terrier. 'Chosen Don of Notts', 6in. £350. Mar 03.

1497

Tring Market Auctions, Herts. Meissen plate, dish, X swords mk. and dot in u/g blue, imp'd 10, dish imp'd 33, plate 9.75in, dish 8.5in. £350. Mar 03.

1498

Gorringes, Bexhill. Pair of German porcelain figures, 16.5in. £350. Oct 02.

1499

Louis Taylor, Stoke on Trent. R. Doulton stoneware vase by Eliza Simmance and Bessie Newbery, monogrammed to base, 8in. £350. June 03.

1500

Gorringes, Lewes. Bow porcelain maiden flower seller, 6.75in. £350. Apr 01.

1501

Tring Market Auctions, Herts. 19thC Palissy style Majolica snake and frog jug as an oak tree, 10in. £350. Nov 02.

1502

Gorringes, Lewes. Royal Worcester kneeling monk in prayer candle extinguisher, 3.75in. £340. Oct 00.

1503

Canterbury Auc. Galleries, Kent. Early 19thC Staffs pottery tureen stand, printed with a view of Canterbury, 16in wide. £340. Oct 00.

1504

David Duggleby, Scarborough. Pair of Doulton Lambeth stoneware candlesticks by Emily Partington, incised marks, 12in. £340. Apr 00.

1505

Dee, Atkinson & Harrison, Driffield. Pair E. Dunderdale, Castleford Pottery pickle dishes, c1800. £340. July 99.

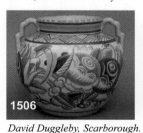

1506

David Duggleby, Scarborough. Carter Stabler and Adams Poole terracotta vase, shape No. 973/EB, painted by Ruth Pavely, impressed and painted marks, 7.25in. £340. Apr 00.

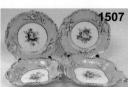

1507

Gorringes, Lewes. Six Ridgway dessert dishes and three comports. £340. July 00.

1508

Woolley & Wallis, Salisbury. Samuel Alcock cat and kitten group, '2' impressed c1830-45, 6.5cm. £340. Mar 00.

Hammer Prices £350-£340

1509

Ambrose, Loughton. Watcombe terracotta jardiniere with hand painted decoration of lilies. £340. Dec 99.

1510

Woolley & Wallis, Salisbury. Leeds creamware cup, c1800, af. 16cm. £340. June 00.

1511

Woolley & Wallis, Salisbury. Bow mug, no mark, c1750-55, 12.3cm. (some damage) £340. June 00.

1512

Wintertons Ltd, Lichfield. Pearlware teapot, painted with Oriental fenced landscape, reverse inscribed Hannah Beard, Stockport, 1783, 6.5in. £340. Nov 01.

1513

Woolley & Wallis, Salisbury. Chinese white glazed pottery vase, Tang dynasty 618-906AD, 23cm. (re-glued rim chip, chip to shoulder) £340. Sep 00.

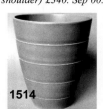

1514

Amersham Auction Rooms, Bucks. Mid 20thC Wedgwood Keith Murray vase, incised rings on a pale green ground, 9in. £340. Apr 01.

1515

Gorringes, Lewes. Signed Satsuma bowl painted with butterflies, 7in. £340. June 00.

1516

Andrew Hartley, Ilkley. Royal Dux porcelain shire horse grazing, gilt embellishment, 10in wide. £340. Apr 01.

1517

Gorringes, Lewes. Two Royal Worcester cups and saucers painted with peacocks, all signed R. Austin, date code 1926. £340. Dec 00.

1518

Woolley & Wallis, Salisbury. Six R. Crown Derby coffee cans/saucers, Imari style with pattern No 2451, c1928. £340. Sep 00.

1519

John Taylors, Louth. Copeland Spode Italian toilet jug, bowl, soap dish and toothbrush pot. £340. Mar 01.

1520

Gorringes, Lewes. Royal Copenhagen figure of an elderly lady wearing a shawl, no 784, 8in. £340. Sep 00.

Hammer Prices £340-£320

Cheffins, Cambridge. 19thC Scottish pottery bread crock, body moulded in relief, 44cm wide. £340. Dec 00.

Gorringes, Lewes. Set of 7 German monkey band group, 6.5in to 4in. £340. Feb 01.

Gorringes, Lewes. Moorcroft MacIntyre aurelian ware vase with red poppies against a gilded blue ground, Rd No. 314901, 6in. £340. Feb 01.

Gorringes, Lewes. 17thC Transitional wucai vase, with courtiers in an interior, 15in. (holed/cracked) £340. Mar 01.

Gorringes, Lewes. Bow porcelain chamberstick as 2 canaries amongst bocage, 6.5in. (sconce deficient) £340. Apr 01.

Sworders, Stansted Mount-fitchet. 'Newstone' 73 piece part dinner service, late 19thC. £340. July 01.

Gorringes, Lewes. Royal Worcester coffee cup/saucer, Chinese pheasants, cup signed R Austin, saucer signed Sedgley. £340. Mar 01.

Gorringes, Lewes. Royal Worcester coffee cup/saucer with pheasants. £340. Mar 01.

Gorringes, Lewes. 18thC Worcester polychrome teapot, manner of James Giles, 6.25in. £340. Mar 01.

Gorringes, Lewes. Worcester sauceboat painted with underglaze flowers, c1760, 6.75in. £340. Mar 01.

Locke & England, Leamington Spa. Art Deco Shelley porcelain teaset for 6. £340. Feb 03.

Gorringes, Bexhill. Parian group, 'Little Boat Builder', by E B Stephens for The Art Union of London', c1872, marked to side of plinth base 'Hit the wrong nail', 18.5in. £340. Feb 03.

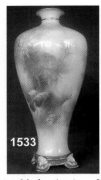

Tring Market Auctions, Herts. Hadleys Worcester vase, 10in high. £340. Nov 02.

Wintertons Ltd, Lichfield. George Jones majolica bread plate, c1865-70, No. 1756, 32cm. £340. July 02.

Locke & England, Leamington Spa. Pair 19thC Chamberlains Worcester armorial plates, latin motto. (some crazing) £340. Sep 03.

W & H Peacock, Bedford. Beswick advertising figure of collie, for Dulux paints. £340. July 03.

W & H Peacock, Bedford. 19thC Staffordshire figure 'Christ Teacheth Nicodemus'. £340. Mar 03.

Gorringes, Lewes. 3 Carlton ware Guinness advertising figures, kangaroo, (foot repaired) toucan and pint (repaired) and an ostrich, 3.7in tallest. £340. Mar 03.

W & H Peacock, Bedford. Pair of 19thC Sampson porcelain armorial chargers. £340. Jan 03.

Locke & England, Leamington Spa. 19thC Minton majolica beer jug, pewter mounted cover, impressed number 1231, 28cm. £340. Sep 03.

Locke & England, Leamington Spa. 8 Samson porcelain Commedia del Arte theatrical figures, false gold anchor mark, 16cm. £340. Sep 03.

Tring Market Auctions, Herts. Set of 4 Staffs white glazed porcelain lobed jugs, 5.25in, 6.5in and 8in. £330. Nov 02.

Wintertons Ltd, Lichfield. Royal Crown Derby Mansion House Dwarf advertising 'Theatre Royal Haymarket....' signed M.Mason, 17cm. £330. July 03.

Andrew Hartley, Ilkley. Early 19thC Brameld pottery meat plate, blue printed with 'The Castle at Rochefort' pattern, impressed 20, 20.75in wide. £330. Sep 99.

Sworders, Stansted Mount-fitchet. Pair of 19thC dishes, 'Colossal Sarcophagus near Castle Rosso', probably Spode, 9.5in. £330. July 01.

Peter Wilson, Nantwich. Slipware shallow baking dish, poss. Staffordshire, 12in. (all over crazing, chips and damage) £330. Nov 00.

Great Western Auctions, Glasgow. Wemyss pig, 16cm long. £330. Feb 01.

Woolley & Wallis, Salisbury. Two Chinese pottery models of figures riding horses, Tang dynasty, 618-906AD, 38cm. (damaged) £320. Sep 00.

Gorringes, Lewes. Clarice Cliff garland pattern sandwich dish, 11in and 4 matching plates. £320. June 00.

1550

Finn & Sons, Canterbury. Majolica ewer and stand, a/f. £320. Sep 99.

1551

Wintertons Ltd, Lichfield. Moorcroft Macintyre Florian vase, design 404017, 20.5cm. £320. Nov 99.

The numbering system aids the editorial analysis at the beginning of each section as well as providing a reader reference.

1552

Wintertons Ltd, Lichfield. Royal Doulton Series Ware 'The Jackdaws of Rheims' jardiniere, printed marks, firing crack to interior and crazing, 26in. £320. Feb 01.

1553

Gorringes, Lewes. Two early 19thC Pratt style cottage money boxes flanked by figures (one missing), 5in. £320. Oct 00.

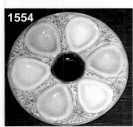

1554

Clarke Gammon, Guildford. Pair of Continental majolica pottery oyster dishes, with pink and cream wells, 10in. £320. Feb 01.

1555

Andrew Hartley, Ilkley. Carter Stabler Adams red earthenware Poole vase, Shape no 960/HE painted with a blue bird amongst stylised flowers, 6.25in high. £320. Oct 00.

1556

Gorringes, Lewes. Royal Worcester blush porcelain jug, No 1227, 10.5in. £320. Apr 00.

1557

Woolley & Wallis, Salisbury. Set 6 Chinese famille rose plates, Qianlong, 1736-96, 22.5cm. (cracks and wear) £320. Sep 00.

1558

Crows, Dorking. Pair of Satsuma vases and one other. £320. Sep 01.

1559

Andrew Hartley, Ilkley. Pair Royal Doulton pottery vases, tube lined stylised leaves in green and blue glaze on a Slater's Patent ground, 16in. £320. Oct 00.

1560

Gorringes, Lewes. Austrian Keramos wall mask of a harlequin, 11in. £320. July 00.

1561

Gorringes, Lewes. Crown Ducal Charlotte Rhead tube lined plate, 14in. £320. Sep 00.

1562

Gorringes, Lewes. Clarice Cliff inverted baluster vase, 8.25in. £320. July 00.

1563

Gorringes, Lewes. Isle of Man on coil of rope teapot with removable head, marked W. Broughton China Rooms, 50 Duke St, Douglas, 10in. (glaze flaking and repair of spout) £320. Feb 01.

1564

Richard Wintertons, Burton on Trent. Minton Secessionist tapered vase, hairline crack. £320. Apr 02.

Hammer Price £320

1565

Gorringes, Lewes. Cantagali vase, serpent handles and masks, with a townscape and soldiers, 16in. £320. Oct 00.

1566

Cheffins, Cambridge. Clarice Cliff Bizarre Biarritz plate, 'Fragrance', black printed marks, 26cm. £320. Dec 00.

1567

Cheffins, Cambridge. Pair of Mintons Secessionist pottery vases, date code 1913, black printed and impressed marks, 31cm high. £320. Dec 00.

1568

Gorringes, Lewes. Cased early 20thC Royal Doulton 12 piece coffee set with 6 silver gilt coffee spoons, H4058. £320. Feb 01.

1569

Gorringes, Lewes. Cased early 20thC Royal Doulton 12 piece coffee set with 6 silver gilt coffee spoons, H3891. £320. Feb 01.

1570

Gorringes, Lewes. Clarice Cliff bonjour crocus pattern biscuit barrel, 6in. (chip to all corners of lid and one foot) £320. Feb 01.

1571

Sworders, Stansted Mountfitchet. Creamware tankard, printed and enamelled with a farmyard scene, 6in high. £320. Apr 01.

1572

Sworders, Stansted Mountfitchet. Pair Chinese moon flasks, 19thC, 14.5in. £320. Apr 01.

1573

Sworders, Stansted Mountfitchet. Bloor Derby part dinner service, (42) (some damage) £320. Apr 01.

1574

Tring Market Auctions, Herts. Chinese Celadon glazed vase. £320. Jan 02.

1575

Gorringes, Lewes. Set of four Capo-di-monte figures of Napoleonic soldiers, signed B Merli, 12in. £320. Mar 01.

1576

Sworders, Stansted Mountfitchet. Six Aynsley plates painted with a Scottish view 'jewelled' borders, signed Harrison, and numbered 3338, 8.5in. £320. July 01.

Hammer Prices £320-£310

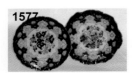

1577

Locke & England, Leamington Spa. 19thC English pottery dessert set. (16) £320. Nov 02.

1578

Gorringes, Lewes. Doulton Lambeth beaker, three birds on a branch by Florence Barlow, 5.25in. £320. Mar 01.

1579

Amersham Auction Rooms, Bucks. Pair of late 19thC Japanese Imari porcelain vases, 9.25in. £320. Aug 02.

1580

Gorringes, Lewes. Linthorpe pottery Christopher Dresser mottled green glazed jug with imp'd decoration, imp'd mark, signed No 339, 9in. (chipped) £320. Mar 01.

1581

Louis Taylor, Stoke on Trent. Fieldings Crown Devon vase, 15in. £320. Sep 03.

1582

Gorringes, Lewes. Pair of Coalport candlesticks, 9in. £320. Apr 01.

1583

Amersham Auction Rooms, Bucks. Early 20thC Moorcroft sugar basin, pomegranate design, hammered pewter mounts, 3.5in. £320. Nov 02.

1584

Richard Wintertons, Burton on Trent. Pair of Arita type moonflasks, one with battle scenes, other water buffalo, 25cm high. £320. Apr 03.

1585

Richard Wintertons, Burton on Trent. Clarice Cliff Killarney vase. £320. July 03.

1586

Amersham Auction Rooms, Bucks. Late 19thC Meissen model of a gentleman, 9.5in. £320. Nov 02.

1587

Tring Market Auctions, Herts. Majolica sardine dish, no marks, interior glaze cracks, 7.25in x 8in. £320. Jan 03.

1588

Louis Taylor, Stoke. Large R. Doulton, 'Paddy' musical jug, D5887. £320. June 03.

1589

Tring Market Auctions, Herts. Early 19thC part tea/coffee service, some damage. (20) £320. Mar 03.

1590

Sworders, Stansted Mount-fitchet. R. Worcester, 'Japan', 3072, 3in. £320. July 01.

1591

Gorringes, Lewes. Pair late 19thC Japanese chargers, painted with dragon amongst waves, 21in. £320. Mar 01.

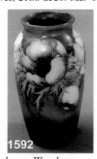

1592

Denhams, Warnham. Moorcroft Anemone pattern vase, signature mark, Potter to HM The Queen, Made in England. £320. Aug 03.

1593

Richard Wintertons, Burton on Trent. Masonic creamware mug, late 18thC, puce transfer printed, 9cm. Old repairs to handle. £320. Apr 03.

1594

Gorringes, Bexhill. Pair of baluster shaped Kutani vases, 24.5in. (one af) £320. July 03.

1595

Denhams, Warnham. Meissen porcelain urn with floral encrusted border, 15in. £320. Aug 03.

1596

Woolley & Wallis, Salisbury. Goebel nativity set in a wooden stable. (12) £310. Sep 00.

1597

Tring Market Auctions, Herts. Pair of early 19thC baskets, printed with 'Net' pattern, one af, 8in long. £310. Sep 02.

1598

Andrew Hartley, Ilkley. Late 18thC creamware tankard, with cattle watering in a landscape, 5in. £310. Feb 01.

1599

Louis Taylor, Stoke on Trent. Beswick shire foal, rocking horse grey gloss, 6.25in. £310. Mar 03.

1600

D. Duggleby, Scarborough. Linthorpe pottery plate by Dr Christopher Dresser, central well decorated with a stylised bird in foliage, factory marks and facsimile sig., 11.5in. (crazing) £310. Apr 00.

1601

Andrew Hartley, Ilkley. 19thC Chinese famille rose teapot. £310. Oct 99.

1602

Tring Market Auctions, Herts. Royal Worcester vase, yr. mk. 1903, 15.5in. £310. Mar 03.

1603

Mervyn Carey, Tenterden. Victorian parian figure of the Duke of Wellington, 10.25in. £310. Dec 99.

1604

Woolley & Wallis, Salisbury. Malcolm Pepper, stoneware vase, 23.5cm & dish, 42.5cm, impressed seal marks, c1970-80. £310. Sep 00.

1605

John Taylors, Louth. 19thC Meissen figurine of a girl with a dog. £300. July 99.

The illustrations in these pages are in descending price order. The price range is indicated at the top of each page.

1606

Andrew Hartley, Ilkley. Leeds Fireclay Co Ltd pottery vase, 7.25in, impressed marks and painted initials. £300. Oct 99.

1607

A. Hartley, Ilkley. French white porcelain figural group, 10.75in wide. £300. Oct 99.

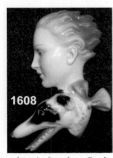

1608

Rosebery's, London. Goebels wall mask. £300. June 00.

1609

A. Hartley, Ilkley. 19thC parian vase, 15.75in, printed mark Copelands Porcelain Statuary. £300. Oct 99.

1610

Great Western Auctions, Glasgow. Dunmore pottery bread crock. £300. May 00.

1611

Gorringes, Lewes. Meissen cupid figure entitled 'Je les unis', 6in. £300. Apr 00.

1612

Woolley & Wallis, Salisbury. Two Mason's meat plates, views from the British Lakes series, printed marks, c1830, 44cm & 39cm. £300. Sep 00.

1613

Gorringes, Lewes. Victorian Staffordshire figure of a lady holding a bird and a spaniel, 16in. £300. July 00.

1614

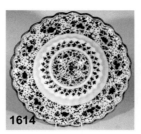

Andrew Hartley, Ilkley. 18thC Continental Delft dish, 13.5in wide. £300. Dec 00.

1615

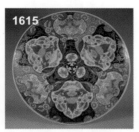

Woolley & Wallis, Salisbury. Japanese Imari dish, Meiji, 1868-1912, 45cm. £300. Sep 00.

1616

John Taylors, Louth. Moorcroft Liberty's pomegranate bowl, damage. £300. Sep 00.

1617

Gorringes, Lewes. Clarice Cliff Fantasque Trees and House pattern plate, 9.75in. £300. July 00.

1618

Crows, Dorking. Plichta clover decorated pig signed Nekola. £300. July 01.

1619

Woolley & Wallis, Salisbury. Minton pot pourri vase, 'Indian Tree', impressed and painted marks, 2nd half 19thC, 30cm. £300. Sep 00.

1620

Woolley & Wallis, Salisbury. Chinese flower vase, panels of figures on diaper ground, 19thC, 23cm. £300. Sep 00.

1621

Gorringes, Lewes. Pair of Victorian Staffordshire zebras, 5in. £300. July 00.

1622

Woolley & Wallis, Salisbury. James Kent Chintz tea set, 'Du Barry', printed marks. (21) £300. Sep 00.

1623

Gorringes, Lewes. 18thC Walton style tithe pig group, 7in. £300. June 00.

1624

Gorringes, Lewes. Pair 19thC Staffs bocage back lamb groups, 3.5in. £300. June 00.

1625

Dee, Atkinson & Harrison, Driffield. Copeland Spode part dinner service, 'Chinese Rose'. (57) £300. Apr 01.

1626

Andrew Hartley, Ilkley. Poole Pottery Delphis charger, printed and painted marks, 16.5in. £300. Feb 01.

1627

Woolley & Wallis, Salisbury. Grainger Worcester reticulated ovoid vase and cover, impressed mark, c1880, 20cm. (knop restored) £300. Sep 00.

1628

Gorringes, Bexhill. Moorcroft powder bowl, impressed to underside, also bearing paper label, 6in dia. £300. Mar 03.

1629

Gorringes, Lewes. Clarice Cliff Aurea pattern sugar sifter, 5.5in. £300. Sep 00.

1630

Amersham Auction Rooms, Bucks. Pair of late 19thC Doulton Lambeth stoneware vases, by Florence Barlow, 7in high. £300. June 01.

73

Hammer Prices £300

1631

Wintertons Ltd, Bakewell. 19thC Alcock & Co majolica jug, impressed beehive mark, 9.5in. £300. Oct 01.

1632

Biddle & Webb, Birmingham. Pair of Cantonese chargers. £300. Sep 01.

1633

Gorringes, Lewes. 19thC tree and well oval meat plate and matching smaller plate, 20.5in and 19in. £300. Oct 00.

1634

Gorringes, Lewes. 18thC Whieldon type cat on a cushion, 3.75in. £300. Oct 00.

1635

Gorringes, Lewes. Royal Worcester vase, and painted with fruit, signed T. Lockyer, No. 2764, date code 1921, 6.25in. £300. Dec 00.

1636

Tring Market Auctions, Herts. 20thC Royal Crown Derby dessert dish. £300. Jan 02.

1637

Biddle & Webb, Birmingham. Japanese Imari charger. £300. Sep 01.

1638

Gorringes, Lewes. Royal Worcester jug painted with blackberries, No. 1094, base chip, and a pair of vases, patt. 957, one chipped/cracked, all signed K. Blake. £300. Dec 00.

1639

Wintertons Ltd, Lichfield. Mid 19thC porcelain florally enamelled two handled tray, 36cm long. £300. Dec 01.

1640

Gorringes, Lewes. Group of three Capo-di-monte figures of British soldiers, signed B. Merli, 12.5in. £300. Mar 01.

1641

Gorringes, Lewes. R. Doulton vase, incised leaf and floral decoration, 8in. £300. Dec 00.

1642

Gorringes, Lewes. Clarice Cliff Bizarre 30 piece part dinner/tea set. £300. Feb 01.

1643

Gorringes, Lewes. 19thC majolica cheese dish, 11in. £300. Apr 01.

1644

Gorringes, Lewes. Pair of Bretby vases relief moulded with mice, cherries, acanthus leaves, No. 544, 11in., one cracked. £300. Feb 01.

1645

Tring Market Auctions, Herts. Set of five famille rose plates painted with two Dogs of Fo, 8.75in. £300. May 02.

1646

Gorringes, Lewes. 19thC Spanish vase painted with a Nelson memorial armorial with motto Junta in uno tiva. £300. Dec 00.

1647

Gorringes, Lewes. Royal Worcester 'Officer of the Coldstream Guards 1815', No. 2676, date code 1917, 11.5in., damaged and restored. £300. Dec 00.

1648

Ambrose, Loughton. Victorian earthenware Rockingham form part teaset. (27) £300. Feb 02.

1649

Rosebery's, London. Pair of Crown Derby gardeners, c1820, 20cm. £300. Mar 02.

1650

Gorringes, Lewes. 18thC Derby figure of Neptune and a dolphin, 8.5in., arm restored. £300. Apr 01.

1651

Gorringes, Lewes. Bow figure of a youth with yellow tricorn hat, holding a cup, 7in. £300. Apr 01.

1652

Gorringes, Bexhill. Meissen figure, 'Goose Girl', under-glaze blue marks and incised J175 and 137. £300. Mar 03.

1653

Gorringes, Lewes. 17thC Isnik dish, with blue, iron red and green serrated edged flowers and leaves, 11.5in. (restored) £300. Apr 01.

1654

Gorringes, Lewes. 18thC German saltglaze bellarmine, with coat of arms. (restored) £300. Mar 01.

1655

Peter Wilson, Nantwich. Royal Doulton John Barley Corn Kingsware decanter, c1913, with silver cork and stopper, 19cm. £300. July 02.

1656

Sworders, Stansted Mount-fitchet. Royal Worcester vase with 2 floral sprays, 1895, 5.5in. £300. July 01.

1657

R. Wintertons, Burton on Trent. Staffs figure of Gladstone, late 19thC, 39cm. £300. Sep 03.

1658

Louis Taylor, Stoke on Trent. Royal Doulton, The Perfect Pair, HN 581. £300. Mar 03.

1659

Fellows & Sons, Hockley, Birmingham. Poole Carter, Stabler, Adams majolica glazed stoneware cherub, imp'd 'Phoebe Stabler 1912', imp'd mks., 7in. £300. July 03.

Prices quoted are hammer prices which excluded the buyer's premium. Adding 15% will give an approximation to the buying price.

1660

Sworders, Stansted Mountfitchet, Two 18thC Delft plates, 10in and 8.5in., chips. £300. July 01.

1661

Woolley & Wallis, Salisbury. Pair of Continental porcelain vases, late 19th/early 20thC, 38cm. £300. Sep 00.

1662

John Taylors, Louth. Beswick Dulux dog. (hairline crack) £300. Sep 03.

1663

Louis Taylor, Stoke. Beswick 'Oceanic Bonito', model 1232, 7.25in. £300. June 03.

1664

Amersham Auction Rooms, Bucks. Doulton Lambeth stoneware table lamp, two part body, imp'd stamp and dated 1884, 9.5in high. £300. July 02.

1665

Sworders, Stansted Mountfitchet. Royal Worcester tea set, painted with flower sprays. (19) £300. July 01.

1666

Rosebery's, London. Vienna porcelain charger, late 19thC, signed W. Meyr, the reverse entitled 'Damen - Portrait H Mahart', 35cm. £300. Sep 02.

1667

Tring Market Auctions, Herts. Royal Worcester tyg, shape No 1421, puce mark, c1886, 8.75in. £300. Jan 03.

1668

Amersham Auction Rooms, Bucks. Pair of late 19thC Continental porcelain figures, 11in high. £300. Mar 03.

1669

Gorringes, Lewes. Clarice Cliff Honolulu pattern honey pot and odd cover with bee handle, Bizarre mark, 3in. £300. June 03.

1670

Gorringes, Lewes. Worcester bowl, underglaze painted with pine prunus blossom, 6in dia. £290. July 00.

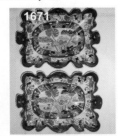

1671

Kivell & Sons, Bude. Pair of Masons dishes. £290. Dec 02.

1672

Gorringes, Bexhill. Pair of Staffordshire flatback spill vases modelled as peacocks, 8.25in high. £290. July 03.

1673

Wintertons Ltd, Lichfield. Clarice Cliff Bizarre 'melon' bowl, printed mk. for Newport Pottery, 8.75in. £290. Sep 01.

Hammer Prices £300-£280

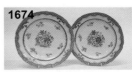

1674

Gorringes, Lewes. Pair of late 18thC Chamberlains Worcester plates in Chinese export palette, 9.25in. £290. Mar 01.

1675

Gorringes, Lewes. Beswick Ware portrait wall plaque, impressed 436 and numbered 8187, 12in. £290. Apr 01.

1676

Canterbury Auc. Galleries, Kent. Pair German porcelain figures of a gentleman and his companion, 16.5in. Formerly the property of Jack Warner OBE. £290. Dec 00.

1677

A. Hartley, Ilkley. Porcelain sugar bowl/saucer painted in polychrome, 18thC, possibly Liverpool, 5in. £290. Aug 02.

1678

Amersham Auction Rooms, Bucks. Early 20thC John Dewdney, Brannam pottery vase, body decorated with scraffito Arts & Crafts floral motifs, incised sig. and dated 1905, 17in. £290. Nov 01.

1679

R. Wintertons, Burton on Trent. Clarice Cliff sugar sifter with crocus pattern. £290. Jan 03.

1680

Gorringes, Lewes. 19thC Riley blue and white Eastern Street Scene pattern drainer, 14in. £280. Apr 00.

1681

Gorringes, Lewes. Clarice Cliff Lydiat pattern fruit bowl, 9.25in. £280. Sep 00.

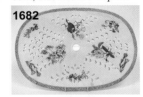

1682

Gorringes, Lewes. Early 19thC Wedgwood drainer printed with garden flowers, 16in. £280. Apr 00.

1683

Gorringes, Lewes. Clarice Cliff 'orange trees and house' plate, 8.5in. £280. June 00.

1684

Andrew Hartley, Ilkley. Berlin porcelain goblet, the gilt bowl painted with cherubs, 5.25in high. £280. Oct 99.

75

Hammer Price £280

1685

Woolley & Wallis, Salisbury. Caughley cup, saucer, dish, 'S' marks, c1780. £280. Sep 00.

1686

Gorringes, Lewes. Mintons earthenware plaque painted with figures beside a thatched cottage, signed Cathcart, 12in square. £280. June 00.

1687

Gorringes, Lewes. Early 19thC Staffs figure of Apollo with lyre, stamped Neale & Co. £280. June 00.

1688

Gorringes, Lewes. Unusual Ruskin vase, blue ice crystal decor, 9.5in. £280. July 00.

1689

Peter Wilson, Nantwich. Mid 19thC Staffs figure, 7in. (firing cracks). £280. Nov 00.

1690

Gorringes, Lewes. Worcester blue and white '100 Antiques' pattern waved edge dish, c1770, 8.25in. £280. Mar 01.

1691

Sworders, Stansted Mount-fitchet. Two pairs of 19thC pottery childs plates, with motto's within moulded and enamelled borders, 6in and 5.5in dia. £280. Apr 01.

1692

Gorringes, Lewes. Cased R. Worcester set of six coffee cups/saucers, with six silver coffee spoons. £280. Feb 01.

1693

Gorringes, Lewes. Egyptian Pre-Dynastic pottery black top jar, 6.25in, inventory number 1595 on base, c4000-3000BC (rim chipped) and a red ware bowl (probably later) 10in. £280. July 00.

1694

Gorringes, Bexhill. First period Worcester 'Plantation' mug. £280. July 01.

1695

Sworders, Stansted Mount-fitchet. Royal Doulton figure, Sir Walter Raleigh, HN 1751, 11.5in. (slight damage) £280. May 01.

1696

Gorringes, Lewes. Moorcroft MacIntyre crested vesta holder, marked Keble & WM in green, 3.5in. £280. June 00.

1697

Gorringes, Lewes. R. Doulton bowl, 6.5in. £280. June 00.

1698

Gorringes, Lewes. Late 19thC Japanese Satsuma koro and cover, 19in. £280. Sep 00.

1699

Gorringes, Lewes. Clarice Cliff beaker, 'Moonlight', 2.75in. £280. Sep 00.

1700

Gorringes, Lewes. Moorcroft Macintyre Florian vesta, 3in. (rim chip) £280. Sep 00.

1701

Gorringes, Lewes. Coalport vase with painted Loch Lomond panel, signed E G Ball, 6in. £280. Sep 00.

1702

Gorringes, Lewes. Worcester cabbage leaf jug, fruit and fir cone and flowers patterns, c1765, 11.25in. £280. Mar 01.

1703

Hamptons, Godalming. Pair of Royal Worcester vases by W Hawkings, printed marks and date code 1911, 15.5cm. (Handles restored, possibly lacking covers) £280. Sep 01.

1704

Gorringes, Lewes. German porcelain group of a couple in oriental costume, 8.5in. £280. Sep 00.

1705

Gorringes, Lewes. 19thC Nankin blue and white mug with a central willow pattern reserve, 6.5in. £280. Oct 00.

1706

Gorringes, Lewes. Clarice Cliff 'Rhodanthe' bonjour sugar caster, 5in. £280. Oct 00.

1707

Gorringes, Lewes. Mid 19thC lavender ground cottage pastille burner encrusted with flowers, 5.25in. £280. Oct 00.

1708

Sworders, Stansted Mount-fitchet. R. Doulton, The Jester, HN 1702, 10in. £280. May 01.

1709

Amersham Auction Rooms, Bucks. Pair of late 19thC German painted porcelain figures, 6.75in. £280. Mar 02.

1710

Wallis and Wallis, Lewes. Blue glazed pottery figure of a devil, skit of Freemasonry. Reg. No. for 1909, 7.75in high. £280. May 02.

1711

Locke & England, Leamington Spa. Midwinter Stylecraft pottery tableware, 'Zambesi', c1950s. (31) £280. Apr 03.

1712

Gorringes, Lewes. 19thC Staffordshire group, 9in and a similar clock face group, 3.5in. £280. Apr 01.

1713

Gorringes, Lewes. Pair of Royal Worcester blush porcelain vases, No. 982, 6.5in. £280. Apr 01.

1714

Tring Market Auctions, Herts. Staffs figure of Wellington, 9.5in. £280. Mar 02.

1715

Tring Market Auctions, Herts. Royal Doulton jardiniere, imp'd artist's mark for Ethel Beard and Francis Pope, 8in high. £280. May 02.

The numbering system aids the editorial analysis at the beginning of each section as well as providing a reader reference.

1716

Thos Mawer & Son, Lincoln. 19thC blue transfer printed vase 'Memphis' pattern, 32cm high. £280. Nov 02.

1717

Thos Mawer & Son, Lincoln. Moorcroft Centenary 'Yacht vase', 1897/1997 23cm, imp'd painted marks, No 1185, with certificate. £280. Apr 02.

1718

Locke & England, Leamington Spa. Clarice Cliff 'Crocus' vase, 15cm. £280. Feb 03.

1719

A. Hartley, Ilkley. Worcester porcelain tea bowl, cup and saucer, 'Hollow Rock Lily', mid/late 18thC. £280. Apr 03.

1720

Gorringes, Lewes. Lovatts Langleyware terracotta jardiniere, 37in. £280. Oct 02.

1721

Dee, Atkinson & Harrison, Driffield. 18thC polychrome Delft charger, 13.75in. £280. Apr 02.

1722

Thos Mawer & Son, Lincoln. 19thC porcelain dessert service. (14) £280. Nov 02.

1723

Potteries Specialist Auctions, Stoke on Trent. R. Doulton Greyhound, HN1067, small size, gloss. £280. Feb 03.

1724

Andrew Hartley, Ilkley. Pair of Pearlware sauce tureens and stands, 7.25in wide, with pair of damaged sauce ladles, early 19thC. £280. Aug 02.

1725

Dreweatt Neate, Newbury. English delft polychrome plate, prob. Bristol, painted in Fazackerly manner, 23cm, c1760. (chips, hairline crack) £280. June 03.

1726

Canterbury Auc. Galleries, Kent. Pr. Crown Staffordshire porcelain, Blue Jay and Blue Hawk, in Meissen manner, decorated by M Doubell-Miller, 8in. £280. Aug 03.

1727

Locke & England, Leamington Spa. Royal Doulton, Gulliver, D6560, 19.5cm. £280. May 03.

1728

Amersham Auction Rooms, Bucks. Mid 19thC Japanese Imari porcelain charger, painted characters to the reverse, 18in. £280. Mar 03.

1729

Andrew Hartley, Ilkley. Worcester porcelain coffee cup/saucer, painted in the Kempthorne pattern, 18thC, fret mark. £270. Feb 03.

Hammer Prices £280-£260

1730

Tring Market Auctions, Herts. Pair early 19thC Davenport toy teapots. £270. Jan 02.

1731

John Taylors, Louth. Moorcroft vase. Anemones. £270. Mar 00.

1732

Rosebery's, London. Wedgewood creamware jelly mould c1780. £270. June 00.

1733

Woolley & Wallis, Salisbury. Sunderland pink lustreware frog mug, with Iron Bridge over the Wear, title including 'Dixon and Co. Sunderland 1813', 12.5cm. £270. Sep 00.

1734

Andrew Hartley, Ilkley. Clarice Cliff Bizarre sugar shaker 'Marguerite', printed and painted marks, 5.5in. £270. Oct 00.

1735

Woolley & Wallis, Salisbury. Malcolm Pepper, stoneware vase, 30.5cm and dish, 35.5cm, imp'd seal marks, c1970-80. £270. Sep 00.

1736

Woolley & Wallis, Salisbury. 4 19thC Staffs figures, some damages, tallest 21.5cm. £270. Sep 00.

1737

Ambrose, Loughton. Clarice Cliff 'Bonjour' shape part tea service, 'Hollyhocks', some damage. (7) £270. Mar 02.

1738

Kivell & Sons, Bude. Torquay pottery cat, 7in high. £270. Mar 03.

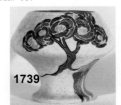

1739

Locke & England, Leamington Spa. Clarice Cliff Bizarre 'Patina' baluster vase, printed marks, 14cm. £270. July 03.

1740

Gorringes, Lewes. Wedgwood lustre vase decorated with carp on a mottled blue ground, 4.25in. £260. July 00.

Hammer Price £260

1741

Sworders, Stansted Mount-fitchet. Pair Satsuma eagles, early 20thC, 12in. (one with damaged claws) £260. Apr 01.

1742

Gorringes, Lewes. Gold-scheider figure of a lady in long plaid skirt, sig. C Weiss, 12.5in, chip. £260. June 00.

1743

Gorringes, Lewes. Clarice Cliff Forest Glen patterned plate, 8.5in. £260. June 00.

1744

Gorringes, Lewes. Minton parian figure, young woman on rock, 15in. £260. June 00.

1745

Rosebery's, London. Wedgwood blue jasper dip teapot, c1780. £260. June 00.

1746

Gorringes, Lewes. Minton majolica oval game dish, replaced handle, 12in. £260. June 00.

1747

Gorringes, Lewes. Royal Worcester sugar bowl, signed H. H. Price, date code 1926, 5.25in dia. £260. Dec 00.

1748

Andrew Hartley, Ilkley. Gold-scheider terracotta wall mask, stamped marks and incised 7910, 8.5in. £260. Dec 99.

1749

Woolley & Wallis, Salisbury. Aston Villa novelty teapot as a leather football, marked 'Aston V' in silver lustre and 'Made in England, Registered No 826551' moulded mark, 19cm wide. £260. Mar 00.

1750

Woolley & Wallis, Salisbury. 2 Caughley toy coffee cups, 'Island' pattern, 'C' marks, c1780, 3.1cm. £260. Sep 00.

1751

Hyperion Auctions, St Ives, Huntingdon. Large 19thC blue and white plate, view of Lancaster. £260. Feb 01.

1752

Gorringes, Lewes. Pair of German monkey band figures, 4.5in. £260. Feb 01.

1753

Woolley & Wallis, Salisbury. 4 18thC Chinese meat plates, one cracked. £260. Sep 00.

1754

Woolley & Wallis, Salisbury. Pair of Staffs King Charles spaniels, mid 19thC, 15cm. £260. Sep 00.

1755

Woolley & Wallis, Salisbury. 2 Staffs flatbacks 'Returning Home' and 'Going to Market', 19thC, 21.5cm. £260. Sep 00.

1756

Gorringes, Lewes. Two pairs of German porcelain figures, 6.5in & 5.5in. £260. June 00.

1757

Gorringes, Lewes. Nankin mug, riverscape decoration, 5.5in. £260. Oct 00.

1758

Gorringes, Lewes. Clarice Cliff melon pattern toast rack, 6.5in. £260. June 00.

1759

Hamptons, Godalming. Moorcroft Cymric 'Dreams' vase, by R J Bishop in a Ltd Edn of 250, after a Liberty design, 21cm. £260. Mar 02.

1760

Gorringes, Bexhill. Pair of Staffs figures, milkman and his wife, 8in. £260. Dec 01.

1761

Cheffins, Cambridge. Pair of late 19thC cantagalli wall plaques, 31cm. £260. Sep 01.

1762

Andrew Hartley, Ilkley. Pair Royal Dux porcelain figures of a Dutchman and woman both in green and red dress, pink triangle marks, 15.5in high. £260. Dec 01.

1763

Andrew Hartley, Ilkley. Royal Dux porcelain horse, 7.25in wide. £260. Apr 01.

1764

Rosebery's, London. Pair of Continental porcelain wall pockets, exotic birds eating fruit, 19cm. £260. Mar 02.

1765

Wintertons, Lichfield. Beswick Ayrshire Bull, 'CH Whitehill Mandate'. £260. Nov 00.

1766

Richard Wintertons, Burton on Trent. Pair of Worcester coffee cans c1750, in famille rose. £260. Sep 01.

1767

Gorringes, Lewes. Burmantofts blue majolica seated dragon, glass inset eyes, 16in. £260. Apr 01.

1768

Thos Mawer & Son, Lincoln. Two Staffs flat back spill vases. £260. Oct 03.

1769

Locke & England, Leamington Spa. Japanese Meiji Imari porcelain dish. £260. Nov 02.

1770

Locke & England, Leamington Spa. 19thC Japanese Imari jar, 64cm. (damage) £260. Jan 03.

1771

Locke & England, Leamington Spa. Italian 19thC faience ewer, Cantagalli mark, 39cm. £260. Jan 03.

1772

Wintertons Ltd, Lichfield. Pair of salt glazed stoneware hunting jugs, mid 19thC, 24cm. £260. Jan 03.

1773

Tring Market Auctions, Herts. Mason's childs toilet jug, bowl, beaker (a/f) and small pot (a/f), jug 9in high, bowl 11.5in dia. £260. Jane 03.

1774

Amersham Auction Rooms, Kent. Late 19thC majolica earthenware jardiniere, 15.5in high. £260. Sep 02.

1775

W & H Peacock, Bedford. A 19thC Grainger & Co Worcester blackberry design preserve set, Mappin & Webb plated stand. £260. July 03.

1776

Denhams, Warnham. 18thC Wedgwood & Bentley plaque, 3in. £260. Aug 03.

1777

W & H Peacock, Bedford. Walter Moorcroft commemorative tankard, Edward VII & Queen Alexandra Coronation Day. £260. July 03.

1778

Tring Market Auctions, Herts Stevenson & Hancock, Derby 'Dr Syntax seated sketching', chip to drake's beak, 5.25in. £260. Nov 02.

1779

Gorringes, Bexhill. Pair of Augustus Rex bottle vases, marked, 12.5in. £260. June 03.

1780

Gorringes, Lewes. Royal Worcester plate, Tantallon Castle, signed J. Stinton, (one signed Hale) W8709, 9.5in. £260. Apr 01.

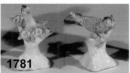

1781

Canterbury Auc. Galleries, Kent. Pair English porcelain mythical birds, 3.25in, poss. 18thC. £260. Aug 02.

1782

Tring Market Auctions, Herts. 18thC globular pearlware teapot. £250. Jan 02.

1783

Gorringes, Lewes. Meissen comport painted with three classical ladies entitled 'Flora', 8.5in. £250. Oct 00.

1784

P. Wilson, Nantwich. Crown Devon Fieldings musical jug, 'Daisy Bell, verse and outdoor scene, 8in. £250. Apr 00.

1785

Woolley & Wallis, Salisbury. Wedgwood creamware vase with agate slip, 'Wedgwood' impressed, c1770, 23.5cm and 5 canary yellow French cream ware plates. (extensive damages) £250. Sep 00.

1786

Rosebery's, London. Sevres style ormolu mounted vase. £250. Sep 01.

1787

Andrew Hartley, Ilkley. Pair of English delft chinoiserie plates, 9in. £250. Feb 02.

1788

Gorringes, Lewes. Victorian Staffs greyhound spill vase group, 11in. £250. Oct 00.

1789

Gorringes, Lewes. Worcester powder blue dish, chinoiserie, Pseudo Chinese mark, 8.25in. £250. July 00.

1790

Dockree's, Manchester. Five Davenport Imari pattern items. £250. Nov 00.

1791

Gorringes, Lewes. Royal Copenhagen group, Boy with a calf, 772. £250. Apr 01.

1792

Louis Taylor, Stoke on Trent. Beswick foal. £250. Sep 02.

1793

Richard Wintertons, Burton on Trent. Brampton salt glazed tobacco jar in the form of a Regency villa. £250. Sep 02.

1794

Sworders, Stansted Mountfitchet. Meissen chocolate cup, cover and stand, 5.75in high. £250. Feb 02.

1795

Richard Wintertons, Burton on Trent. Pair of Staffordshire hounds, mid 19thC, 11cm high. £250. Apr 03.

1796

Peter Wilson, Nantwich. Capodimonte figure group 'The Cheats', in polychrome, blue printed mk., on wooden plinth. 21in. £250. Nov 00.

1797

Woolley & Wallis, Salisbury. Pair Chinese dishes, with figures and pagodas, and a small scalloped dish, 18thC, 20cm & 8cm. £250. Sep 00.

1798

Gorringes, Lewes. Victorian Staffordshire clock face figure of Reverend Wesley, 12in. £250. Apr 01.

1799

Sworders, Stansted Mountfitchet. Pr. 19thC childs plates, printed centres. £250. Apr 01.

1800

Gorringes, Lewes. Crown Devon Fieldings musical John Peel spirit flask, 8in. £250. Apr 01.

1801

Amersham Auction Rooms, Bucks. Mid 17thC Kraak Chinese porcelain dish, 14in. £250. June 03.

Sample Analysis

Section 6 is the largest section in this volume with about 820 examples of lots sold in this category. This is by far the most prolific price range for ceramics at auction. Almost every manufacturer is represented from Adams, Ashworth and Augustus Rex to Worcester, Westerwald, Factory Z and Zsolnay Pecs. The analyses will be pursued on a page by page basis. The reader is again reminded of the links which should be made to other sections using the *Index*. This Section is almost certainly, for the collector or dealer the most potentially productive of all Sections in the sense that there are literally dozens and dozens of lots to be found here that represent excellent value for money and excellent investment potential. Indeed many of the lots sold, in terms of their relative cheapness, whilst representing the market, would also appear to defy it! The reader will benefit time and time again if they make a particular study of this Section.

On page 81, the hybrid hard-paste porcelains of Factory Z catch the eye, not so much for their price as for the mystery surrounding this and other similar hard-paste productions from the late eighteenth/early nineteenth century. For many years these have been known as Factories X,Y and Z, as they are unmarked and have only been tentatively identified and no archaeology is available to substantiate research.

Clarice Cliff sifters abound in this volume and fetch a fairly standard price. See 1813. Reproductions are also common. The Poole jug at 1840 and only £240, was possibly sold too cheaply and should show good long term profit; and the possible Baddeley-Littler tea bowl and saucer (1850) is very modest if the attribution proves correct. Notice the Spode miniatures at image 1833. Davenport also made these and there are a lot of collectors who would buy at this price or higher.

The first Sitzendorf in this volume appeared on page 62, image 1322. There are a lot more pieces to choose from now and the Sitzendorf trail may be followed through the *Index*. Note the 'Derby' Samson on page 63, image 1880. You need to know your 'pastes' to detect these spurious pieces. Can you identify English soft-paste porcelain? And can you spot the differences between this and French hard-paste?

Painting on majolica is rare. See page 83 (1858). Surely the Queen Caroline commemorative pearlware plate on page 84 has potential or for that matter the Queen Caroline pearlware jug on page 94 which appears to be seriously underpriced. Check out the price of one Lowestoft tea cup on page 85 (1920) and the price of a Linthorpe Christopher Dresser plate (1927). This is the cheapest Linthorpe item in this volume. See *Index*.

The juxtaposition in the price range at £210 of a Pendelfin *Kipper*, a nineteenth century Staffordshire pottery zebra and a Staffordshire figure of Elijah (early nineteenth century), along with an eighteenth century Worcester jug suggests the market is crazy! But is it? Creamware named botanicals are very collectable. These display scientific accuracy and £200 on page 87 (1981) is modest. The Crown Devon art deco nude on the same page is even better value and should prove to be a very sound investment.

The Rockingham trail may be followed through the *Index* but it is now time for the promised discussion. Images 2005, 2023, and 2121 are all models of dogs and all sold at Gorringes in Lewes for £180-£200. It is our opinion that these prices are probably very modest by any standard. Would they have fetched the same, or perhaps a lot more, if they had appeared in an auction in South Yorkshire where there would probably

have been a bidding punch-up before the hammer finally fell? The Editor would welcome further comments from Rockingham collectors. In these pages you can practise on the prices of pairs of Staffordshire spaniels, but I believe the £190 paid for a Brownfields majolica kitten holding a ball of wool will prove to be one of the best investments around! On page 90 note the price paid for a Beswick Bill Badger. Does this have investment potential? And on the same page the Wadeheath Donald Duck represented surely an excellent investment at what appears to be an incredible price. The bisque group on page 90 at 2061 and the English Delft on pages 91 and 93 (2087, 2144) will certainly go up in value as will the child's blue and white pearlware chamber pot (2133). Also it is the Editor's opinion that readers should at least consider Royal Worcester Doughty figures for the future. There is an example on page 92 at 2112.

Cornishware (T G Green in the *Index*) makes its first appearance on page 94 at 2167. This is one of the dodgiest areas of all in which to buy with many cunning and diabolical fakes around. The essentials for novice collectors are: keep up to date with the Cornishware Collectors' Club bulletins; only use reputable specialist dealers and insist on a receipt when purchasing. This should always provide an approximate date of manufacture and in addition state the condition.

Has Chintz peaked? See page 94 (2163) and page 101 (2360) for examples. Or if you think it hasn't just compare what you can buy for the same money that will provide you with a far safer investment and much more to talk about, rather than what is more often than not quite boring, second-hand teawares.

This Section is full of fascinating alternatives, for example, good eighteenth century soft-paste porcelains such as the Worcester asparagus server at 2189 on page 95. Or the fascinating Brannams Griffin candlesticks on page 96 which simply must increase in value considerably in years to come. Incidently, Watcombe Pottery appears again on this page. And look at the incredible Vidler bird money-box with the thick marmalade glaze at 2243 which brought only £150, the same as a Derby mug on page 98 (2278) which many Derby collectors would die for. Don't under-estimate early Mason's mugs. I would judge that the example on page 99 (2310) is worth getting on for £200 today. And if you are ever presented with the opportunity of buying antiquities, give it some consideration. How many collectors can ever have the chance to own a piece of rare Chinese celadon ware such as the example shown which fetched only £140 (damaged) on the same page. Your can check out celadon in the *Glossary of Terms*.

There is much opportunity to study Satsuma with over twenty images. This Japanese pottery (as opposed to porcelain) can frequently be found quite undervalued where the dealers have failed to appreciate the quality of the decoration. Check out a fine example at a modest £140 on page 100 and use the *Index* to follow the Satsuma trail. Other items of interest are the Poole Carter, Stabler, Adams vases on page 101 and the bargain Staffordshire rabbit on the same page. The reader should also spot the potential of the bisque pepperettes on page 103, which will always sell on for a profit. Note the Beswick Rupert on the same page and the incredible pair of lobster match holders on page 107 at £110. Finally, the 'Plymouth style' baluster mug on page 108 which fetched only £100, another French fake? Certainly, Samson was well practised at copying eighteenth century English 'soft-paste' baluster mugs.

1802

John Taylors, Louth. Clarice Cliff bizarre vase. £240. Jan 00.

1803

Gorringes, Lewes. Clarice Cliff orange autumn plate, 9in. £240. June 00.

1804

Andrew Hartley, Ilkley. Parian ware female figure 'Terpsichore' by Beattie, 14.25in high. £240. Oct 99.

The illustrations in these pages are in descending price order. The price range is indicated at the top of each page.

1805

Gorringes, Lewes. Factory Z milk jug and a pair of coffee cans painted with bird panels. £240. Oct 00.

1806

Andrew Hartley, Ilkley. Pair of late 19thC Staffordshire pottery seated spaniels, 12.5in high. £240. Feb 00.

1807

Gorringes, Lewes. Miniature Moorcroft leaf and fruit pattern vase, green script signature mark. £240. Apr 00.

1808

Woolley & Wallis, Salisbury. Four modern Royal Crown Derby animals, comprising a snail, a wren, a quail and a rabbit. £240. Sep 00.

1809

Great Western Auctions, Glasgow. Noritake coffee set. (one saucer damaged) £240. Mar 01.

1810

Woolley & Wallis, Salisbury. Pair of Coalport vases with a matching tray, signed 'M Cooke', gilt details, modern, 32.5cm. £240. Sep 00.

1811

Gorringes, Lewes. Victorian 14 piece porcelain part dessert service with named topographical views of Great Britain. £240. Feb 01.

1812

Richard Winterton, Burton on Trent. Mintons secessionist vase. £240. Apr 01.

1813

Gorringes, Lewes. Clarice Cliff orange/yellow flower sifter, 5.5in. £240. June 00.

1814

Gorringes, Lewes. Pair of Grainger & Co small ovoid vases painted with riverscapes, 2.75in. £240. June 00.

1815

Gorringes, Lewes. Pair of 18thC Imari fan shaped dishes, prunus decoration, 11in. £240. July 00.

1816

Dee, Atkinson & Harrison, Driffield. Set of 12 Victorian plates, transfer printed in flo-blue 'Pekin' pattern, gilded edge, 10in dia. £240. Apr 01.

1817

Cheffins, Cambridge. Mid 20thC Wedgwood Dragon Lustre Bowl, marks in gold, 23cm. £240. Dec 00.

1818

Gorringes, Lewes. Early 20thC Staffordshire group of The Night Watchman, 9.5in. £240. Feb 01.

Hammer Price £240

1819

Gorringes, Lewes. Wemyss style charger, painted with a cockerel, 14.5in. £240. Oct 01.

1820

Gorringes, Lewes. Clarice Cliff stile and trees pattern sugar caster of ribbed form, 5in. £240. Oct 00.

1821

Amersham Auction Rooms, Bucks. Early/mid 20thC Japanese porcelain vase, blue and white figures in a formal garden, 12in. £240. Dec 01.

1822

Sworders, Stansted Mountfitchet. Westerwald stoneware jug, 9in high. £240. Apr 01.

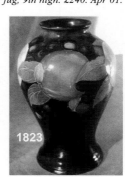

1823

Great Western Auctions, Glasgow. Moorcroft vase, 17cm high. £240. Apr 00.

1824

Gorringes, Lewes. Moorcroft pomegranate vase, 5in, a Clarice Cliff crocus pattern bowl, 3.5in and a modern dish. £240. Dec 00.

1825

Cheffins, Cambridge. Mid 20thC Moorcroft pottery lamp base, painted shade, traces of a label, imp'd and painted marks, 14cm. £240. Dec 00.

1826

Gorringes, Lewes. Signed Satsuma bowl painted with carp, 6in. £240. Apr 00.

1827

Gorringes, Lewes. Worcester jar and cover with floral knop and Chinese fisherman pattern, 4.25in. £240. June 00.

1828

Hamptons, Godalming. Grainger blush ivory pierced vase, printed green mark, shape No. G565, puce No. 893, date code 1898, 15.8cm high. £240. Sep 01.

Hammer Prices £240-£230

1829

Sworders, Stansted Mount-fitchet. Royal Winton 'Marguerite' chintz part dessert service. (20) (some damage) £240. Apr 01.

1830

Sworders, Stansted Mount-fitchet. Doulton Burslem ewer and basin, Glore-De-Dijon pattern, the basin 17in wide. (chips to basin) £240. Apr 01.

1831

Thos Mawer & Son, Lincoln. Clarice Cliff. 'Orange Trees & House', plate, printed mk., 15cm. £240. Apr 02.

1832

Hamptons, Godalming. Pair Clarice Cliff Crocus tureens, printed Bizarre marks, 24.5cm dia. £240. Nov 01.

1833

Tring Market Auctions, Herts. Early 19thC Spode toy wash jug and bowl. £240. Jan 02.

1834

Tring Market Auctions, Herts. Pair of 19thC Cantonese famille rose vases, 9in high. £240. Sep 02.

1835

Lambert & Foster, Tenterden. 19thC Staffs cow creamer spill, 23cm. £240. May 02.

1836

Tring Market Auctions, Herts. 19thC Meissen basket coaster as a 4 wheeled carriage, 10in long. restored. £240. Mar 02.

1837

Gorringes, Lewes. Clarice Cliff orange roof cottage bowl, 6.25in. £240. Apr 01.

1838

Gorringes, Lewes. Pair of Staffordshire spaniels on cushions, 5in. £240. Apr 01.

1839

Canterbury Auc.Galleries, Kent. 19thC Staffs arbour group, 8in high and a pair of late 19thC Staffs white and encrusted pottery figures of ewes, 2.5in. £240. Aug 02.

1840

Amersham Auction Rooms, Bucks. Mid 20thC Poole pottery jug, impressed Carter, Stabler, Adams mark, 14.5in high. £240. Oct 03.

1841

Tring Market Auctions, Herts. 19thC majolica Stilton dish, 9.5in high, minor damage. £240. May 02.

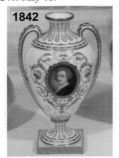

1842

Andrew Hartley, Ilkley. Royal Worcester porcelain vase by James Callowhill, portrait of Van Dyke, initialled, gilt embellished, 7in. £240. Apr 02.

1843

Amersham Auction Rooms, Bucks. Early 19thC Derby porcelain meat dish, painted mark, 19.5in. £240. June 02.

1844

Sworders, Stansted Mount-fitchet. Wedgwood three piece teaset, Cauliflower pattern., imp'd marks, 30/24 4YD, teapot 16cm high. (cream jug handle riveted) £240. Feb 03.

1845

Fellows & Sons, Hockley, Birmingham. Minton pottery Art Nouveau vase, printed 'Minton Ltd', and 'No 34', impressed mark and numbers, 14.5in. £240. July 03.

1846

Tring Market Auctions, Herts. 18thC Meissen 'blanc de chine' coffee cup, u/g blue mark, small hairline crack, possibly glazed over factory fault, 3in. £240. Nov 02.

1847

Gorringes, Bexhill. Burmantofts faience jardiniere, 11.5in dia. £240. June 03.

1848

Rosebery's, London. Italian faience holy water stoop, 19thC, 35cm. £240. June 03.

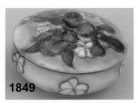

1849

Gorringes, Bexhill. Moorcroft powder bowl, impressed marks, bearing paper label, 6in dia. £240. Mar 03.

1850

Andrew Hartley, Ilkley. English porcelain tea bowl/saucer, late 18thC, possibly Baddeley-Littler. £240. Feb 03.

1851

Gorringes, Bexhill. Chinese blue and white porcelain sauce tureen cover and stand, 7in max. £240. Oct 02.

1852

Rosebery's, London. Pair of Sevres style porcelain candlesticks, 17cm. £240. Mar 02.

1853

Amersham Auction Rooms, Bucks. Late 19thC Satsuma earthenware bowl, painted marks, 4.75in. £240. Sep 02.

1854

John Taylors, Louth. Late 18thC Worcester teapot (damaged). £230. Feb 00.

1855

Gorringes, Lewes. Part set of 6 Sitzendorf porcelain frog musicians including tuba and kettle drum players, largest 4.5in. (damage) £230. Dec 00.

1856

Rosebery's, London. Ruby lustre vase by E R Wilkes. £230. June 00.

1857

Woolley & Wallis, Salisbury. Royal Doulton model of two rabbits, impressed, printed marks, 9cm. £230. Sep 00.

1858

Lambert & Foster, Tenterden. 19thC Continental majolica jardiniere with land and sea scape. AF. £230. June 00.

1859

Woolley & Wallis, Salisbury. Meissen Bottger porcelain saucer, no mark, c1720, 12.8cm. (wear) £230. June 00.

Prices quoted are hammer prices which excluded the buyer's premium. Adding 15% will give an approximation to the buying price.

1860

John Taylors, Louth. Early 19thC pierced edge basket 'Gothic Ruins'. £230. Oct 00.

1861

Bristol Auction Rooms, Bristol. George Jones & Sons Aesthetic Movement pair of vases. £230. Sep 03.

1862

Dockree's, Manchester. 19thC blue and white oval charger, 17in overall. £230. Sep 00.

1863

Dockree's, Manchester. Pair of Royal Worcester plates, 8.75in, date code 1892. £230. Nov 00.

1864

Woolley & Wallis, Salisbury. Pair of Derby figures of the Welsh tailor and companion, he inscribed 'No 62', she with faint Stevenson and Hancock mark, both 19thC, 15cm. (restoration) £230. Sep 00.

1865

Sworders, Stansted Mount-fitchet. Lustre jug impressed 'Enoch Wood', 5in, and early 19thC pottery jug and a 'semi-china' jug. £230. Apr 01.

1866

Richard Wintertons, Burton on Trent. Beswick figure of Rupert the Bear snowballing. £230. July 01.

1867

Wintertons Ltd, Lichfield. Parian figure, c1870, impressed OPUS W THEED SCULP 1856 Published MAY 1 1861, COPELAND, 49cm. chip to base and left forefinger. £230. Dec 01.

1868

Gorringes, Lewes. Clarice Cliff coral firs pattern plate, 9.75in. £230. Feb 00.

1869

Sworders, Stansted Mount-fitchet. Miniature creamware tankard, printed crest, 2in (chips to foot) and a Staffs pottery tankard inscribed 'Every one to his liking', 5in. £230. Apr 01.

1870

Woolley & Wallis, Salisbury. Caughley mustard pot and cover, 'C' mark, c1780, 9cm. (tiny chip) £230. Sep 00.

1871

Lambert & Foster, Tenterden. 18thC blue/white Chinese tea caddy, jug and two shallow shaped dishes. (jug damaged) af. £230. May 02.

1872

Richard Wintertons, Burton on Trent. Staffordshire pot lid and base, c1850, Drayton Manor, 13cm dia. (container chipped) £230. Apr 03.

1873

John Taylors, Louth. Early 19thC blue and white tureen 'Gothic Ruins. £220. Oct 00.

Hammer Prices £230-£220

1874

Gorringes, Lewes. Victorian Wedgwood jasper ware 2-handled pot pourri bowl and cover, 6.5". £220. Apr 00.

1875

G W Finn & Sons, Canterbury. Meissen hot milk jug. £220. Sep 99.

1876

Richard Wintertons, Burton on Trent. Linthorpe Art Pottery plaque no. 929, dated 1884. £220. Jan 01.

1877

Dee, Atkinson & Harrison, Driffield. Carter Stabler Adams Ltd Poole vase, incised No 970 and painted /BX, 9.5in. £220. Dec 00.

1878

Dockree's, Manchester. Staffordshire lustreware jug, Josh and Sally Saxton, 1824, 7in high. £220. Sep 00.

1879

Andrew Hartley, Ilkley. 19thC Art nouveau terracotta bust of Auriels, stamped Cologne, 22.75in high. £220. Aug 00.

1880

Andrew Hartley, Ilkley. Pair of 19thC Samson porcelain cornucopia wall vases, Derby mark, 8.25in. £220. Aug 00.

1881

Locke & England, Leamington Spa. Royal Worcester ewer, printed mark in puce and pattern 1047, date code 1909, 23cm. £220. Oct 03.

1882

John Taylors, Louth. Belleek shell teapot. £220. Feb 00.

1883

Woolley & Wallis, Salisbury. Chinese polychrome boy, c1800, 18cm. £220. Sep 00.

Hammer Price £220

Woolley & Wallis, Salisbury. Pair of Japanese Kenjo Imari bowls, 19thC, 16cm. (rim chips) £220. Sep 00.

1885

Andrew Hartley, Ilkley. Pair of 19thC Canton porcelain vases, 12in. £220. Dec 00.

1886

Woolley & Wallis, Salisbury. Two small Dresden cups and saucers, (printed marks) and a small pair of porcelain baskets, c1900. £220. Sep 00.

1887

Woolley & Wallis, Salisbury. 4 small Royal Crown Derby Imari coffee cans/saucers, No 2451, date codes 1923, 1937 and 1938. £220. Sep 00.

1888

Gorringes, Lewes. Royal Worcester square dish with fruit centre and floral panels, 9in. £220. June 00.

1889

Gorringes, Lewes. Wedgwood lustre vase with gilt dragon and locust on mottled blue ground, 5in. £220. July 00.

1890

Gorringes, Lewes. 18thC Chinese export armorial teapot, arms of the Lennard family, 6.5in. £220. July 00.

1891

Gorringes, Lewes. Wedgwood lustre bowl, 5in. £220. June 00.

1892

Gorringes, Lewes. Clarice Cliff Gardenia pattern plate, 9in. £220. July 00.

1893

Gorringes, Lewes. 19thC Staffs deer with bocage back, 4.25in and later Continental lamb, 2.5in. £220. Oct 00.

1894

Sworders, Stansted Mount-fitchet. Royal Worcester vase painted with cabbage roses, 5.5in high, signed M Hunt. (shape G702) £220. May 01.

1895

Gorringes, Lewes. 19thC Commemorative Queen Caroline plate, 6.5in. £220. Sep 00.

1896

Gorringes, Lewes. Victorian Staffordshire figure of Gilpin, 7.5in. £220. Mar 01.

1897

Sworders, Stansted Mount-fitchet. Westerwald stoneware jug, 9in high. £220. Apr 01.

1898

Sworders, Stansted Mount-fitchet. Pottery jardiniere and stand, 38in. £220. Apr 01.

1899

Amersham Auction Rooms, Bucks. Carlton Ware china 'Guinness' table lamp as a toucan and pint of Guinness, 9.25in high. £220. June 01.

1900

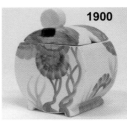

Gorringes, Lewes. Clarice Cliff bonjour, Rhodanthe pattern preserve jar and cover, 4in. £220. Dec 00.

1901

John Taylors, Louth. Delft plate with bianco-sopra-bianco border. £220. June 01.

1902

Gorringes, Lewes. Sampson Chinese armorial vase, 12.5in. £220. Mar 01.

1903

Sworders, Stansted Mount-fitchet. Carltonware 'Rouge Royale' vase and lid, 20in high. £220. Apr 01.

1904

Gorringes, Lewes. Linthorpe Christopher Dresser vase with dimpled brown and trailed green body, 9in. £220. Mar 01.

1905

Gorringes, Lewes. Royal Worcester blue budgerigar No. 2663 and another No. 2664. £220. Oct 00.

1906

Gorringes, Lewes. Royal Worcester cup and saucer with pheasants amidst foliage signed Jas Stinton, dated code 1912. £220. Dec 00.

1907

Gorringes, Lewes. Royal Worcester porcelain vase of quartre lobed form, No. 261, 10-54, 4in. £220. Oct 00.

1908

Gorringes, Bexhill. Pair of Volkstadt Rudolfstadt groups, ladies dancing with cherubs, 5.75in. £220. Dec 01.

1909

Gorringes, Lewes. Worcester lozenge shaped spoon tray with u/g blue panels and floral polychrome decoration, c1770, 6in. £220. Mar 01.

1910

Gorringes, Lewes. Clarice Cliff delecia milk jug, 5in. £220. Apr 01.

1911

Rosebery's, London. 23 Delft blue and white tiles, 19thC, depicting ships and figures on horseback. £220. Mar 02.

1912

Rosebery's, London. Pair of Continental pottery wall plaques, 19thC, painted iron red monogram WP to base, 26cm. £220. Mar 02.

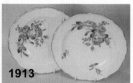

1913

Sworders, Stansted Mount-fitchet. Pair Meissen plates, X swords marks, pommelled hilts, 9in. £220. July 01.

The numbering system aids the editorial analysis at the beginning of each section as well as providing a reader reference.

1914

W & H Peacock, Bedford. 19thC Staffordshire figure 'Charity'. £220. Mar 03.

1915

Gorringes, Bexhill. Victorian Minton parian statuette, Margaret of Anjou, date code 1851, 17in. £220. Oct 02.

1916

Gorringes, Lewes. Pr. 19thC Dillwyn Swansea creamware plates, each printed with a frigate, 8.5in. £220. Apr 01.

1917

Lambert & Foster, Tenterden. Royal Worcester vases, aster pattern flowers and foliage, mark and dated on base 1888, 31cm. £220. May 02.

1918

Andrew Hartley, Ilkley. Pair Pearlware vegetable tureens, Arcadian landscape, 9in wide, early 19thC. £220. Aug 02.

1919

Gorringes, Lewes. Late 18thC Derby figure of a goddess, 10.5in. £220. Apr 01.

1920

Andrew Hartley, Ilkley. Lowestoft porcelain tea cup, Thomas Curtis style flowers, late 18thC. £220. Apr 03.

1921

Richard Wintertons, Burton on Trent. Royal Doulton jardiniere, children playing hide and seek around a tree, 24cm high. £220. Apr 03.

1922

Andrew Hartley, Ilkley. Pair of Staffordshire pottery spills of sheep, 5in. £220. Aug 02.

1923

Wintertons Ltd, Uttoxeter. Minton majolica blue tit and oak leaf dish. £220. June 03.

1924

Tring Market Auctions, Herts. Chinese porcelain bowl, 6 character reign mark, chip to rim, 6in dia. £220. Nov 02.

1925

Phillips, Bath. Masons Ironstone pot pourri vase and cover, impressed mark, 14cm high. £210. May 00.

1926

Gorringes, Lewes. Pair of Doulton Lambeth faience vases with crab apples on blue grounds by Mary M Arding, 7in. £210. Apr 00.

1927

David Duggleby, Scarborough. Linthorpe pottery plate by Dr Christopher Dresser, artist Fred Brown, impressed factory marks and facsimile signature, 11.5in. £210. Apr 00.

Hammer Prices £220-£210

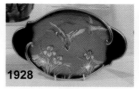

1928

A. Hartley, Ilkley. Carlton Ware Bleu Royale dish, 10.25in wide. £210. Oct 00.

1929

Woolley & Wallis, Salisbury. Japanese Imari teapot, with birds in flight over blossom, 18thC, 13cm. £210. Sep 00.

1930

Woolley & Wallis, Salisbury. Royal Winton Chintz ware part tea service, Delphinium pattern, various marks. (24) £210. Sep 00.

1931

Gorringes, Lewes. Pair of Sitzendorf lamp bases, 6in. (chips to leaves) £210. Sep 00.

1932

Gorringes, Lewes. Pair of Doulton Lambeth Carrara vases, dolphin like animals and vine leaves by Eliza Simmance, 11in. £210. Feb 01.

1933

Andrew Hartley, Ilkley. Pair Doulton Lambeth pottery candlesticks, urn shaped socket on baluster stem, tube line with stylised flowers and leaves, 5.5in. £210. June 02.

1934

Dockree's, Manchester. Six Minton dessert plates, date code c1870. £210. Sep 00.

1935

Gorringes, Lewes. Crown Ducal tube lined plate by Charlotte Rhead, 12in. £210. Sep 00.

1936

Woolley & Wallis, Salisbury. Royal Crown Derby, two handled cup, patt. No 1128, 7.5cm, a watering can, a dish, No ?6299, 23.5cm and a Stevenson & Hancock Derby cup and saucer, various dates. £210. Sep 00.

1937

Gorringes, Bexhill. Worcester club shape 2-handled vase, 9.5in. £210. Dec 00.

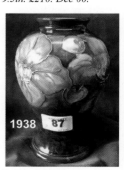

1938

Biddle & Webb, Birmingham. Moorcroft pottery clematis pattern vase. £210. Sep 01.

Hammer Prices £210-£200

1939
Gorringes, Lewes. Royal Copenhagen figure, Faun with crow, 2113. £210. Feb 01.

1940
Sworders, Stansted Mount-fitchet. 19thC creamware jug, copper lustre and enamelled decoration, 5in high and a similar jug with enamelled decoration, and a sailors rhyme, 4.5in. £210. Apr 01.

1941
W & H Peacock, Bedford. Ruskin pottery vase. £210. Jan 03.

1942
Tring Market Auctions, Herts. 19thC Staffordshire frog and newt loving cup. £210. Jan 02.

1943
Gorringes, Bexhill. Clarice Cliff sugar sifter with orange-roofed house and light green banding. £210. Mar 03.

1944
Sworders, Stansted Mount-fitchet. 1920s Staffordshire bocage group of 2 young cricketers, 6.5in. £210. Apr 01.

1945
Richard Wintertons, Burton on Trent. Wedgwood blue Jasper dip vase, Portland shape, classical subjects, 21cm high. £210. Jan 02.

1946
Gorringes, Lewes. Late 19thC Vienna cabinet plate entitled 'Prisonniere', 8.75in. £210. Mar 01.

1947
Bristol Auction Rooms, Bristol. Wedgwood cream-ware chestnut basket on stand, c1800. £210. Oct 02.

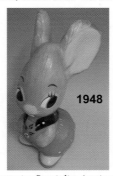

1948
Potteries Specialist Auctions, Stoke. Pendelfin. Kipper the father rabbit, out of production. £210. Apr 03.

1949
Andrew Hartley, Ilkley. Staffordshire pottery zebra on oval rustic base, 19thC, 5.5in wide. £210. Feb 03.

1950
W & H Peacock, Bedford. 19thC Staffordshire figure 'Elijah being fed by a Raven'. £210. Mar 03.

1951
Thos Mawer & Son, Lincoln. Mid 19thC Coalport vase, 17cm high, gilt 'ampersand mark c1861/75'. (minor damage to rim) £210. Feb 03.

1952
Andrew Hartley, Ilkley. Worcester porcelain sparrow beak jug, late 18thC, 3.25in high. £210. Feb 03.

1953
Potteries Specialist Auctions, Stoke. Lladro Gres Balinese dancers. £210. Mar 03.

1954
Lambert & Foster, Tenterden. Fantasque Bizarre by Clarice Cliff, 'Clog', printed marks, 14cm wide. £210. Dec 02.

1955
Sworders, Stansted Mount-fitchet. Ruskin Pottery vase, signed 'W Howson Taylor' in script, imp'd 'Ruskin, England, 1930', 30cm. £210. July 03.

1956
Tring Market Auctions, Herts. 19thC Minton child's part teaset, with Dresden Flowers pattern. Some damage. (9) £205. May 02.

1957
Woolley & Wallis, Salisbury. Royal Worcester plate, signed 'A Hughes', titled 'Ripley Woods', black factory mark, c1957, 27cm. £200. Sep 00.

1958
Academy Auctioneers, Ealing. Large Lladro figure of King Arthur. Escul. V. Martinez, Decor. V. Navarro - No 210, impressed 5368 and E 23 A. £200. Oct 99.

1959
Woolley & Wallis, Salisbury. Two Continental porcelain figures, a man wearing black tricorn hat, 2nd half 19thC, 22cm, other a white glazed Berlin figure of Juno, late 18thC, 19.5cm. (both some damage) £200. Sep 00.

1960
Sworders, Stansted Mount-fitchet. Large stoneware jardiniere designed by Gertrude Jekyll. £200. Nov 99.

1961
Gorringes, Lewes. French terracotta plaque, with a wooded landscape, signed M. Bouquet, imp'd on the reverse Dumas Rue Fontaine au Roi, 12 x 10in. £200. Apr 00.

1962
Woolley & Wallis, Salisbury. 4 Staffordshire Toby jugs, all 19thC, 28cm the tallest, minor damages. £200. Sep 00.

1963
Academy Auctioneers, Ealing. Art Deco Boch Freres Keramis stoneware vase, possibly by Charles Catteau, c1925, pattern no. D1084, 12in high. £200. July 99.

1964

John Taylors, Louth. Moorcroft vase. Clematis. £200. Mar 00.

1965

Phillips, Scotland. Cylindrical vase, painted with fairies, 22cm. £200. June 00.

1966

John Taylors, Louth. 19thC Commemorative earthenware plate. £200. June 00.

> The illustrations in these pages are in descending price order. The price range is indicated at the top of each page.

1967

John Taylors, Louth. Late 19thC blanc-de-chine vase. £200. July 00.

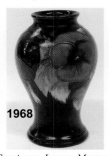

1968

Gorringes, Lewes. Moorcroft baluster vase decorated with pansies, 6.5in. £200. July 00.

1969

Gorringes, Lewes. Victorian Royal Worcester lemonade jug, silver plated mounts and a matching pair of beakers. £200. Apr 00.

1970

Gorringes, Lewes. Pair of Sevres style vases with rams heads and cupid panels on pink grounds, 6.25in, and an oval porcelain dish, 11.5in. af. £200. Oct 00.

1971

Woolley & Wallis, Salisbury. Four Continental porcelain figures, a Meissen girl with a vine, Marcolini mark, a pair as a vintner and companion, gold anchor marks, fourth as a woman in Turkish dress, cross mark, 19th/early 20thC, 15cm tallest. £200. Sep 00.

1972

Gorringes, Lewes. Crown Devon art deco nude holding a ball by Kathleen Parsons, 7in. £200. Sep 00.

1973

Gorringes, Lewes. Wedgwood lustre vase with gilt butterflies on an orange ground, 5in. £200. July 00.

1974

Peter Wilson, Nantwich. Late 19thC bisque figure, 14.5in high. £200. Nov 00.

1975

Woolley & Wallis, Salisbury. Two Staffs Punch & Judy jugs, late 19thC, 25cm. (Judy hair cracks to base) £200. Sep 00.

1976

Gorringes, Lewes. Moorcroft shallow bowl with irises and cornflowers, paper label to base, 9.75in. £200. Sep 00.

1977

Gorringes, Lewes. Pair of Royal Doulton square section vases printed with golfers, D5947E, 3in. £200. Dec 00.

1978

Gorringes, Lewes. Two small Moorcroft vases with hibiscus against yellow green grounds, largest 3.5in. £200. Sep 00.

1979

Gorringes, Lewes. Royal Worcester jug, pattern no. 1136, 4.5in. £200. Apr 00.

Hammer Price £200

1980

Woolley & Wallis, Salisbury. Dutch Delft dish, in the 'kraak' porcelain style, late 17thC, 39.5cm. (cracked, small chips) £200. Sep 00.

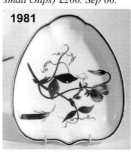

1981

Andrew Hartley, Ilkley. Early 19thC creamware botanical fruit dish, inscribed verso, 8.5in wide. £200. Aug 00.

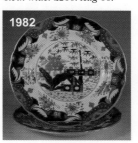

1982

Woolley & Wallis, Salisbury. Pair of Spode porcelain plates, pattern No 967 in red, c1820, 21.5cm. £200. Sep 00.

1983

Woolley & Wallis, Salisbury. Royal Worcester plate, signed, 'A Hugh' and title 'Burnham Beeches', black mark, c1957, 27cm. £200. Sep 00.

1984

Lambert & Foster, Tenterden. Pair 19thC German porcelain figures, 8.5in high, mark on base R, prob. Rodelstadt or Ludwigsburg. £200. Dec 00.

1985

Gorringes, Lewes. Clarice Cliff cafe au lait handkerchief vase, 6in. (small crack) £200. June 00.

1986

Woolley & Wallis, Salisbury. Derby biscuit model of Andromache, factory mk. and 'N 100' incised, late 18thC, 25cm. (fire cracks and lacking garland) £200. Sep 00.

1987

Gorringes, Lewes. 19thC gilt metal and porcelain mounted inkwell with floral back and 2 receivers, 7in. £200. June 00.

1988

Gorringes, Lewes. Worcester teapot with floral knop and polychrome floral decoration. (cracked) £200. July 00.

1989

Andrew Hartley, Ilkley. Pair Burmantofts faience candle-sticks, Shape No 1198, imp'd marks, 11.25in. £200. Oct 00.

Hammer Price £200

Gorringes, Lewes. Royal Copenhagen group, small Goosegirl, 528. £200. Feb 01.

Andrew Hartley, Ilkley. Clarice Cliff Bizarre pottery butter dish, printed marks, 7.5in wide. £200. Apr 01.

Crows, Dorking. Walton figure of St Matthew. £200. Sep 01.

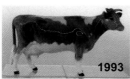

Wintertons Ltd, Bakewell. Beswick Guernsey cow, 4.25in high. £200. Oct 01.

Wintertons Ltd, Lichfield. Derby sauceboat, c1765, 9.5in. £200. Nov 01.

Wintertons Ltd, Lichfield. Soft paste porcelain printed cream jug, c1785, poss. Seth Pennington, Chinese landscape, 3.5in. £200. Nov 01.

Gorringes, Lewes. Pair of Davenport cornucopia vases with floral panels, 6in. (one af.) £200. Oct 00.

Gorringes, Lewes. Pair of Sitzendorf floral encrusted urn shaped vases, 12in. (1 lid repaired) £200. Feb 01.

Thos Mawer & Son, Lincoln. Pair of Minton ewers, in blue and gilt on a cream ground, 29cm. (crack and reglued to one rim) £200. Apr 02.

Andrew Hartley, Ilkley. Samuel Alcock pottery reproduction Portland vase, 19thC, 10.5in high. £200. Oct 01.

Rosebery's, London. 19thC saltglaze tobacco jar in the round with four faces, two taking snuff, one with a pipe and another with a tobacco pouch, 20cm. £200. Mar 02.

Dockree's, Manchester. Late 19thC Vienna vase, 35cm overall. £200. June 01.

Dee, Atkinson & Harrison, Driffield. Four Royal Crown Derby Imari plates dated 1884, 1901, 1917 and 1925, 9in. £200. Apr 01.

Andrew Hartley, Ilkley. Minton parian 'Sleeping Children', unmarked, (glass dome missing) 14in wide. £200. Dec 01.

Cheffins, Cambridge. Mid 20thC Wedgewood Butterfly Lustre bowl, decorated with insects, black printed marks and 25068 in green, 22cm dia. £200. Dec 00.

Gorringes, Lewes. Rockingham figure of a hound, 4.25in. £200. Mar 01.

Gorringes, Lewes. 19thC Mason's Ironstone hydra jug, 6in and a similar cream jug, 4in. £200. Feb 01.

Gorringes, Lewes. Coalport inkwell gilded with flowers and insects with white metal American top, stamped Sterling, 4in. £200. Dec 00.

Andrew Hartley, Ilkley. Chamberlain's Worcester porcelain armorial plate, 10.25in. £200. Feb 01.

Gorringes, Lewes. Victorian Brownfield & Sons stoneware barrel shaped cheese dish, 11in. £200. Mar 01.

Amersham Auction Rooms, Bucks. Late Victorian Cauldon Ware china vase in u/g cobalt blue, 21in. £200. June 02.

Gorringes, Lewes. Victorian Copeland parian urn shaped vase, Celliniesque decoration, 14.5in. £200. Mar 01.

Sworders, Stansted Mountfitchet. Dresden porcelain jardiniere, gilt goats mask handles, 7in. £200. Apr 01.

Gorringes, Lewes. Early 19thC Derby cup and saucer, with painted panel 'Sudbury Church, Derbyshire', saucer with 'View in Cornwall'. (restored) £200. Dec 00.

Hamptons, Godalming. Clarice Cliff Crocus pattern preserve jar, Bizarre marks, 10cm high. £200. Nov 01.

Richard Wintertons, Burton on Trent. Pair of Fairing dog figures, titled 'Taking a walk', 13cm high. £200. Jan 02.

Sworders, Stansted Mountfitchet.19thC jug and basin, view with bridge & waterfall, 10in high. £200. Apr 01.

Richard Wintertons, Burton on Trent. Pair of Royal Doulton stoneware vases. £200. Oct 02.

2018

Locke & England, Leamington Spa. Moorcroft jardiniere, iris pattern, Moorcroft signature, imp'd Burslem 66, 26cm high, chip to base. £200. Oct 03.

2019

Gorringes, Lewes. 18thC Worcester bridge and pagoda pattern footed bowl, 8in. (star crack to base and chip to rim) £200. Apr 01.

2020

Gorringes, Lewes. Pair of Victorian Staffs ram and child groups, 5.5in. £200. Apr 01.

Prices quoted are hammer prices which excluded the buyer's premium. Adding 15% will give an approximation to the buying price.

2021

Locke & England, Leamington Spa. Pr. Derby figures, c1775, 13cm. (restored). £200. Jan 03.

2022

Sworders, Stansted Mountfitchet. R. Doulton, Maureen HN 1770. £200. June 03.

2023

Gorringes, Lewes. Staffs pottery poodle, 3.5in and a Rockingham porcelain recumbent dog, 5.5in. (hair crack) £200. Apr 01.

2024

Gorringes, Lewes. Clarice Cliff orange gardenia bowl, 6.5in. £200. Apr 01.

2025

Amersham Auction Rooms, Bucks. Royal Doulton loving cup, Coronation of Queen Elizabeth, Ltd. Edn. 1000 original certificate, 10.5in high. £200. July 02.

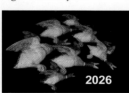

2026

Sworders, Stansted Mountfitchet. Set of five Beswick ducks, and two further ducks, largest 12in long. £200. Jul 01.

2027

Louis Taylor, Stoke on Trent. Wade 'Aqua' vase, c1939. £200. Mar 03.

2028

W & H Peacock, Bedford. R. Doulton, Ugly Duchess, jug D6599. £200. July 03.

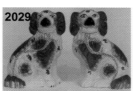

2029

Andrew Hartley, Ilkley. Pair Staffordshire pottery spaniels, 19thC, 10in. £200. Apr 03.

2030

Richard Wintertons, Burton on Trent. Royal Dux group, early 20thC, Dutch fishing family, model 1594, pink triangle mark, sig. 'Hampel', 48cm. Damage. £200. Apr 03.

2031

Andrew Hartley, Ilkley. Pair Staffs pottery figures of Gillies in blue frock coats, 19thC, 9in high. £200. Feb 03.

2032

Louis Taylor, Stoke on Trent. Beswick large action shire horse, 8.25in. £200. Mar 03.

2033

Andrew Hartley, Ilkley. Staffordshire pottery figure Garibaldi, 19thC, 19.75in high. £200. Apr 03.

Hammer Prices £200-£190

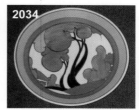

2034

John Taylors, Louth. Clarice Cliff plate. £190. Nov 99.

2035

Dee, Atkinson & Harrison, Driffield. Maling, Ringtons tea caddy, sides showing different cathedrals, 7.5in high. £190. July 99.

2036

John Taylors, Louth. Staffordshire figure of dog with young girl. £190. Sep 99.

2037

Denhams, Warnham, Sussex. Oriental blue/white shaped tulip vase, 12in. £190. Oct 03.

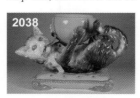

2038

Woolley & Wallis, Salisbury. Brownfield's Majolica model of a kitten lying on its back holding a ball of wool which forms a box, 'Brownfield, 1/78' impressed, 2nd half 19thC. £190. Mar 00.

2039

Rosebery's, London. Doulton Titanian ware covered pot with tusk finial. £190. June 00.

2040

Dee, Atkinson & Harrison, Driffield. Early 19thC Crown Derby style Imari teapot and stand, fire breathing dragons in cobalt blue and gilt, 5.5in high. £190. Feb 00.

2041

Gorringes, Lewes. Sitzendorf floral basket supported by cherubs, 12in. £190. Apr 00.

2042

Woolley & Wallis, Salisbury. Continental porcelain oval basket, crowned monogram mark, late 19thC, 42.5cm. (restoration) £190. Sep 00.

2043

John Taylors, Louth. 19thC Lobster pot, Rd 110991 and a very poorly impressed mark WEDGWOOD. £190. Oct 00.

2044

Great Western Auctions, Glasgow. Crown Devon vase. £190. Feb 01.

Hammer Prices £190-£185

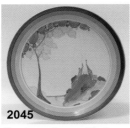

2045

Gorringes, Lewes. Clarice Cliff 'Secrets' plate, green border, 9in. £190. July 00.

2046

Woolley & Wallis, Salisbury. Chinese baluster jug, pagoda landscape, and three cups, one teabowl and seven saucers, similar decoration, all 18thC. £190. Sep 00.

2047

Woolley & Wallis, Salisbury. Two Caughley toy bowls, 'Island' pattern, 'C' marks c1780, 4cm dia. £190. Sep 00.

2048

Gorringes, Lewes. Worcester cream jug with an oriental pattern, 3in. £190. June 00.

2049

Dockree's, Manchester. Carltonware chinoiserie bowl, 10in dia. £190. Sep 00.

2050

Great Western Auctions, Glasgow. Carlton Ware Rouge Royale ginger jar, 37cm high. £190. Mar 01.

2051

Gorringes, Lewes. Pair mid 19thC Staffs King Charles spaniels, 8in. £190. July 00.

2052

Richard Wintertons, Burton on Trent. Beswick Bill Badger no. 2720. £190. July 01.

2053

Gorringes, Lewes. Sitzendorf floral encrusted centrepiece, 14in. £190. Feb 01.

2054

Gorringes, Lewes. Moorcroft chrysanthemum pattern vase, 8.5in. £190. Feb 01.

2055

Marilyn Swain Auctions, Grantham. Royal Worcester tapering vase, date code 1903, 5.5in high. £190. Aug 01.

2056

Gorringes, Lewes. Set of six Beswick pig musicians with original labels. £190. Dec 00.

2057

Sworders, Stansted Mountfitchet. R. Winton 'Cheddle' chintz, (19) £190. Apr 01.

2058

Gorringes, Bexhill. Poole, Carter Stabler Adams Summer Flowers plaque, c1921, 14 x 10.5in. £190. Dec 01.

2059

Gorringes, Lewes. Worcester oval basket, fruit and pine cone pattern, c1770, 6.75in. (handle restored) £190. Mar 01.

2060

Canterbury Auc. Galleries, Kent. 19thC Staffs pottery toilet bowl, British Scenery Series, 12.5in dia and a toilet basin with Wild Rose pattern, 13.25in dia. (latter repaired) £190. Aug 02.

2061

Tring Market Auctions, Herts. Bisque figure group of two boys bird nesting, incised numerals to base, 6in high. £190. Nov 02.

2062

Tring Market Auctions, Herts. Pair of transfer printed Bow tea bowls, painted in yellow, cerise, turquoise and blue, small rim chips and glaze fault. £190. Sep 02.

2063

Sworders, Stansted Mountfitchet. Pair of Samson melon shaped bowls in Chantilly style, 7in wide. £190. July 01.

2064

Tring Market Auctions, Herts. Pearlware ring flask, printed with a floral design, the neck af, 7in high. £190. Sep 02.

2065

Sworder & Sons, Stansted Mountfitchet. Newhall teapot, decorated with Pattern No. 253, 9.5in wide. £190. July 01.

2066

Amersham Auction Rooms, Bucks. Late 19th/20thC Doulton Lambeth stoneware spirit barrel, 8in high, 6in wide. £190. Sep 03.

2067

W & H Peacock, Bedford. Grainger & Co, Royal China Works, vase. £190. Dec 02.

2068

Andrew Hartley, Ilkley. Royal Dux figure of a female water carrier, pink triangle mark, 20in. £190. Oct 02.

2069

Tring Market Auctions, Herts. 18thC famille rose tankard, 6.25in high. £190. Nov 02.

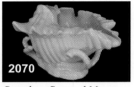

2070

Sworders, Stansted Mountfitchet. Belleek sugar bowl, Shell pattern, 2nd period, 4.25in high. £190. July 01.

2071

Tring Market Auctions, Herts. Pair of Royal Doulton dessert plates, centres painted with castles, signed in mono J.H.P., 8.75in. £190. Nov 02.

2072

Dockree's, Manchester. Wadeheath Donald Duck teapot, damaged. £185. Sep 99.

2073

Richard Wintertons, Burton on Trent. Clarice Cliff Bizarre cruet set in crocus pattern. (chips) £185. Jan 03.

2074

Academy Auctioneers, Ealing. R. Worcester 'Blush Ivory' Nautilus vase, shape no. 94, c1900, 8.5in. £185. Dec 99.

2075

Crows, Dorking. Large creamware jug, William of Orange, floral motifs, text, dated 1826. af. £185. Jan 03.

The numbering system aids the editorial analysis at the beginning of each section as well as providing a reader reference.

2076

Gorringes, Lewes. Clarice Cliff delicia pattern cauldron, 3in. £180. Apr 00.

2077

Hamptons, Marlborough. 19thC blue and white strainer. £180. Jan 00.

2078

Woolley & Wallis, Salisbury. Staffordshire pearlware toby jug, 19thC, (damage) 24cm. £180. June 00.

2079

Peter Wilson, Nantwich. 19thC Clews plate, 'Death of a Bear' u/g blue, imp'd mk., 10in., wear. £180. Apr 00.

2080

Gorringes, Lewes. French Empire coffee pot and sucrier. £180. Apr 00.

2081

Gorringes, Lewes. Early 19thC Spode Italian pattern meatplate, 20in. £180. Apr 00.

2082

Gorringes, Lewes. 19thC Masons Patent Ironstone drainer, 12in £180. Apr 00.

2083

Woolley & Wallis, Salisbury. R.Worcester teapot, date code 1895, 23cm. £180. Sep 00.

2084

Phillips, London. Doulton. The Duchess of York, by Eric Griffiths, HN3086, 1986, No 1 of 1500. £180. Nov 99.

2085

R. Wintertons, Burton on Trent. Early 19thC Masonic creamware jug. Restorations. £180. Jan 01.

2086

Dockree's, Manchester. Royal Doulton Drake jug with verse, numbered 135, 7in high. £180. Nov 00.

2087

Morphets, Harrogate. 18thC English tin glaze plate, c1740, possibly Bristol or Lambeth, 9in. £180. Mar 01.

2088

Crows, Dorking. Pair Walton bocage figures of a man and a woman. £180. Sep 01.

2089

Woolley & Wallis, Salisbury. French porcelain plaque, signed 'Lachassaigne' and dated probably for 1831, 23 x 20cm. £180. Sep 00.

2090

Woolley & Wallis, Salisbury. Faience two division letter holder, 'VP' monogram, late 19thC, 20cm. £180. Sep 00.

2091

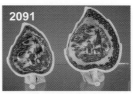

Woolley & Wallis, Salisbury. Two Caughley butter boats, Fisherman pattern, no marks, c1775, 8.5cm & 7cm. (larger with rim flakes) £180. Sep 00.

2092

Woolley & Wallis, Salisbury. Pair of Staffs King Charles spaniels, late 19th/early 20thC, 13.5cm. £180. Sep 00.

2093

Gorringes, Lewes. Susie Cooper milk jug painted with circles and zig-zag pattern, 4.5in £180. July 00.

2094

Gorringes, Lewes. Clarice Cliff 'Spring Crocus' fruit bowl, 9.25in. £180. June 00.

2095

Denhams, Warnham, Sussex. 19thC Royal Worcester vase by Charles 'Chappie' White, green mark and 16 dots, 12in. £180. Oct 03.

2096

Gorringes, Lewes. Worcester dish, panels of birds, rococo borders, 5in. £180. June 00.

2097

Gorringes, Lewes. Moorcroft vase decorated with hibiscus, 4in. £180. Sep 00.

2098

Andrew Hartley, Ilkley. 19thC English yellow glaze silver lustre jug, 4.75in, and a yellow glaze pink lustre bowl. £180. Feb 01.

2099

Gorringes, Lewes. George Jones majolica tazza, cartouche mark and number 1804, 9.25in. £180. Oct 00.

2100

Gorringes, Lewes. 19thC Staffs spaniel on a rococo base, 4.75in. £180. Oct 00.

2101

Woolley & Wallis, Salisbury. Crown Devon vase, black printed mark and gilt pattern No. probably '2115', 11cm. £180. Sep 00.

Hammer Price £180

2102

Gorringes, Lewes. 19thC Staffordshire inkwell, sporting dog on a blue base, 3in. £180. Oct 00.

2103

Gorringes, Lewes. 19thC Sevres bisque group of 3 wrestling cherubs inscribed 3-81, 8in. £180. Oct 00.

2104

Wintertons Ltd, Lichfield. Worcester teapot, c1780, printed with three flower pattern, 5.5in. £180. Nov 01.

2105

Gorringes, Lewes. 19thC German porcelain mug with riverscape panel inscribed Der Muhl Newbrunn, 4.5in. £180. Dec 00.

2106

Tring Market Auctions, Herts. 19thC Wedgwood brown jasper cream jug and stand, jug 2.25in high, stand 4.75in long, impressed Wedgwood in upper case. £180. Jan 03.

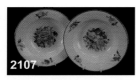

2107

Sworders, Stansted Mount-fitchet. Pair of Derby soup bowls, 9.75in. £180. July 01.

2108

Dee, Atkinson & Harrison, Driffield. 19thC Staffordshire watch holder, 10.5in high. £180. Apr 01.

2109

Gorringes, Lewes. Coalport vase with landscape vignette, lion head handles and claw feet, pattern No. 7404/C 1st 200, 6.75in. (chip to knop and re-stuck) £180. Dec 00.

2110

Sworders, Stansted Mount-fitchet. 19thC Minton set comprising: centre piece and a pair of bough pots (one arm to centrepiece putti damage), pots 6.5in. £180. July 01.

2111

Hamptons, Godalming. Meissen cup/saucer, 19thC, Hausmaler, inscribed 'Immer Lustig!', bearing u/g blue X swords and 'I' mark for 1814-15, 13.5cm. £180. Nov 01.

2112

Gorringes, Lewes. Royal Worcester Doughty July figure, girl playing in waves, No. 3440, 7in. £180. Dec 00.

2113

Andrew Hartley, Ilkley. Pair Wedgwood pearlware pickle dishes, 18thC. £180. Apr 02.

2114

Gorringes, Lewes. Outside decorated Meissen cabinet cup and saucer painted with lovers in a landscape, yellow grounds. £180. Feb 01.

2115

Hamptons, Godalming. Prince Albert earthenware plate, c1862, depicting the achievements of his reign, 'published by J T Close', 28cm. £180. Nov 01.

2116

Gorringes, Lewes. Art Nouveau Continental bisque plaque of nymphs in a river, 11.5in. £180. Mar 01.

2117

Canterbury Auc. Galleries, Kent. R. Doulton porcelain figure of a lady, Janice, 7.5in high, HN2165. £180. Aug 02.

2118

Tring Market Auctions, Herts. Pair of late 18thC pearlware plates, 14in. £180. Sep 02.

2119

Gorringes, Lewes. Pair of 20thC Continental porcelain figures of British Guard's Officers, 1821, 1822, 12in. £180. Mar 01.

2120

Gorringes, Lewes. Pair of Continental Derby style figures of a lady and gallant shepherd and shepherdess, 7.25in. £180. Mar 01.

2121

Gorringes, Lewes. Rockingham group of a child and dog, 4.5in. £180. Mar 01.

2122

Gorringes, Lewes. Dresden teapot, fete gallant panels, 3.5in and a similar cabinet cup and saucer. £180. Apr 01.

2123

Tring Market Auctions, Herts. Pair of K'ang Hsi beaker vases with figures, bamboo, prunus, 10in. £180. May 02.

2124

Gorringes, Lewes. 17thC saltglazed Rheinish Bartmann ewer, 10in. (af) £180. Apr 01.

2125

Gorringes, Lewes. Moorcroft vase with wisteria pattern, 4in. £180. Apr 01.

2126

Gorringes, Lewes. 19thC Bow style bagpiper and dog, 7in. £180. Mar 01.

2127

Thos Mawer & Son, Lincoln. A.G. Richardson & Co. Ltd. Crown Ducal. Chintz four piece toilet set, bowl cracked, together with a soap dish and an oval pottery container. (7) £180. Nov 02.

2128

Gorringes, Lewes. Royal Copenhagen group, Farmer with 2 sheep. £180. Feb 01.

2129

W & H Peacock, Bedford. Clarice Cliff preserve jar. £180. Dec 02.

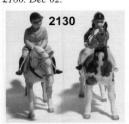

2130

Locke & England, Leamington Spa. Two Beswick figures of children riding ponies. £180. Dec 02.

The illustrations in these pages are in descending price order. The price range is indicated at the top of each page.

2131

Thos Mawer & Son, Lincoln. Moorcroft, Woodside Farm vase, 102/5, 13cm high. £180. Nov 02.

2132

Rosebery's, London. Victorian Staffordshire Toby jug, 27cm high. £180. June 03.

2133

Andrew Hartley, Ilkley. 19thC blue and white child's pearlware chamber pot, 6in wide. £170. Oct 99.

2134

Lambert & Foster, Tenterden. Pair of Staffordshire figures of females seated side saddle on goats. £170. Dec 99.

2135

Great Western Auctions, Glasgow. Clarice Cliff bowl, 15cm long. £170. Mar 00.

2136

Gorringes, Lewes. Royal Worcester jug, pattern no. 1094, 5in. £170. Apr 00.

2137

Peter Wilson, Nantwich. Mid 19thC blue and white pottery tankard, a scene of the 1851 Great Exhibition, Crystal Palace, 5in. £170. Apr 00.

2138

Woolley & Wallis, Salisbury. Pair of English porcelain candlesticks, no marks, mid 19thC, 20.5cm. (some restoration) £170. Sep 00.

2139

Dee, Atkinson & Harrison, Driffield. Late 19thC Royal Crown Derby plate, signed, 8.75in. £170. Feb 00.

2140

Gorringes, Lewes. Royal Worcester coffee cup and saucer with highland cattle by H. Stinton. £170. Apr 00.

2141

Gorringes, Lewes. Early 19thC Mason's ironstone vase gilded with vine leaves and grapes on a Mazzarine blue ground (cracked), 11in £170. Apr 00.

2142

Gorringes, Lewes. Martin Ware vase with orange peel green glaze, inscribed R. W. Martin & Bros Southall, 6.5in. £170. Apr 00.

2143

Dee, Atkinson & Harrison, Driffield. Wardle vase, Delhi pattern no. 211, incised mark & GN.A, 14in. £170. Dec 00.

2144

Dee, Atkinson & Harrison, Driffield. 18thC Delft plate, c1750, 9.75in. £170. Dec 00.

Hammer Prices £180-£170

2145

Woolley & Wallis, Salisbury. Five Pratt ware printed pot lids decorated with 'The Rivals', 'A Pair', 'Contrast', 'I See You My Boy' and 'On Guard', 19thC. £170. Sep 00.

2146

Woolley & Wallis, Salisbury. 2 miniature Caughley bowls, 'Island' pattern, one with an 'S' mark, c1780, 4.8cm and 4.5cm. £170. Sep 00.

2147

Gorringes, Lewes. 19thC Adams blue and white 'Cattle Scenery' footed punch bowl, 13.5in. £170. Feb 01.

2148

Woolley & Wallis, Salisbury. Four English bone china teacups/saucers, 19thC and one c1900. £170. Sep 00.

2149

Gorringes, Lewes. Victorian B & S 'Royal Cottage' soup tureen and stand, with ladle, 14in. £170. Sep 00.

2150

Woolley & Wallis, Salisbury. Blue Jasper biscuit barrel on silver plated stand, no marks, 19thC, 25cm. £170. Sep 00.

2151

Woolley & Wallis, Salisbury. Pair of creamware plates, no marks, late 18thC, 19cm. £170. Sep 00.

2152

Woolley & Wallis, Salisbury. Longton Hall dish, no marks, c1755-60, 22.5cm. (3cm hair crack) £170. Sep 00.

2153

Gorringes, Lewes. Meissen gardener figure, 5.5in and a Naples Cupid, 4in. £170. June 00.

2154

Dee, Atkinson & Harrison, Driffield. Pair of late 19thC vases, painted with, three children huddled together in woodland, impressed 6746 HK, 16.5in. £170. Apr 01.

2155

Hamptons, Godalming. Porcelain figure of a grape picker, possibly Meissen Marcolini period, late 18th/ 19thC, indistinct inscribed mark, 9cm. £170. Sep 01.

Hammer Prices £170-£160

2156

Gorringes, Lewes. Crown Ducal Charlotte Rhead tube lined jug, 9in. £170. Oct 00.

2157

Tring Market Auctions, Herts. 19thC Imari charger, 18.5in. £170. Sep 02.

2158

Gorringes, Lewes. Victorian Staffs spill vase group with a girl on a bridge and a fox below, 9.5in. £170. Oct 00.

2159

Hamptons, Godalming. General Gordon: Doulton Lambeth stoneware, 'Hero of Heroes, Governor General, General Gordon', imp'd mks., 18.5cm. £170. Nov 01.

2160

Canterbury Auc. Galleries, Kent. Copeland & Garrett pottery invalid's feeding cup with landscape, 2 Masons ironstone octagonal jugs with moulded dragon handles, 4.25in & 5.25in. £170. Aug 02.

2161

Locke & England, Leamington Spa. Royal Doulton figure of the year 'Mary', HN 3375, c1992, modelled by M Pedby, 22cm. £170. Apr 03.

2162

Ambrose, Loughton. Clarice Cliff waterlily bowl, width 22cm. £170. Aug 02.

2163

Gorringes, Lewes. Royal Winton 'Julia' chintz tray, 10.5in and matching plate, 9in. £170. Mar 01.

2164

Wintertons Ltd, Lichfield. Clarice Cliff Bizarre jug and tea plate, 'Blue Chintz', moulded, impressed, incised marks, jug 11cm. £170. Sep 02.

2165

Canterbury Auc. Galleries, Kent. Pair of Continental pottery baluster vases in the Chinese manner, 6.75in high, unmarked. £170. Aug 02.

2166

Gorringes, Lewes. Worcester cannonball and lake scene small bowl, workman's mark, c1760, 4.75in and cannonball pattern teapot. (af) £170. Mar 01.

2167

Richard Wintertons, Burton on Trent. Cornish Kitchen ware. 'Ginger', 'Cream of Tartar' and 'Almonds' jars. £170. June 03.

2168

Amersham Auction Rooms, Bucks. Continental porcelain dessert service, early 20thC transfer decorated. (14) £170. Sep 01.

2169

Gorringes, Bexhill. Late 19thC oval plaque, painted scene of a young woman, 14in long. £170. July 03.

2170

Tring Market Auctions, Herts. 19thC gaudy Welsh miniature toilet jug and bowl, jug 4in high. £170. Mar 03.

2171

W & H Peacock, Bedford. R. Doulton, The Coachman figure. £170. July 03.

2172

Sworders, Stansted Mount-fitchet. 3 Pendelfin pottery rabbits, 19.5cm. £170. July 03.

2173

Gorringes, Lewes. Liverpool Penningtons coffee pot with stylised floral decoration, c1775, 7.5in. (chip and 2 hairlines) £170. Mar 01.

2174

Dockree's, Manchester. Pair of poodles. £160. Nov 99.

2175

Rosebery's, London. Watcombe 'Disraeli' terra-cotta charger. £160. Feb 00.

2176

Dee, Atkinson & Harrison, Driffield. Pair of mid 18thC London Delft plates, c1750. £160. Dec 00.

2177

Andrew Hartley, Ilkley. Royal Worcester vase, painted blue roundels depicting swallows, 12.75in high. £160. Apr 00.

2178

Dockree's, Manchester. Three Royal Doulton flambé ware bowls. £160. May 00.

2179

Andrew Hartley, Ilkley. 19thC pottery 'Yorkshire Cricketing' mug, printed in black with images of George H Hirst and Wilfred Rhodes, 4.25in. £160. Oct 99.

2180

Hamptons, Marlborough. Wedgwood majolica cheese dish. Damaged. £160. Jan 00.

2181

Woolley & Wallis, Salisbury. English pearlware commemorative jug, with half length portrait of Queen Caroline above a banner inscribed 'God Save Queen Caroline', c1820, 8cm. £160. Sep 00.

2182

Woolley & Wallis, Salisbury. Chinese white glazed ewer, lobed body and tall flared neck, 18cm, and a Chinese white glazed small jar, 7cm, both probably Song dynasty. £160. Sep 00.

2183

Woolley & Wallis, Salisbury. Set of six R. Worcester coffee cups/saucers, pink factory marks, c1936. £160. Sep 00.

2184

Woolley & Wallis, Salisbury. Four Royal Worcester figures, Lullaby, February '3453' (fingers chipped) Market Day, Masquerade Boy '3359' (finger chipped) and a Royal Doulton David Copperfield. £160. Sep 00.

2185

Gorringes, Lewes. Caughley lemon strainer, Chinese fisherman pattern, 3.25in. £160. June 00.

Prices quoted are hammer prices which excluded the buyer's premium. Adding 15% will give an approximation to the buying price.

2186

Gorringes, Lewes. Victorian Copeland parian/gilt centrepiece, 8.5in. £160. Oct 00.

2187

Gorringes, Lewes. Clarice Cliff Autumn pattern beaker, 3.5in. £160. July 00.

2188

Gorringes, Lewes. 19thC Continental majolica cheese cover, 9in. £160. Feb 01.

2189

Gorringes, Lewes. 18thC Worcester asparagus server, 3in. £160. June 00.

2190

Woolley & Wallis, Salisbury. English porcelain plaque, in the manner of Steele, 19thC, 15cm wide. £160. Sep 00.

2191

Gorringes, Lewes. Wedgwood lustre bowl with butterflies on a green ground. £160. June 00.

2192

Richard Wintertons, Burton on Trent. Beswick figure of Algy no 2710. £160. July 01.

2193

Gorringes, Lewes. Late 18thC Chinese sauce boat, floral decoration and another with landscape decoration, 8in. £160. July 00.

2194

Gorringes, Lewes. Victorian Staffs bust of 'Shakespeare', 8.5in. £160. Oct 00.

2195

Gorringes, Lewes. Moorcroft shallow bowl, irises, paper label, 6in. £160. Sep 00.

2196

Dee, Atkinson & Harrison, Driffield. Pair of early 19thC Staffordshire spaniels, with mustard coloured collars, 4.5in high. £160. Apr 01.

2197

Gorringes, Lewes. Royal Doulton vase moulded with flowers on a mottled blue ground, 8in. £160. Dec 00.

2198

Gorringes, Lewes. Royal Copenhagen group, Faun with kid, 498. £160. Feb 01.

2199

Gorringes, Lewes. Sunderland lustre Sailor's Farewell bowl, 9in. £160. Dec 00.

2200

Marilyn Swain Auctions, Grantham. R. Worcester jug, date code 1906, 4.5in high. £160. Aug 01.

Hammer Price £160

2201

Richard Wintertons, Burton on Trent. Bretby Art Pottery tray with false biscuits, c1897. £160. Mar 02.

2202

Gorringes, Lewes. Minton Secessionist vase, stylised leaf decoration, no 42, 5.5in. £160. Sep 00.

2203

Gorringes, Lewes. Moorcroft pomegranate pewter mounted ash tray, 4in. £160. Feb 01.

2204

Gorringes, Lewes. Moorcroft vase, hibiscus, paper label, 7in. £160. Oct 00.

2205

Gorringes, Lewes. Clarice Cliff crocus pattern preserve jar and cover, 3in, a matching salt and pepper and 2 other pieces. £160. Dec 00.

2206

Biddle & Webb, Birmingham. Moorcroft pottery clematis vase with purple flowers on a green ground, paper label, 3.75in high. £160. Feb 02.

2207

Cheffins, Cambridge. Pair of 19thC transfer printed cheese dishes, c1870, 20cm high. £160. Dec 00.

2208

Sworders, Stansted Mountfitchet. Royal Worcester vase, registration mark for 1864, 16cm high. £160. Apr 01.

2209

Gorringes, Lewes. Crown Devon musical earthenware jug 'Daisy Bell', inscribed with verse, 9in. £160. Jan 02.

2210

Hamptons, Godalming. Royal Doulton stoneware jug inscribed 'Marshal Foch, Armistice, signed Nov. 11th 1918', impressed marks, 18cm high. £160. Nov 01.

2211

Thos Mawer & Son, Lincoln. Moorcroft. Cleopatra pattern 65/6 vase, 16cm. £160. Nov 02.

Hammer Prices £160-£150

2212
Gorringes, Lewes. Victorian pierced oval Whieldon style dish, 9.5in. £160. Apr 01.

2213
Gorringes, Lewes. Worcester teabowl and saucer, 'landslip' pattern, c1758. £160. Apr 01.

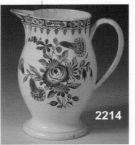

2214
Peter Wilson, Nantwich. Creamware jug, prob. Leeds, 18cm, cracks. £160. July 02.

2215
Sworders, Stansted Mountfitchet. 16thC Italian maiolica alberello, badly damaged, 10.5in high. £160. July 01.

2216
Amersham Auction Rooms, Bucks. Royal Doulton china figure 'The Shepherd', HN1975, designer H Fenton, 8.5in high. £160. Feb 02.

2217
Lambert & Foster, Tenterden. Late Spode tea set, 34 pieces. af. £160. May 02.

2218
Sworders, Stansted Mountfitchet. Two Royal Worcester tankards, 1920 & 1950, tallest 2.25in high. £160. July 01.

2219
Gorringes, Lewes. Victorian Staffordshire spaniel, 5.5in, and a Victorian copper lustre jug, 5in. £160. Apr 01.

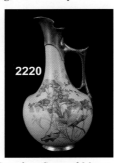

2220
Sworders, Stansted Mountfitchet. Royal Worcester ewer, (gilding rubbed) No. 1028, 13.5in. £160. July 01.

2221
John Taylors, Louth. Large blue and white meat dish. £160. Oct 03.

2222
Thos Mawer & Son, Lincoln. 19thC Staffordshire toby jug, inscribed 'Home Brewed Ales', 27cm. £160. Feb 03.

2223
Gorringes, Bexhill. Pair of C H Brannam chambersticks, modelled as griffins, signed to bases and dated 1897, 6in high. £160. June 03.

2224
Thos Mawer & Son, Lincoln. Moorcroft. Jumeriah vase 403/5, 13.5cm. £160. Nov 02.

2225
Andrew Hartley, Ilkley. Staffordshire group depicting an actor and actress, 19thC, 12in high. £160. Feb 03.

2226
Denhams, Warnham, Sussex. 19thC Worcester porcelain vase, scalloped shell with lizard. £160. Aug 03.

2227
Andrew Hartley, Ilkley. 19thC Staffs figure depicting a shepherd, sheep and dog, 9.75in. £160. Feb 03.

2228
Amersham Auction Rooms, Bucks. Mid late 18thC porcelain bowl, 9in dia. £160. Mar 03.

2229
Tring Market Auctions, Herts. Late 18thC pearlware spill group, minor damage, poss. Neale, 7in. £160. Sep 02.

2230
Locke & England, Leamington Spa. Pair of 19thC porcelain vases, probably Continental, 24.5cm. £160. Oct 03.

2231
Locke & England, Leamington Spa. Midwinter bud vase by Jessie Tate, 17cm high. £160. Apr 03.

2232
Canterbury Auc. Galleries, Kent, 19thC Parianware figure, 'Summer', unmarked, 15.5in high. £160. Aug 03.

2233
Woolley & Wallis, Salisbury. Copeland meat plate and a Copeland vase, Spode's Italian pattern, printed and impd marks, early 20thC, 37cm & 19.5cm. £160. Sep 00.

2234
Gorringes, Lewes. Clarice Cliff volcano pattern bowl, 7.25in, chip. £150. Apr 00.

2235
Lambert & Foster, Tenterden. Pair Staffs black and white Spaniels, based marked 5, 7in high. £150. June 00.

2236
Academy Auctioneers, Ealing. Watcombe Pottery Co, terracotta jug with silver mounted rim, design reg. for 1872, 8in, Designed by Christopher Dresser. £150. July 99.

2237
Trembath Welch, Great Dunmow. Staffordshire brown glazed lion standing with a forepaw upon an orb, 26cm high. £150. Nov 99.

2238
Woolley & Wallis, Salisbury. Three Staffordshire groups, all painted with coloured enamels, 19thC. £150. Sep 00.

2239

Clevedon Salerooms, Bristol. 19thC Staffs pottery mug, (possibly Friendly Society), 10.5in. £150. Nov 00.

2240

Gorringes, Lewes. 19thC jug with slip moulded frieze of vines, cherubs and gryphons, 6.5in. £150. Apr 00.

> The numbering system aids the editorial analysis at the beginning of each section as well as providing a reader reference.

2241

Andrew Hartley, Ilkley. 19thC Davenport pottery meat plate with gravy gunnel, blue printed, 20.5in £150. Feb 01.

2242

Woolley & Wallis, Salisbury. Two similar Chinese green glazed pottery vases, Han dynasty, 206BC-220AD, 44cm approx. £150. Sep 00.

2243

Gorringes, Lewes. Sussex. Pottery bird money box with thick marmalade glaze inscribed 'e. Vidler August 1904', 7in. £150. Apr 00.

2244

Woolley & Wallis, Salisbury. Chinese teapot and teabowl, decorated en grisaille with European lovers in landscape, 18thC, 12cm. £150. Sep 00.

2245

Woolley & Wallis, Salisbury. Pair of R. Doulton stoneware ewers, impressed marks, 33.5cm, and a R. Doulton stoneware vase, 20.5cm, all early 20thC. £150. Sep 00.

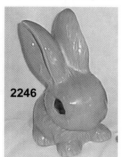

2246

John Taylors, Louth. Sylvac pink bright glaze rabbit, no. 1028. £150. Apr 01.

2247

Crows, Dorking. Walton bocage figure. £150. Sep 01.

2248

Woolley & Wallis, Salisbury. R. Doulton 'Springflowers', HN 1807, 18.5cm. (minute chip) £150. Sep 00.

2249

Great Western Auctions, Glasgow. Dresden plate with classical scene. £150. Mar 01.

2250

Andrew Hartley, Ilkley. Clarice Cliff Bizarre pottery three piece condiment set, Autumn Crocus, printed marks, 3in. £150. Apr 01.

2251

Gorringes, Lewes. Clarice Cliff orange flower conical sifter, 5.5in. £150. June 00.

2252

Gorringes, Lewes. Victorian stone china childs part dinner service. (12) £150. June 00.

2253

Gorringes, Lewes. Victorian bargeware teapot, cover and stand, with motto 'Present to a Friend', 9in. £150. June 00.

2254

Gorringes, Lewes. Spodes New Stone meatplate with floral decoration, 16.5in. £150. Oct 00.

2255

Gorringes, Lewes. Spode scallop dish painted with a view of Bruton, Somerset, gilt border, 8.5in. £150. June 00.

2256

Gorringes, Lewes. Early 19thC mug with Oriental style decoration, 5in. £150. July 00.

2257

Sworders, Stansted Mountfitchet. 21 piece Shelley tea set. £150. Apr 01.

2258

Gorringes, Lewes. Pair of German porcelain lady musicians, 7in. £150. Sep 00.

2259

Wintertons Ltd, Bakewell. Beswick Hereford bull, 6in high. £150. Oct 01.

2260

Woolley & Wallis, Salisbury. Royal Worcester Hadley Ware vase, green mark, 1905, 8cm. £150. Sep 00.

2261

Andrew Hartley, Ilkley. Leeds Pottery pearlware basket, chinoiserie landscape, 11.25in. £150. Apr 01.

2262

Gorringes, Lewes. Clarice Cliff autumn crocus pattern milk jug, cream jug, sugar & 3 other items. £150. June 00.

2263

Andrew Hartley, Ilkley. Royal Dux porcelain figure of a Golden Labrador, 4.75in wide. £150. Apr 01.

2264

Gorringes, Lewes. Royal Worcester ivory porcelain jug with rustic handle and bird and lizard in relief, No. 1116, 7.5in. £150. Oct 00.

2265

Crows, Dorking. Walton bocage figure of a shepherd. £150. Sep 01.

Hammer Price £150

2266

Gorringes, Lewes. 19thC Staffordshire model of a red deer, 4.5in. £150. Oct 00.

2267

Andrew Hartley, Ilkley. Kutani porcelain charge, signed, 14in wide. £150. Aug 01.

2268

Dee, Atkinson & Harrison, Driffield. Two 19thC Staffs figures, boy with a dog 9.25in high and a boy seated upon a bundle of wheatsheaves, 8.25in. £150. Apr 01.

2269

Gorringes, Lewes. Pair of Samson vases with blue scale grounds and beaded borders, 6in. £150. Dec 00.

2270

Gorringes, Lewes. Early 19thC Staffordshire figure of a goddess with trophies of war, 8.5in. £150. Mar 01.

2271

Cheffins, Cambridge. 19thC P. Ipsen of Copenhagen terracotta plaque, in oils by P. A. Schepper, 41cm. £150. Dec 00.

2272

Gorringes, Lewes. Royal Worcester vase painted with roses, No. 2491, date code 1922, 3.25in. £150. Dec 00.

2273

Gorringes, Lewes. 19thC Royal Crown Derby imari tea cup and saucer, vase/cover, 4in and a trumpet shaped vase, 4in. £150. Mar 01.

2274

Gorringes, Lewes. Pair of Victorian Semi Nankeen China floral dishes, 10in. (chipped) £150. Feb 01.

2275

Gorringes, Lewes. Clarice Cliff crocus pattern honey pot and cover, 4in. £150. Feb 01.

2276

Gorringes, Lewes. Large early 19thC 'Moss Rose' charger, 15in. £150. Feb 01.

2277

Gorringes, Lewes. Pair of Wedgwood lustre vases, gilt dragons and grasshoppers, Z4829, 5.25in. (both necks damaged) £150. Feb 01.

2278

Rosebery's, London. Regency Crown Derby porcelain mug, c1820, entitled 'In Germany', 11cm. £150. Mar 02.

2279

Gorringes, Lewes. Chinese blue crackle glazed squat baluster vase, with lug handles, 9in. £150. Apr 01.

2280

Gorringes, Lewes. Majolica jug moulded with a strawberry plant, 3.5in. £150. Feb 01.

2281

Sworders, Stansted Mount-fitchet. Chinese porcelain ginger jar and cover, 7in high and another. £150. Apr 01.

2282

Tring Market Auctions, Herts. Vienna porcelain chocolate cup, cover and trembleuse saucer, 4.75in high overall. £150. Mar 02.

2283

Gorringes, Lewes. Worcester fisherman patt. sparrowbeak jug, c1765, 3.25in and a feather moulded bowl with floral decoration, workman's mk., c1760, 4in. £150. Mar 01.

2284

Gorringes, Lewes. Victorian Staffordshire group of a girl and ram, 5.5in and a seated figure with goblet, 5.5in. £150. Oct 00.

2285

Gorringes, Lewes. Wemyss vase, decorated with roses, pattern no. 213, 12in. £150. Apr 01.

2286

John Taylors, Louth. Staffordshire greyhound holding a hare. £150. July 02.

2287

Sworders, Stansted Mount-fitchet. R. Worcester shell dish, date code 1903, 6.75in. £150. July 01.

2288

Sworders, Stansted Mount-fitchet. Lowestoft tea bowl/saucer in the Green Redgrave pattern, saucer 5in. (minor chip/cracks) £150. July 01.

2289

Tring Market Auctions, Herts. Delft plate with houses, plants and rocks, possibly Lambeth, 11in, rim chips. £150. May 02.

2290

Gorringes, Lewes. Derby porcelain figure of a Youth as a Turk, 4.5in. £150. Apr 01.

2291

Tring Market Auctions, Herts. Pratt type Toby jug, caryatid handle, af and cover missing, 10in high. £150. Sep 02.

2292

Andrew Hartley, Ilkley. Staffordshire pottery spill vase of a spaniel and geese, 19thC, 8in. £150. Feb 03.

Lambert & Foster, Tenterden. Royal Doulton. Tawny Owl surmounting dish, No. 3667. £150. June 03.

Andrew Hartley, Ilkley. Arts & Crafts W H Goss parian ware charger, relief moulded and painted with a shield, 13.75in. £150. June 03.

W & H Peacock, Bedford. 19thC Staffordshire figure 'Pomona'. £150. Mar 03.

Richard Wintertons, Burton on Trent. Clarice Cliff Bizarre Athens jug, crocus pattern, 16cm. £150. Apr 03.

Andrew Hartley, Ilkley. Arts & Crafts W H Goss parian ware charger, relief moulded and painted with a crest, 13.75in. £150. June 03.

Wintertons Ltd, Lichfield. 19thC majolica dish, s.d., 28cm. £140. Nov 99.

Sworders, Stansted Mountfitchet. Clarice Cliff Woodland pattern bread plate, printed and inscribed marks verso, 22.5cm. £140. Mar 03.

The illustrations in these pages are in descending price order. The price range is indicated at the top of each page.

Andrew Hartley, Ilkley. 19thC silver lustre pottery jug painted with fruiting vine, 5.75in high. £140. Feb 00.

Woolley & Wallis, Salisbury. Chinese famille rose plate, maiden in garden, Qianlong, 1736-95, 26cm. £140. Sep 00.

David Duggleby, Scarborough. Early 19thC Belper & Denby stoneware gimmal flask for 'Broughams Reform cordials' as a judge holding 'The second Magna Carta', c1832, 7in. (nose damage) £140. Apr 00.

Woolley & Wallis, Salisbury. Four Chinese meat plates, all 18thC, (one chipped) 37cm - 25cm. £140. Sep 00.

Dee, Atkinson & Harrison, Driffield. Manner of Carlo Dolci. Oval miniature on porcelain La Dollorosa, with a similar miniature, 3.5 x 2.5in. £140. Dec 00.

Woolley & Wallis, Salisbury. Royal Worcester jug, puce factory mark No 1094, c1899, 13cm. £140. Sep 00.

Gorringes, Lewes. Italian pattern shaped dish, and a 19thC Willow pattern boat shaped tureen. £140. Oct 00.

Woolley & Wallis, Salisbury. Royal Worcester cup and saucer, pink mark, c1926, 15cm. £140. Sep 00.

Dee, Atkinson & Harrison, Driffield. German Art Deco figure, Bock-Wallendorf factory, 10.5in. £140. Feb 00.

Hammer Prices £150-£140

Woolley & Wallis, Salisbury. Four Staffs dogs, tallest 18cm, all 19thC. £140. Sep 00.

Woolley & Wallis, Salisbury. Mason's ironstone mug, blue printed mark, 19thC, 10.5cm high. £140. Sep 00.

Woolley & Wallis, Salisbury. Worcester with 'Royal Lily' pattern. Saucer dish, open crescent mark, 20cm, plate, no mark, 18cm, two handled cup and saucer, incised 'B', late 18thC. £140. Sep 00.

Gorringes, Lewes. Royal Worcester blush porcelain ewer vase, No. 1026, 6.25in. £140. Oct 00.

Dee, Atkinson & Harrison, Driffield. R. Doulton, Sweet Anne May, 1930s, Rd No 743560, 4in. £140. Dec 00.

Gorringes, Lewes. 19thC Staffordshire huntsman and his dog, 7.5in. £140. Oct 00.

Amersham Auction Rooms, Bucks. Pair of late 19thC Continental porcelain table centres, 12in. £140. June 01.

Andrew Hartley, Ilkley. 19thC Staffordshire pottery pastille burner as a pagoda encrusted with flowers, gilt embellishment, 6.5in. £140. Feb 01.

Woolley & Wallis, Salisbury. Chinese celadon vase, 14thC, (neck reduced) 32cm, wood stand/cover. £140. Sep 00.

Hammer Price £140

2318 Gorringes, Bexhill. Royal Worcester Crownware bowl with a galleon at sea, CW162, 11in. £140. Oct 01.

2319 Bonham's, Bath. Susie Cooper for Crown Works Burslem. Pr. Art Deco plates, printed factory mark no. E/249, 22.5cm. £140. Nov 01.

2320 Marilyn Swain Auctions, Grantham. Royal Worcester. Globular vase, 3.5in, date code 1916. £140. Aug 01.

2321 Gorringes, Lewes. Dresden floral encrusted trinket box, 3.5in. £140. Dec 00.

2322 Gorringes, Lewes. Pair of Victorian Staffordshire seated shepherd and shepherdess figures, 7in. £140. Feb 01.

2323 Clarke Gammon, Guildford. Victorian Taylor, Tunnicliffe & Co Ltd pottery tobacco jar. £140. Sep 01.

2324 Sworders, Stansted Mountfitchet. Pair of Prattware plates, 9.5in. £140. Apr 01.

2325 Gorringes, Lewes. Royal Copenhagen, Amager woman knitting, 1317. £140. Feb 01.

2326 Gorringes, Lewes. Moorcroft bowl and cover with russet and dark blue glaze, 6.5in. £140. Feb 01.

2327 Sworders, Stansted Mountfitchet. Three 19thC pottery childs plates, largest 6in. £140. Apr 01.

2328 Tring Market Auctions, Herts. Pair of 18thC Chinese famille rose plates, painted with vase of flowers in brown and gilt cell and sopra bianco sopra borders, 9in. £140. May 02.

2329 Sworders, Stansted Mountfitchet. Chinese baluster vase and cover, 24in. (extensive damage) £140. Apr 01.

2330 Sworders, Stansted Mountfitchet. Davenport 'Frisburg' oval meat plate, 47cm long. (crazed) £140. Apr 01.

2331 Sworders, Stansted Mountfitchet. R. Doulton charger 'under the greenwood tree', 15in. £140. Apr 01.

2332 Sworders, Stansted Mountfitchet. Late 19thC Japanese charger, 18in. £140. Apr 01.

2333 Andrew Hartley, Ilkley. Pearlware dish printed in an Arcadian landscape design, early 19thC, 10.25in wide, and a shell shaped dish to match 5.25in wide, and an oval dish. £140. Aug 02.

2334 Sworders, Stansted Mountfitchet. Newhall teapot and cover, with pattern No. 312, 10in wide. £140. July 01.

2335 Amersham Auction Rooms, Bucks. Pair of early 19thC Pearlware tea cups and three saucers, monochrome transfer prints. £140. Apr 02.

2336 Hamptons, Godalming. Rare George IV Coronation buff stoneware jug, 22cm. £140. Nov 01.

2337 Gorringes, Lewes. Early 19thC Staffs figure of a boy holding dog, bocage damage, 6in, and boy with seated dog and lamb, 6in. £140. Mar 01.

2338 Gorringes, Lewes. Samson porcelain figure of lady with a wicker box, bocage damage, 6in. £140. Mar 01.

2339 Gorringes, Bexhill. Pair of Burmantofts Venetian blue glaze pedestals, with trailing ivy, 3ft 6in. £140. Dec 01.

2340 Gorringes, Lewes. Unusual Satsuma hexagonal vase with Egyptian style decoration, 8in. £140. Apr 01.

2341 Gorringes, Lewes. Sevres bleu celeste and gilt coffee can and saucer painted with birds. £140. Apr 01.

2342 Peter Wilson, Nantwich. Royal Worcester vase hand painted with fruit, signed Bill Roberts, late 20thC, 15cm high. £140. July 02.

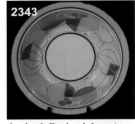

2343 Locke & England, Leamington Spa. Clarice Cliff Fantasque bowl, pomegranate design, 22.5cm. £140. Sep 02.

2344 Tring Market Auctions, Herts. Victorian white parian bust of an unknown gentleman, 12.5in high. £140. Jan 03.

2345 Sworders, Stansted Mountfitchet. Parianware bust of a veiled lady, unsigned, 9.5in high. £140. July 01.

2346

Gorringes, Bexhill. Pair of Samuel Alcock porcelain vases, Etruscan style showing Victors of Public Games fulfilling their vows in Temple of Venus, 8.5in. £140. July 03.

2347

Tring Market Auctions, Herts. 18thC Worcester tea bowl and saucer, Kakiemon style, blue seal mark, saucer with small rim chip. £140. Jan 03.

2348

Lambert & Foster, Tenterden. Pr. vases, green ground, 8340t, Wh, 27cm. £140. June 03.

2349

Andrew Hartley, Ilkley. Carter Stabler and Adams Poole Pottery vase, Blue Bird pattern, imp'd and painted marks, 7in. £140. Feb 03.

2350

Tring Market Auctions, Herts. Doulton Lambeth ewer by Frank Butler, chip to one leaf, 7.5in. £140. Jan 03.

2351

Lambert & Foster, Tenterden. Set of three Carltonware plates, Rd No. 462037 and 519343. £140. Dec 02.

2352

Amersham Auction Rooms, Bucks. Late 19thC Royal Worcester porcelain vase, 10.5in wide. £140. Dec 02.

2353

Tring Market Auctions, Herts. Pair of Zsolnay Pecs vases, bases drilled with holes for lamps, 11in. £140. Nov 02.

2354

Locke & England, Leamington Spa, Leamington Spa. Wemyss pottery jardiniere, impressed mk., 19.5cm. af. £140. July 03.

> Prices quoted are hammer prices which excluded the buyer's premium. Adding 15% will give an approximation to the buying price.

2355

Locke & England, Leamington Spa. 19thC Staffordshire pottery black and white rabbit, 8cm. £140. Jan 03.

2356

R. Wintertons, Burton on Trent. Doulton Burslem waste pail, 'Iris' pattern, printed factory mark, 30cm. £135. Dec 01.

2357

John Taylors, Louth. Doulton Flambe vase. £135. Feb 01.

2358

Gorringes, Lewes. 19thC Rogers Elephant pattern plate, 10in. £130. Apr 00.

2359

Dee, Atkinson & Harrison, Driffield. Old English loving cup, hand painted, 4.5in and a christening mug, 'John Briggs Davey', born April 20th 1878, 3in. £130. July 99.

2360

Gorringes, Lewes. Royal Winton Evesham pattern serving dish and six matching bowls. £130. Apr 00.

2361

Andrew Hartley, Ilkley. Early 19thC pearlware loving cup, 5.5in high. £130. Oct 99.

2362

Woolley & Wallis, Salisbury. Pearlware bowl, decorated with chinoiserie scenes, no mark, early 19thC, 23.5cm. (hair crack and rim chip) £130. Sep 00.

2363

Gorringes, Lewes. Late 19thC Milan cornucopia chariot pulled by two cherubs, 12in. £130. Apr 00.

2364

Lambert & Foster, Tenterden. Old Staffordshire 'Hen' egg nest. £130. June 00.

2365

Gorringes, Lewes. Royal Worcester blush porcelain jug, pattern no. 1116, 6in. (gilding rubbed) £130. Apr 00.

2366

Gorringes, Lewes. Carter Stabler Adams ovoid Poole vase with fan tailed birds, 6.5in. £130. July 00.

2367

Andrew Hartley, Ilkley. Pair of Bloor Derby encrusted vases, 8in. £130. Feb 01.

Hammer Prices £140-£130

2368

Woolley & Wallis, Salisbury. Four Staffordshire groups, 19thC, tallest 23cm. (some damages) £130. Sep 00.

2369

John Taylors, Louth. Late 18thC 'Salopian' scalloped dish. £130. Oct 00.

2370

Gorringes, Lewes. British Anchor Pottery Co. 12-piece Japan pattern part dinner service. £130. Apr 00.

2371

Woolley & Wallis, Salisbury. Barr Worcester coffee cup and saucer with matching teabowl and saucer, incised 'B' marks, Worcester spiral fluted teabowl and saucer and a fluted coffee cup, all late 18thC. (7) £130. Sep 00.

2372

Amersham Auction Rooms, Bucks. Late 19thC majolica earthenware sardine dish, 4in high, 8in wide. £130. Mar 01.

2373

Gorringes, Lewes. Majolica Continental ewer, mask spout and panelled body, marked Pesaro, 16in. £130. July 00.

Hammer Price £130

2374

Hamptons, Godalming. Set of three 'Four Castles' diamond jubilee plates, with Victoria's portrait and four residences, 24.5cm. £130. Nov 01.

2375

Gorringes, Lewes. Clarice Cliff Celtic harvest teapot and cover, 8in. £130. June 00.

2376

Gorringes, Lewes. 19thC Sevres vase with landscape and fete gallant panels, 6in. £130. June 00.

2377

Gorringes, Lewes. Victorian Staffs group of a Scottish couple, 7in. £130. June 00.

2378

D.Duggleby, Scarborough. Burmontofts faience tile, two birds feeding their young, in turquoise/green, stamp mark, c1890, 30cm sq. £130. Dec 01.

2379

Gorringes, Lewes. Moorcroft vase with anemones on green ground, 3.5in. £130. Mar 01.

2380

Gorringes, Lewes. Victorian Staffordshire clock group with highland couple, 14in and a Little Red Riding Hood, 9.5in. (cracked) £130. July 00.

2381

Gorringes, Lewes. Staffordshire cottage pastille burner and a cottage with pink roof, 5in. £130. Oct 00.

2382

Cheffins, Cambridge. 19thC Burmantoft's Iznik jardiniere, design No 52 and 240, 27.5cm dia. £130. Sep 01.

2383

Gorringes, Lewes. Royal Worcester vase painted with roses, No. 2491 and date code 1925, 5in. £130. Dec 00.

2384

Gorringes, Lewes. Three Moorcroft floral decorated ashtrays, paper labels to bases, 4.25in. £130. Sep 00.

2385

Richard Wintertons, Burton on Trent. Chamber candlestick c1900, green and ochre majolica and lustre glazes, handle as a lizard, impressed 'Burmantoft Faience 834', 12cm at base. £130. Sep 01.

2386

Gorringes, Lewes. Two Staffs cottage pastille burners, largest 5in. £130. Oct 00.

2387

Gorringes, Lewes. 18thC famille rose teapot with floral decoration. £130. Oct 00.

2388

Gorringes, Lewes. Royal Worcester ovoid vase painted with roses, G161, date code 1924, 2.75in. £130. Dec 00.

2389

Gorringes, Lewes. Royal Copenhagen figure, Whittler, 905. £130. Feb 01.

2390

Dee, Atkinson & Harrison, Driffield. Set of Losol ware jugs printed and painted exotic birds and foliage, 7in to 5.5in high. £130. Apr 01.

2391

Gorringes, Lewes. Moorcroft wisteria pattern vase, 3.5in and a pomegranate vase, 3.5in. (af) £130. Feb 01.

2392

Denhams, Warnham, Sussex. David Leach Art Pottery vase, 7in. £130. Oct 03.

2393

Sworders, Stansted Mountfitchet. Japanese vase and lid, with cut decoration, 7in high and a pair of Noritaki vases. (lids af) £130. Apr 01.

2394

Gorringes, Lewes. German porcelain basket surmounted by cherubs embracing, 8.5in. £130. July 00.

2395

Dee, Atkinson & Harrison, Driffield. Royal Doulton Kingsware tea caddy, profile of an old lady drinking tea, 4.5in. £130. Apr 01.

2396

Richard Wintertons, Burton on Trent. Clarice Cliff Crocus pattern bowl. £130. Aug 01.

2397

Gorringes, Lewes. Early 19thC Pratt style plate with a steam driven carriage titled 'Dampf Coach Von London Nach Liverpool', 7in. £130. Feb 01.

2398

Gorringes, Lewes. Victorian Staffordshire spaniel with red sponged decoration on blue base, 6.75in. £130. Mar 01.

2399

Gorringes, Lewes. Victorian Staffordshire figure of Shakespeare leaning on a pillar, 7in. £130. Mar 01.

2400

Gorringes, Lewes. French figural faience double salt entitled Salies de Bearn, 7.5in. £130. Mar 01.

2401

Gorringes, Lewes. Royal Worcester cream jug painted with a bullfinch by W Powell, 3.25in. £130. Mar 01.

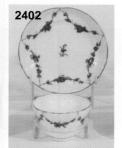

2402

Andrew Hartley, Ilkley. Bristol type porcelain tea bowl/saucer, 18thC, possibly Coalport. £130. Feb 03.

2403

W & H Peacock, Bedford. Royal Doulton, The Potter figure. £130. July 03.

2404

Gorringes, Bexhill. Majolica teapot, with flowers, and a blue and white self pouring teapot. £130. Mar 03.

2405

Canterbury Auc. Galleries, Canterbury. German bisque porcelain figure of W G Grace, 9.5in. £130. Aug 03.

2406

Gorringes, Lewes. Worcester fence pattern teapot, (ex Bushell Collection) 5.5in. (restored) £130. Mar 01.

2407

Gorringes, Lewes. Crown Devon John Peel musical mug, 1930s, 5in. £130. Apr 01.

2408

Hamptons, Godalming. Crown Ducal Charlotte Rhead charger, with bands of stylised fruits, painted and printed marks. £130. July 02.

2409

Sworders, Stansted Mountfitchet. Beswick Beatrix Potter figure, Duchess, 4in, brown stamp. £130. July 01.

2410

Tring Market Auctions, Herts. Derby figure of a grotesque boy eating a bowl of curds and whey, incised No. 69, 4.5in high. £130. Nov 02.

2411

Gorringes, Lewes. Pair of Continental txfr. decorated vases, 11in. £130. Apr 01.

2412

Andrew Hartley, Ilkley. Worcester porcelain tea cup and saucer, mid to late 18thC. £130. Apr 03.

2413

Ambrose, Loughton. Collection of porcelain cake decorations, c1930, 2 polar bears, 3 snow babies, 5 piece cat band and 4 Father Christmases. £130. Aug 02.

The numbering system aids the editorial analysis at the beginning of each section as well as providing a reader reference.

2414

Sworders, Stansted Mountfitchet. Tudric pottery vase, candlestick, pewter mounts, 9.5in high. (candlestick broken) £130. July 01.

2415

Gorringes, Lewes. Early Victorian creamware nursery plate of a child praying in a leaf moulded border, imp'd A, 5in. £130. Apr 01.

Hammer Prices £130-£120

2416

Lambert & Foster, Tenterden. 19thC Canton china. (11) £130. Apr 03.

2417

Amersham Auction Rooms, Bucks. Mid 19thC Staffs china bowl, decorated with flora, 11in dia. £130. Nov 02.

2418

Sworders, Stansted Mountfitchet. Four Carlton Ware Guinness egg cups, 3.5in. £130. July 01.

2419

Tring Market Auctions, Herts. Satsuma figure of a male Lion of Fo, af. £125. May 02.

2420

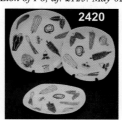

R. Wintertons, Burton on Trent. Series 1950s Midwinter plates, salad design, Terrance Conran. £125. Nov 00.

2421

Richard Wintertons, Burton on Trent. Beswick figure of Rupert the Bear no. 2694. £125. July 01.

2422

Gorringes, Lewes. Four bisque figure pepperettes, 4in. £120. Apr 00.

2423

Gorringes, Lewes. Late 18thC creamware bowl of basket weave form, 10in. £120. Apr 00.

2424

Andrew Hartley, Ilkley. Staffordshire pottery figural spill vase on oval base, 8in high. £120. Feb 01.

2425

Gorringes, Lewes. Royal Doulton flambe seated puppy, onyx base, 4in. £120. Apr 00.

2426

Rosebery's, London. Oldhall pottery ewer. £120. June 00.

Hammer Price £120

2427

Gorringes, Lewes. Early 19thC Pountney & Allies Dromedary pattern plate, 10in. £120. Apr 00.

2428

John Taylors, Louth. Caughley 18thC butter boat. £120. Oct 00.

2429

John Taylors, Louth. 18thC Caughley pickle dish. £120. Oct 00.

2430

Woolley & Wallis, Salisbury. English earthenware mug, 'Piper' pattern, printed mark including the title, c1820-40, 12.5cm. (foot chips and a 4cm hair crack) £120. Sep 00.

2431

Andrew Hartley, Ilkley. Leeds Pottery creamware basket, 10.25in. £120. Apr 01.

2432

Woolley & Wallis, Salisbury. Japanese Satsuma model of two fighting shi shi, Meiji, 1868-1912, 17.5cm high. (chips) £120. Sep 00.

104

2433

A. Hartley, Ilkley. 19thC Continental porcelain snuff box, gilt metal mounts, with lovers in a landscape, 1.75in wide. £120. Dec 00.

2434

Gorringes, Lewes. Mason's ironstone jug with serpent handle, 4in and a smaller ditto, 2.75in £120. Oct 00.

2435

Gorringes, Lewes. Staffordshire cottage money box and 2 pastille burners, largest 4.25in. £120. Oct 00.

2436

Woolley & Wallis, Salisbury. Barr Worcester breakfast cup and saucer with the 'Dragon in Compartments' pattern, cup with an incised 'B' mark, c1792-1807. £120. Sep 00.

2437

Gorringes, Lewes. Pair of Rockingham pot pourri vases, one with cover, encrusted with floral spray, 8in. af. £120. Oct 00.

2438

Dee, Atkinson & Harrison, Driffield. Clarice Cliff vase, moulded '904 Clarice Cliff' to the base. £120. Dec 00.

2439

Dockree's, Manchester. 19thC Copeland Spode bread basket, 12.5in and an oval trough, 4.5in, both in blue and white Italian pattern. £120. Sep 00.

2440

Gorringes, Lewes. Pair of urn shaped vases on square bases, 9.5in. £120. June 00.

2441

Andrew Hartley, Ilkley. 19thC Continental porcelain snuff box of circular bombe form, 1.75in wide. £120. Oct 00.

2442

Gorringes, Lewes. Moorcroft anemone vase, paper label to base, 4in. £120. Sep 00.

2443

Gorringes, Lewes. Staffordshire figure of Wallace, 15in. £120. Oct 00.

2444

Gorringes, Lewes. Clarice Cliff harvest pattern teapot and cover and matching milk jug. £120. July 00.

2445

Gorringes, Lewes. Dresden porcelain group of lovers with a nest, 7.5in. £120. June 00.

2446

Hogbens, Folkestone. Damaged 19thC Bargeware teapot. £120. May 01.

2447

Gorringes, Lewes. 18thC Staffordshire enamelled oval patch box with motto 'I love too well to kiss and tell', 1.5in. £120. June 00.

2448

Gorringes, Lewes. Royal Doulton Puppy HN1158, a kingfisher and a Watney's Ale ashtray. £120. Oct 00.

2449

Gorringes, Lewes. Clarice Cliff geometric dwarf candle-stick, 3in. £120. July 00.

2450

Andrew Hartley, Ilkley. 18thC Davenport pearlware plate, figures by a church, 9.5in, two other blue printed plates. (3) £120. Apr 01.

2451

Richard Wintertons, Burton on Trent. Pair of Robinson & Leadbeater parian busts, 'Lord Roberts' and 'Lord Kitchener', each incised 'By W C Lawton, Copyright 1900', 20cm. £120. Sep 01.

2452

Gorringes, Lewes. Pair of early 19thC Staffs zebras, 5in. (restoration) £120. Oct 00.

2453

John Taylors, Louth. Staffordshire loving cup with frog. £120. Dec 01.

2454

Gorringes, Lewes. Early 19thC Sunderland lustre christening jug inscribed Thomas Bailey 1838, 8in. £120. Dec 00.

2455

Gorringes, Lewes. Clarice Cliff crocus pattern dish, 11.5in and a viscaria pattern side plate, 6in. £120. Dec 00.

2456

Gorringes, Lewes. Pair of Samson vases with exotic birds against blue scale grounds, 5in. £120. Dec 00.

2457

Gorringes, Lewes. Royal Copenhagen figure, Great Dane, 1679. £120. Feb 01.

2458

Gorringes, Lewes. Wemyss honey pot (no cover) with a bee hive, 3.25in. (small base rim chip) £120. Feb 01.

The illustrations in these pages are in descending price order. The price range is indicated at the top of each page.

2459

Tring Market Auctions, Herts, 18thC Delft dish painted with oriental flowers, rim chips, 12in. £120. Sep 02.

2460

Amersham Auction Rooms, Bucks. Clarice Cliff 'China Harvest' jug, bears printed Newport backstamp, 13in wide. £120. June 02.

2461

Sworders, Stansted Mount-fitchet. 19thC Doulton water filter and lid, 16in high. (restored) £120. Apr 01.

2462

Hamptons, Godalming. Porcelain loving cup, c1869, 'Benjamin Wild, born January 27th 1848, a present from his affectionate Mother on attaining his 21st birthday', 14cm. £120. Nov 01.

2463

Sworders, Stansted Mount-fitchet. Blue jasperware oil lamp, shade and funnel, 17in high overall. £120. Apr 01.

2464

Thos Mawer & Son, Lincoln. Royal Worcester 'Crownware' bowl, pattern number CW162, with castles, islands, stylised gilt trees, 23cm. £120. Apr 02.

2465

Richard Wintertons, Burton on Trent. Cornish Kitchen ware. 'Bread Crumbs' jar. £120. Jan 03.

2466

Gorringes, Lewes. Staffs group of a shepherd with dog, lambs and bocage, 6in. £120. Apr 01.

2467

Tring Market Auctions, Herts. Imari bowl, 12.5in dia. £120. May 02.

2468

Sworders, Stansted Mount-fitchet. Four Beswick Beatrix Potter figures, 'Little Black Rabbit' 'Jemima Puddleduck', 'Old Mr Brown', and 'Foxy Whiskered Gentleman'. £120. July 01.

2469

Amersham Auction Rooms, Bucks. Early 20thC Samson porcelain bowl, 12in dia. £120. Sep 02.

2470

Sworders, Stansted Mount-fitchet. Pair of green glazed Chinese pottery lion dogs, 12in high. £120. July 01.

2471

Thos Mawer & Son, Lincoln. 19thC Staffordshire flatback figure of a boy and girl, 29cm. £120. Nov 02.

Hammer Price £120

2472

Sworders, Stansted Mount-fitchet. Nymphenburg porcelain plate, with a view, 8.5in. Pair of English leaf and flower plates and Vienna style cup/saucer. £120. Apr 01.

2473

Rosebery's, London. Sunderland lustre plaque, with psalm, 'Prepare to meet they God', 17cm. £120. Sep 02.

2474

Gorringes, Lewes. Clarice Cliff Rhodanthe pattern plate, 9in. £120. Sep 02.

2475

Sworders, Stansted Mount-fitchet. Wedgwood pottery blue glazed salad bowl, plated rim, matching servers, 20cm dia. £120. Oct 02.

2476

Gorringes, Lewes. Poole vase with geometric green and grey leaf decoration, 4.5in. £120. Apr 01.

2477

Richard Wintertons, Burton on Trent. Brewery advertising match striker for Ind Coope of Burton. £120. Feb 03.

2478

Thos Mawer & Son, Lincoln. Pair of Staffs King Charles Spaniels, 32cm. £120. Nov 02.

2479

Tring Market Auctions, Herts. Royal Worcester bowl of blush apricot ground, shape No. 1910, year marks for 1906, 4.5in high. £120. Jan 03.

2480

Sworders, Stansted Mount-fitchet. Late 19thC porcelain figural centrepiece, 9in high. £120. July 01.

2481

Sworders, Stansted Mount-fitchet. Poole Pottery freeform vase, printed and painted marks X/PKT, 15cm. £120. July 03.

2482

Sworders, Stansted Mount-fitchet. Three Victorian white stoneware relief moulded jugs incl: Four Seasons, Charles Meigh & Sons, and Naomi by Sm Alcock & Co, tallest 9.5in. £120. July 01.

Hammer Prices £120-£110

2483

Potteries Specialist Auctions, Stoke on Trent. Pendelfin. Picnic basket rabbit, dressed in green and red, out of production. (2) £120. Apr 03.

2484

Andrew Hartley, Ilkley. Worcester porcelain teacup, polychrome painted, late 18thC. £120. Apr 03.

2485

John Taylors, Louth. Late 18thC Lowestoft teabowl with Redgrave patt.. £120. July 03.

2486

Lambert & Foster, Tenterden. Royal Doulton. Pair of small blue ground vases, 1297/2767. £120. June 03.

2487

Gorringes, Lewes. Pair of Samson vases with exotic birds, 4.25in. £120. Feb 01.

2488

Sworders, Stansted Mount-fitchet. R. Worcester 'Sunday Boy', 4.75in. £115. July 01.

2489

Dee, Atkinson & Harrison, Driffield. Two early 19thC copper lustre jugs, 6.5in high. £115. Dec 00.

2490

Tring Market Auctions, Herts. New Hall tea bowl/saucer pattern no. 78. £115. Mar 02.

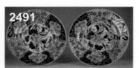

2491

Woolley & Wallis, Salisbury. Pair Japan Coalport plates, no marks, c1820, 23.5cm. £110. Sep 00.

2492

Gorringes, Lewes. Kerr and Binns Worcester cabinet cup with pierced double skin body, 3in. £110. Apr 00.

2493

Andrew Hartley, Ilkley. Early 19thC Wedgwood creamware tureen, 6.5in. £110. Aug 00.

2494

Dee, Atkinson & Harrison, Driffield. Ringtons Maling Ware jug, 8.5in. £110. Feb 01.

2495

Lambert & Foster, Tenterden. Royal Doulton De Luxe patt. no. V1284 breakfast set. (8) £110. Aug 00.

2496

Andrew Hartley, Ilkley. Pair 19thC 'stone china' dishes by John & William Ridgway, Japan Flowers pattern, 9.5in wide and a Spode blue printed porcelain oval sugar bowl and cover, 7in wide. £110. Aug 00.

2497

Gorringes, Lewes. 19thC Davenport Mosque and Fisherman pattern plate, a Spode plate and one other plate. £110. Apr 00.

2498

Woolley & Wallis, Salisbury. Three Chinese pottery items, two groups of a sow and piglets, and a standing figure of a dwarf, all Han dynasty, 206BC-220AD. £110. Sep 00.

2499

Gorringes, Lewes. Pair of R. Worcester blush porcelain ewers, dragon handles, shape 1048, 4.5in. £110. June 00.

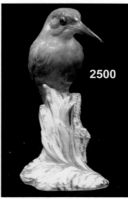

2500

Sworders, Stansted Mount-fitchet. Royal Worcester Kingfisher, stamped 986, 6in. £110. May 01.

2501

John Taylors, Louth. Pair of Masons jugs. £110. Oct 99.

2502

Lambert & Foster, Tenterden. Royal Worcester blush jug, Rd no. 29115 date code 1894, 5in and a ditto jug. (cracked) £110. Dec 00.

2503

Gorringes, Lewes. Two Victorian willow pattern soup tureens and a cheese stand, 11in. £110. Sep 00.

2504

Andrew Hartley, Ilkley. Early 19thC Sunderland pottery spill vase in the form of seven turrets, yellow and brown, 8.25in wide. £110. Feb 00.

2505

Andrew Hartley, Ilkley. Clarice Cliff Bizarre pottery jug, Autumn Crocus, printed mark, 7in. £110. Apr 01.

2506

Woolley & Wallis, Salisbury. Royal Worcester vase, shape 2260, puce mark, c1910, 10.5cm. £110. Sep 00.

2507

Woolley & Wallis, Salisbury. Two porcelain cups/saucers, one Coalport with cockerel and hen, gilt ampersand mks., (fine hair crack) the other probably Ridgway, patt. 2/63, both 19thC. £110. Sep 00.

2508

Lambert & Foster, Tenterden. 18thC famille rose export bowl, flowers and foliage, 10.25in dia. af. £110. Dec 00.

2509

Gorringes, Lewes. Moorcroft vase decorated with hibiscus against a green ground, label to base, 7in. £110. Sep 00.

2510

Gorringes, Lewes. Victorian Staffordshire swan and child inkwell, 6in. (restored base) £110. June 00.

2511

Gorringes, Lewes. Victorian Staffs figure of a dancing lady, 12in. £110. July 00.

2512

Wintertons Ltd, Lichfield. Beswick Hereford 'Champion of Champions' bull and cow. £110. Nov 00.

2513

Andrew Hartley, Ilkley. Clarice Cliff Bizarre pottery candlestick, No. 331 Autumn Crocus, printed marks, 3.5in wide. £110. Apr 01.

2514

Dee, Atkinson & Harrison, Driffield. Limoges style cabaret set painted yellow and purple irises on a green ground. (8) £110. Apr 01.

Prices quoted are hammer prices which excluded the buyer's premium. Adding 15% will give an approximation to the buying price.

2515

Hamptons, Godalming. Royal Doulton, Lord Nelson stoneware pot, with portrait and ship medallions, printed marks, 6.5cm. £110. Nov 01.

2516

Marilyn Swain Auctions, Grantham. Royal Worcester. Pair of Locke & Co. pheasant vases, 2.5in. £110. Aug 01.

2517

Gorringes, Lewes. Majolica 'sweetcorn' water jug, 7in. £110. Oct 00.

2518

Cheffins, Cambridge. Carlton pottery 'Bull Nose Morris' wire windscreen, red petrol can, black printed marks, 14cm. £110. Dec 00.

2519

Gorringes, Lewes. Royal Copenhagen, Amager girl knitting, 1314. £110. Feb 01.

2520

Cheffins, Cambridge. Staffordshire Dalmatian with gilt locket and chain, c1900, 12.75cm high. £110. Apr 01.

2521

Sworders, Stansted Mount-fitchet. Japanese ginger jar, with internal and outer lid, 12in. £110. Apr 01.

2522

Richard Wintertons, Burton on Trent. 19thC Coalport jug, transferred floral sprays, 22cm high. £110. Jan 02.

2523

Biddle & Webb, Birmingham. Royal Doulton character jug of Gulliver. £110. Feb 02.

2524

Ambrose, Loughton. Pair of Zsolnay Pecs moulded leaf shaped dishes with floral and gilt decoration, and boat shaped bowl. £110. Feb 02.

2525

Hamptons, Godalming. Large flatback/spill vase modelled as an elegant farmer and his wife, 40cm. £110. May 02.

2526

Thos Mawer & Son, Lincoln. Charlotte Rhead. Jug, 20cm high, printed Crown Ducal mark and hand written signature. £110. Apr 02.

2527

Ambrose, Loughton. Limoges porcelain 18 piece dessert set, painted transfers. £110. Feb 02.

2528

Locke & England, Leamington Spa. Three Beswick Beatrix Potter figures. £110. Dec 02.

2529

Gorringes, Lewes. Early 19thC Sunderland lustre water jug, moulded hunting scene, (af) and similar jug, 5in. £110. Apr 01.

2530

Gorringes, Lewes. Royal Worcester blush porcelain jug with basket body applied with a lizard and branch handle, No. 1714, 5.75in. £110. Apr 01.

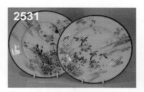

2531

Sworders, Stansted Mount-fitchet. Pair of Kutani plates decorated with flowers and birds, 8.25in. £110. July 02.

2532

Richard Wintertons, Burton on Trent. c1815 Spode soap box. £110. Oct 02.

2533

Ambrose, Loughton. Late 19thC Chinese u/g blue ginger jar, foliate scroll deco., 26cm. £110. Feb 02.

Hammer Price £110

2534

Sworders, Stansted Mount-fitchet. Pair of porcelain lobster match holders, tallest 6in high. £110. Apr 01.

2535

Sworders, Stansted Mount-fitchet. Various Newhall tea bowls, cups and saucers. (11) £110. July 01.

2536

Amersham Auction Rooms, Bucks. Early 20thC Belleek porcelain four piece tea set, bears black backstamps. £110. June 02.

2537

Sworders, Stansted Mount-fitchet. Pair Persian pottery tiles with coloured birds and flower decoration, each 13 x 9.5in. £110. July 01.

2538

Gorringes, Lewes. 19thC Staffs bust of Wesley, 7.5in. £110. Apr 01.

2539

Locke & England, Leamington Spa. Set of 3 19thC pottery jugs, prob. Davenport, largest 13cm. (discoloured) £110. May 03.

Hammer Prices £110-£100

2540

Tring Market Auctions, Herts. 19thC Coalport inkstand, 4in, hairline cracks. £110. Nov 02.

2541

Gammon, Guildford. Delft pottery charger painted with central garden, 18thC, 13.5in dia. £110. Feb 03.

2542

Tring Market Auctions, Herts. 19thC Wedgwood amphora vase, 7in. £110. Nov 02.

2543

Amersham Auction Rooms, Bucks. 1930s Art Deco china coffee set, (14). £110. Oct 03.

2544

Clarke Gammon, Guildford. Tin glazed pottery charger, 19thC, 13.75in, and a later Italian charger. £110. Feb 03.

2545

Denhams, Warnham. Large Royal Doulton character jug, Santa Claus with toy sack handle, D6690. £110. Aug 03.

2546

Gorringes, Lewes. Moorcroft anemone bowl, blue monogram and incised signature mark, 6.5in. £100. Apr 00.

2547

Lambert & Foster, Tenterden. Late 19thC Staffordshire blue and white meat dish, 16.5 x 13.5in. £100. Aug 99.

2548

Dee, Atkinson & Harrison, Driffield. Early 19thC Staffordshire cottage, c1830, 4.5in high. £100. Dec 00.

2549

Gorringes, Lewes. Clarice Cliff style Hollyhocks pattern sugar sifter, unmarked, 5in. £100. July 00.

2550

Edgar Horn, Eastbourne. Royal Doulton 'Winston S Churchill, HN3433. £100. Dec 99.

2551

Andrew Hartley, Ilkley. Early 19thC pearlware sauce boat, blue printed with classical figures, 8in. £100. Feb 00.

2552

Gorringes, Lewes. Clarice Cliff Gayday pattern bowl, 7.25in. £100. June 01.

2553

Woolley & Wallis, Salisbury. Chinese tureen and cover with a matched underdish and a Chinese oval dish, all decorated with pagoda landscapes, all Qianlong, 1736-95, 38.5cm max. (all damaged) £100. Sep 00.

2554

Lambert & Foster, Tenterden. Sunderland copper lustre jug, three flower spray panels, 6in high. £100. Aug 99.

2555

Woolley & Wallis, Salisbury. Chinese vase with two panels of auspicious objects, 17cm, and a blue and white cup, both 18thC. £100. Sep 00.

2556

Andrew Hartley, Ilkley. Pair 19thC Continental porcelain 'Schneeballen' vases, 13.75in. £100. Aug 00.

2557

Woolley & Wallis, Salisbury. Chinese sparrow beak jug, decorated with a pavilion in a rocky landscape, early 18thC, 12cm. £100. Sep 00.

2558

Lambert & Foster, Tenterden. Pair of R. Doulton stoneware vases, incised 8079, initials E.B., 7in high. £100. Apr 01.

2559

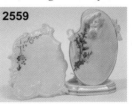

Gorringes, Lewes. Carltonware menu holder and another figural menu holder. £100. Sep 00.

2560

Gorringes, Lewes. Newhall cream jug, floral decoration, 4in. £100. Sep 00.

2561

Gorringes, Lewes. Royal Worcester floral decorated blush porcelain vase, G70, 5in. £100. June 00.

2562

Gorringes, Lewes. Clarice Cliff Kelverne pattern sugar sifter, 5in. £100. Sep 00.

2563

Woolley & Wallis, Salisbury. Plymouth style baluster mug, '2,4' mark, 19thC, 14cm. (tiny rim chip) £100. Sep 00.

2564

Wintertons Ltd, Lichfield. Beswick Guernsey bull, 'CH Sabrina's Sir Richmond 14th'. £100. Nov 00.

2565

Woolley & Wallis, Salisbury. Chinese bactrian camel, Tang dynasty, 618-906AD, 59cm. (restored) £100. Sep 00.

2566

Gorringes, Lewes. Poole vase with daffodil and tulip, 9.5in. £100. July 00.

108

2567

Woolley & Wallis, Salisbury. Seven Continental porcelain figures, various marks, late 19thC and early 20thC, 18cm tallest. £100. Sep 00.

2568

Gorringes, Lewes. Clarice Cliff 'My Garden' sugar sifter, 5.5in. £100. Sep 00.

2569

Amersham Auction Rooms, Bucks. Mid Victorian Staffs pottery model of an English setter, 11in. £100. June 01.

The numbering system aids the editorial analysis at the beginning of each section as well as providing a reader reference.

2570

Gorringes, Lewes. Victorian porcelain inkstand with butterflies, 7in. £100. Sep 00.

2571

Hamptons, Godalming. Meissen cabinet cup/saucer, late 19thC, u/g blue X swords mark, 13cm. £100. Nov 01.

2572

Gorringes, Lewes. Victorian Staffordshire spill vase group, 8.5in. £100. Sep 00.

2573

Lambert & Foster, Tenterden. Poole Pottery, The Queen's Silver Jubilee 1952-1977 plate No. 143, Ltd. Edn. of 250, by Tony Morris, box and certificate. £100. Feb 02.

2574

Crows, Dorking. Meissen style guinea fowl. £100. Aug 01.

2575

Dee, Atkinson & Harrison, Driffield. Royal Doulton, Bess, HN2002, designed by Leslie Haradine 1947-1969, 7.5in. £100. Apr 01.

2576

Gorringes, Lewes. Dresden pug dog, 5in. £100. Oct 00.

2577

Sworders, Stansted Mountfitchet. Three Staffs jugs, one treacle glazed, one painted, one transfer printed, 19thC, highest 9.75in. £100. Oct 01.

2578

Sworders, Stansted Mountfitchet. Two pottery tobacco jars, each of an Abbe, with detachable hats. (possibly by B. Bloch of Hohenstein in Bohemia) £100. Apr 01.

2579

Sworders, Stansted Mountfitchet. Pair of 19thC childs plates, printed and enamelled 'Robinson Crusoe' centres, 7in. £100. Apr 01.

2580

Dee, Atkinson & Harrison, Driffield. Two early 19thC Staffordshire spill vases, a country couple with a dog by their feet, 6.5in and three Regency children reading a book, 6in. £100. Apr 01.

2581

Gorringes, Lewes. 19thC Staffordshire model of a cat with sponged decoration, 3.5in. £100. Sep 00.

Hammer Price £100

2582

Dee, Atkinson & Harrison, Driffield. Victorian commemorative jar transfer printed, painted flags and 'Britannia Rules the Waves', 5in dia., and commemorative Boer War mug by Linley Sambourne, 4.5in. £100. Apr 01.

2583

Sworders, Stansted Mountfitchet. Victorian pottery bowl, 12in. £100. Apr 01.

2584

Gorringes, Lewes. 20thC Shelley oval 'Baby's Plate' decorated with children and a poem, 8.5in and another similar. £100. Feb 01.

2585

Gorringes, Lewes. Royal Copenhagen crab tray, 2465. £100. Feb 01.

2586

Hamptons, Godalming. 'Balance of Payments' earthenware plate by Wallis Gimson and Co, Rd No. 63164, 25cm. £100. Nov 01.

2587

Sworders, Stansted Mountfitchet. Victorian stoneware jardiniere with putti supports, 11in high. £100. Apr 01.

2588

Crows, Dorking. Susie Cooper floral decorated dinner service. £100. July 01.

2589

Cheffins, Cambridge. Early 19thC Paris Angouleme Sprig Butter Dish, M stencilled in red, 24cm. £100. Dec 00.

2590

Gorringes, Lewes. Pair of Clarice Cliff dwarf candlesticks with printed paisley bands on mustard grounds, 3in. £100. Dec 00.

2591

Gorringes, Lewes. Worcester bowl with fence and Chinese landscape patterns, c1765, 6in. £100. Mar 01.

2592

Sworders, Stansted Mountfitchet. Five continental porcelain pin cushion dolls. £100. Apr 01.

2593

Gorringes, Lewes. Early 19thC Continental porcelain figure of a classical man standing beside an eagle, 9in £100. Apr 01.

Hammer Price £100

2594

Gorringes, Lewes. Clarice Cliff 'My Garden' jardiniere with floral handles, 6in. £100. Mar 01.

2595

Gorringes, Lewes. Early 19thC Staffordshire figure of a rogue in salmon pink cloak, 7in. £100. Mar 01.

2596

Thos Mawer & Son, Lincoln. 19thC Staffs pen holder as a greyhound, 14cm long. (chip to ear) £100. Apr 02.

2597

Sworders, Stansted Mountfitchet. 19thC Imari bowl, 5.5in high. (cracks to base) £100. Apr 01.

2598

Denhams, Warnham, Sussex. Victorian Royal Worcester porcelain candle snuffer as an owl with night cap, 3in, chip to base. £100. Aug 03.

2599

Canterbury Auc. Galleries, Kent. 19thC Minton majolica charger, 14in, imp'd mark, date code indistinct, crack, rim damage. £100. Aug 02.

2600

Gorringes, Lewes. 19thC Staffordshire church spill vase, 9in and a figure of a Scotsman, 9in. £100. Apr 01.

2601

Tring Market Auctions, Herts. 18thC Persian dish with stylised flowers and scrolling leaves surrounding a floral motif, 15in. af. £100. May 02.

2602

Tring Market Auctions, Herts. Royal Worcester jug of blush apricot ground, shape No. 1116, spout restored, year mks. for 1903, 6in. £100. Jan 03.

2603

Sworders, Stansted Mountfitchet. Three Victorian white stoneware relief moulded jugs, incl: The sacrifice of Iphigeniea by SM. Bevington, all with pewter lids, tallest 9.5in. £100. July 01.

2604

Thos Mawer & Son, Lincoln. Glazed terracotta figure of a lady making pillow lace, 22cm high. £100. Apr 02.

2605

Gorringes, Lewes. Two small Staffordshire dogs, figure and 2 other items. £100. Apr 01.

2606

Sworders, Stansted Mountfitchet. 19thC parian ware bust of a classical man, 9in high. (Originally on a stand) £100. July 01.

2607

Gorringes, Lewes. Staffs double sided Gin and Water figure. £100. Mar 01.

2608

Gorringes, Lewes. Carltonware vase, chinoiserie decoration of gilded pagodas on a mottled blue ground, 9.5in. £100. Mar 01.

2609

John Taylors, Louth. Staffordshire greyhound pen stand. £100. July 02.

2610

Gorringes, Lewes. Goss novelty ashtray entitled 'That The One Daddy Told Nurse', 3in and model of Shakespeare's House, 3in. £100. Apr 01.

2611

Thos Mawer & Son, Lincoln. Clarice Cliff. 'Autumn', Fantasque Bizarre bowl, 20.5cm. (wear) £100. Apr 02.

2612

Locke & England, Leamington Spa. Three porcelain and gilt bronze floral sculptures by R van Ruyckevelt, marble plinths titled St Denis, Languedoc and Argenteuil. £100. Jan 03.

2613

Andrew Hartley, Ilkley. 19thC Pearlware plate, 'Mausoleum of Sultan Purveiz near Allahabad' poss. Herculaneum, 9.75in. £100. Feb 03.

2614

Sworders, Stansted Mountfitchet. Pearlware sugar sifter. 5.75in. £100. July 01.

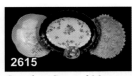

2615

Sworders, Stansted Mountfitchet. Three R. Worcester plates, W9130A, a Grainger Worcester moulded plate, a saucer painted with fruits and oval dish. (6) £100. July 01.

2616

Sworders, Stansted Mountfitchet. Japanese plate with gilt and enamel decoration, signed, 17.5in. £100. July 01.

2617

Sworders, Stansted Mountfitchet. 19thC blue and white ginger jar, and two other oriental bowls. £100. July 01.

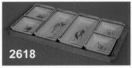

2618

W & H Peacock, Bedford. Susie Cooper entree dish. £100. Dec 02.

2619

Andrew Hartley, Ilkley. Samson porcelain teacup and saucer, copying Worcester's Lord Henry Thyme pattern, late 19thC. £100. Apr 03.

2620

Andrew Hartley, Ilkley. Staffs pottery spill vase of harvester and his companion, 19thC, 9in. £100. Feb 03.

Sample Analysis

The under £100 price range is smaller in size than previous sections. This leads us automatically to the notion of multiple lots where the auctioneer groups similar cheaper items together and sells them as one lot, saving time and costs. Another recurring theme in this price range will be damaged, restored or reproduction lots.

You can still buy eighteenth century lots here although you might expect that quite a number of these pieces will be quite mundane and commonplace. Check through page 112 for examples. The eighteenth century Delft brick at 2626 is an exception. The Rodgers pearlware blue and white plates are standard, see 2623 and 2662, as is the Christian's Liverpool cup at 2634 although these lots are good collectors' pieces. The Royal Crown Derby Japan pattern vase at 2648 represents a ubiquitous porcelain group. Check out the *Index*. Whilst holding its price in today's market it doesn't have the huge following of twenty years ago. No doubt someone may object to this analysis. Certainly prices are flat and probably too high.

Regarding the theme of mixed lots, there are plenty in evidence in these pages. Check out examples 2641, 2665, 2671 and 2676. Mixed lots are a mixed blessing and we may be able to pick up on the best and worst of these as we progress. For example 2676 and 2691 are acceptable to collectors of early tea wares but do beware of damage and check particularly for cracks by tapping items with a fingernail! The Booths at 2690 is currently popular and probably a good buy, but lot 2710 has no theme whatsoever and very unlikely ever to yield a profit or show investment potential. Better to save your money and put it into a more astute purchase. If your kitchen has the right ambience you could opt for something like the three 2000-year-old Chinese granary jars standing almost 12in high which are quite unusual and a good talking point. See 2651 on page 113. You could become the envy of your friends and it is almost certain that they will show a good profit if you sell on.

We have several examples of Chameleon Ware in this volume. See 2678 and 2687 on page 114. These wares are not that common and fetch good prices at this level. The maker was George Clews operating at the Brownhills Pottery at Tunstall between 1906 and 1961. Check the *Index* for further Chameleon Ware lots.

The Satsuma vase at 2694 looks familiar and there it is again at 2805! Both images show the same lot number so are undoubtedly the same vase. The 3000 plus images in this book have been checked and re-checked for every possible type of error. This just goes to show that neither an auction catalogue, nor auction house post-sale press releases, nor indeed a work of this kind, which relies on information from hundreds of sources can offer definitively, 100% accuracy. These vases have been left in place to stress this point.

The Rudoltstadt Volkstedt figures on page 114 at 2702 could belong to a whole range of factories operating over a considerable period. If buying continental porcelain, ensure you have the Ludwig Danckert *Directory of European Porcelain*. It is worth its weight in gold!

On page 115, the Bretby kitten wasn't particularly cheap at £80, but three years later, has it shown any investment 'profit'? Check out the prices of Chinese seventeenth or eighteenth century pieces also on page 115, but note they are damaged or have missing parts. Once again, a continental hard-paste baluster mug with the 2,4 mark, which we last came across on page 108, appears again on page 115. This was discussed in the previous analysis. It is essential that the student of ceramics learns to identify 'pastes' i.e. the various porcelain bodies. Local ceramics clubs and groups offer an answer. Here you can rub shoulders with experts, and professionals are hired to give talks and demonstrations in an absorbing hands-on environment. Without years of knowledge-building experiences at *Canterbury Ceramics Circle* meetings, the Editor could not possibly have presented this book.

Damage is a problem when buying second-hand. The Staffordshire figure at 2717 is straightforward. It is early and would have been much more money if perfect. But what if damage or restoration is found after you have bought? Auctions deal with this in their terms and conditions. Some auctions will rescind a sale, within for example fourteen days, if you can prove a lot was mis-described in the catalogue.

The pearlware font on page 116 (2735) is a survivor! This is almost certain to increase in value and was a good buy at £80. As were five early nineteenth century pearlware plates averaging only £16 each. See 2749. It is the Editor's opinion that the mid eighteenth century Meissen miniature model of a lady could turn out to be worth a great deal more than the £80 hammer paid in September 2002. This is my best buy on page 116, although the charming Royal Dux children group at 2745 was inexpensive. Children in ceramics are as popular as animals. Eighteenth century Worcester/Caughley fisherman pattern lots keep cropping up: standard pieces at standard prices which can offer only long term investment. The Beswick figures are no different. Two items on page 117 are of interest. The Davenport caneware preserve pot at 2783 is exceedingly rare and in my opinion should have fetched at least several hundred pounds. Terry Lockett the well-known Davenport collector has an example but the Editor doesn't know of any other similar preserve pot. Also rare is the Lloyd's spill vase (probably c1830-40) at 2781. We last come across Lloyds on page 25. Do you recall the pair of porcelain lions (367) which fetched £1,900? The Editor would welcome opinions from those with specialist knowledge on these two subjects.

Is the Chinese Emperor at 2824 from antiquity? Surely £200-£300 would be nearer the mark? The Delft plate and the Delft tile on page 121 (2871, 2883) show the lower end of the Delft range. The Mason's ironstone jug at 2897 fetched a standard price at £55 but is it a common or a rare pattern? And how common is the Rodgers zebra pattern plate on page122? Books answer questions. Do you remember the Chinese hawks on page 9 which fetched £25,000? Do you think the pair of parrots at 2920 are old or new? The cradle group at 2903 will almost certainly be early. £55 is modest. Such items can retail for a couple of hundred. On page 123 you can pick up the Guinness and breweriana trail. See 2929 and 2931. Compare also the prices of Pendelfin, Beatrix Potter and Hummel, against a rare eighteenth/nineteenth century pottery lion. Which is the better buy? Are the pair of Chinese kylin at 2944 new or old? Better to pay £50 for the Doulton flambe vase at 2932! See also the Caughley and Worcester damaged blue and white at 2943. Does it make more sense to buy the less common, undamaged, Newhall trio of 'boy in the window' pattern at 2974 on page 124? And could you buy the Beswick courting couple at 2951 for only £40 today? Finally on page 126 you will have to ask yourself, are these original Sylvac pieces or are they from the later output? Only buy Sylvac from reputable Sylvac specialist dealers. Are the pair of German porcelain prams modern? You would be better off buying the genuine early nineteenth century tureen or the eighteenth century Worcester cup.

Hammer Prices £95-£90

2621

Gorringes, Lewes. 19thC Yorkshire pig money box, 5in. £95. Apr 00.

2622

Gorringes, Lewes. Brownfields stoneware fruit bowl and 12 matching bowls in 2 sizes. £95. Apr 00.

2623

Gorringes, Lewes. Early 19thC John Rogers & Son plate, camel in Eastern landscape, 9.75in. £95. Apr 00.

2624

Woolley & Wallis, Salisbury. Chamberlain's pastille burner, painted mark, 1st half 19thC, 12.5cm. chips. £95. Sep 00.

2625

W & H Peacock, Bedford. Victorian Staffordshire figure of 2 children with a spaniel and bird. £95. July 03.

112

2626

Gorringes, Lewes. 18thC Delft flower brick painted with a jester, 5in. £95. Oct 00.

2627

Amersham Auction Rooms, Bucks. Late Victorian china pot, 13in high. £95. Sep 01.

2628

Clarke Gammon, Guildford, Surrey. Royal Doulton figure. £95. Sep 01.

2629

Gorringes, Lewes. Pair of Capodimonte figures, 7.5in. (one restored) £95. Feb 01.

2630

Locke & England, Leamington Spa. Coalport pot pourri, oval reserves of Loch Katrine, 17cm, printed mks. £95. Oct 03.

2631

Sworders, Stansted Mountfitchet. 8 stoneware/pottery items incl. a tiny Doulton jug, largest 2.5in. £95. Apr 01.

2632

Gorringes, Lewes. French art deco brass mounted comport with a trailed blue glaze, 15in and a similar slender vase, 15in. £95. Mar 01.

2633

Gorringes, Lewes. Early 19thC Derby sucrier and cover, 4.5in. £95. Mar 01.

2634

Andrew Hartley, Ilkley. Christian's Liverpool porcelain coffee cup, £95. Apr 03.

2635

Hamptons, Godalming. Pearlware mug, c1820, 'My Dear Boy' above floral sprigs, 3.5in high. (chipped and cracked) £95. July 02.

2636

Sworders, Stansted Mountfitchet. 5 Victorian stoneware relief moulded jugs incl: 'Naomi' by Samuel Alcock & Co, (one repaired and one with star crack to base) tallest 9in high. £95. July 01.

2637

Ambrose, Loughton. Collection of porcelain sets and part sets 'Bonzo Dog' cruets. (11) £95. Mar 2002.

2638

Gorringes, Lewes. Fieldings Crown Devon musical mug with Auld Lang Syne, 6in. £95. Apr 01.

2639

Sworders, Stansted Mountfitchet. 19thC copper lustre jug, titled 'Charity', 5.5in high and a copper lustre teapot with applied figures, 5in high. £95. Apr 01.

2640

Andrew Hartley, Ilkley. Chelsea Derby tea bowl, late 18thC and a Worcester tea bowl printed in black with seated lovers on a terrace. £95. Feb 03.

2641

Sworders, Stansted Mountfitchet. Famille Verte plaque, and a Chinese plate, plaque 9.5in dia. £95. July 01.

2642

Gorringes, Lewes. Early 19thC Staffordshire youth with cup and bunch of grapes, 7.5in. £95. Mar 01.

2643

Amersham Auction Rooms, Bucks. 19thC Staffs pottery group, 5.75in. £95. Sep 02.

2644

Gorringes, Lewes. Moorcroft vase with hibiscus, label to base, 4.75in. £95. Sep 00.

2645

Denhams, Warnham, Sussex. Continental porcelain snow leopard, 7in. £90. Oct 03.

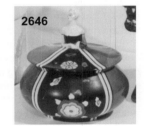

2646

Andrew Hartley, Ilkley. Carltonware pottery powder bowl, 5.75in. £90. Feb 00.

2647

Gorringes, Lewes. Early 19thC Derby vase, (handles restored) 6.5in. £90. Apr 00.

2648

Phillips, Bath. Royal Crown Derby vase, with rich Japan pattern, no 1474, printed marks, 9.5cm. £90. May 00.

2649

Gorringes, Lewes. 19thC J. D. Baxter plate with a Scottish shepherd, 10in and Whampoa pattern plate. (2) £90. Apr 00.

2650

Gorringes, Lewes. Victorian Staffordshire clock group of a highland couple, 14in. (head restored) £90. July 00.

2651

Woolley & Wallis, Salisbury. 3 similar Chinese pottery brown glazed granary jars, each standing on 3 feet, Han dynasty, 206BC - 220AD, 29cm approx. £90. Sep 00.

> The illustrations in these pages are in descending price order. The price range is indicated at the top of each page.

2652

Gorringes, Lewes. Victorian Staffordshire figure of a sailor, 9in. £90. Mar 01.

2653

Richard Winterton, Burton on Trent. Ruskin crystaline glaze vase, c1930, imp'd 'Ruskin' mark, 13cm. £90. Dec 01.

2654

Andrew Hartley, Ilkley. Neale & Co creamware tureen on stand, brown lid banding, 7.5in wide. £90. Aug 00.

2655

Gorringes, Lewes. Maling lustre bowl decorated with fruit, 8.5in. £90. July 00.

2656

Gorringes, Lewes. Graduated set of 3 19thC Continental majolica water jugs, largest 8in. £90. Mar 01.

2657

Gorringes, Lewes. Porcelain group of lovers and a dog, Continental. 5in. £90. Mar 01.

2658

Gorringes, Lewes. Moorcroft 'hibiscus' jar, (no cover) 7.5in and two similar ash trays, 4.5in. £90. Feb 01.

2659

Canterbury Auc. Galleries, Kent. Royal Worcester porcelain figure, Tuesday's Child, a young boy skating, 8in high, black printed mark with date code 1956, No. 3534. £90. Aug 02.

2660

Gorringes, Lewes. Art deco Maling bowl with geometric polychrome decoration, 10in. £90. Sep 00.

2661

Gorringes, Lewes. Wemyss tyg with flying ducks, 13in dia. af. £90. Sep 00.

2662

Andrew Hartley, Ilkley. 19thC Rogers pearlware plate, with Fallow Deer pattern, 9.75in wide. £90. Apr 01.

2663

Clarke Gammon, Guildford. Victorian pottery blue and white jug. £90. Sep 01.

2664

Sworders, Stansted Mount-fitchet. 18thC creamware plate, poss. Leeds, black transfer printed pheasant, 9.25in, (2 hair cracks) and a pottery plate. £90. Apr 01.

2665

Sworders, Stansted Mount-fitchet. K.P.M. porcelain plaque, 3.25in, another 3in, and a pot lid 'The Queen God bless her!' £90. Apr 01.

Hammer Price £90

2666

Tring Market Auctions, Herts. 19thC Staffs pastille burner, 6.5in high. af. £90. May 02.

2667

Gorringes, Lewes. Royal Worcester dish painted with apples, cherries and a strawberry, signed A. Shuck, date code 1918, 6.5in across handles. £90. Dec 00.

2668

Gorringes, Lewes. Royal Copenhagen group, Faun on a tortoise, 858. £90. Feb 01.

2669

Sworders, Stansted Mount-fitchet. Three Beswick Beatrix Potter figures, Cousin Ribby, Hunca Munca Sweeping and Lady Mouse. £90. July 01.

2670

Amersham Auction Rooms, Bucks. R. Doulton china Miss Muffet, HN1936 by L. Harradine issued 1940-1950, 5.5in. £90. Mar 02.

2671

Woolley & Wallis, Salisbury. Two porcelain trios, one bone china, Rd. mark for Brown, Westhead, Moore & Co, 1868, the other Noritake, blue factory marks. £90. Sep 2000.

2672

Gorringes, Lewes. Moorcroft magnolia pattern vase, 10.5in. £90. Feb 01.

2673

Woolley & Wallis, Salisbury. R. Doulton figure of Queen Anne, HN 3141, No. 1.102, Queens of the Realm series, and a Franklin Porcelain model of Arabella, The Waltz, both modern. £90. Sep 00.

2674

Andrew Hartley, Ilkley. Japanese porcelain vase with moulded dragon handles, 19thC, 12.25in. £90. Oct 01.

2675

Edgar Horn, Eastbourne. R. Doulton. The Home Coming, HN 3295. £90. Dec 99.

Hammer Prices £90-£85

2676

Sworders, Stansted Mount-fitchet. Spode teacup/saucer, pattern No. 2123, a Derby teacup/saucer and an English ceramic bowl. £90. July 01.

2677

Sworders, Stansted Mount-fitchet. Victorian toilet basin, floral printed, 'The Sanitas wash down closet', rim chip. £90. July 01.

2678

Potteries Specialist Auctions, Stoke. Chameleon Ware jug decorated with Flame pattern, 11/113, 9in high. £90. Mar 03.

2679

Potteries Specialist Auctions, Stoke. Pendelfin. Megan the harp rabbit, in blue, out of production. £90. Apr 03.

2680

Gorringes, Bexhill. Victorian parian, Queen Eleanor, prob. Copeland, 19.5in, formerly painted. £90. Oct 02.

2681

Locke & England, Leamington Spa. Pair of Royal Doulton stoneware vases. £90. Nov 02.

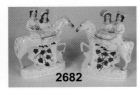

2682

Thos Mawer & Son, Lincoln. Pr. of Staffs flatbacks, Going to Market and Returning Home, 22cm. £90. Feb 03.

2683

Tring Market Auctions, Herts. Staffordshire group, young man holding a goat, a child riding on its back, 7.5in high. £90. Nov 02.

2684

Sworders, Stansted Mount-fitchet. Two white stoneware relief moulded jugs, 'The jolly toper', by W T Copeland, and another, 8in. £90. July 01.

2685

Locke & England, Leamington Spa. Lladro porcelain figure of a female seated in high backed chair, 29cm. £90. Jan 03.

2686

Tring Market Auctions, Herts. Pair of 18thC Chinese plates with pagodas, trees, rocks, 11.5in. af. £90. May 02.

2687

Potteries Specialist Auctions, Stoke. Chameleon ware vase, 65/117, 11in. £90. Mar 03.

2688

Gorringes, Lewes. 19thC Staffs figure of an elderly woman, 7in. £90. Apr 01.

2689

Gorringes, Lewes. Staffs blue and white cow creamer, 7.5in, and a later cow, 6.5in. £90. Mar 01.

2690

Sworders, Stansted Mount-fitchet. Booths 'Real Old Willow' 6 setting tea service, additional items. £85. July 01.

2691

Woolley & Wallis, Salisbury. Worcester spiral fluted tea bowl and saucer, crescent marks, and a Worcester spiral fluted coffee cup and saucer, no mark, both late 18thC. £85. Sep 00.

2692

Andrew Hartley, Ilkley. Clarice Cliff Bizarre pottery jug, Autumn Crocus, printed marks, 3.5in. £85. Apr 01.

2693

Gorringes, Lewes. German figure of a seated gentleman, 5in. af. £85. Oct 00.

2694

Biddle & Webb, Birmingham. Japanese Satsuma vase with figures engaged in building, 8.25in high. £85. Sep 01.

2695

Gorringes, Lewes. Late 19thC Sitzendorf maiden holding a posy of flowers and standing by a lamb, 9in. £85. Apr 01.

2696

Hamptons, Godalming. Prince Albert memorial jug, in violet with his portrait and Britannia, printed mark 'Albert', 19cm. £85. Nov 01.

2697

Sworders, Stansted Mount-fitchet. Pr. Samson porcelain figures of Bacchanalian Putti with goats, 3in. £85. Apr 01.

2698

Gorringes, Lewes. Two Continental porcelain slippers. £85. Mar 01.

2699

Gorringes, Lewes. Royal Worcester blush caddy, cover chipped, 4.5in. £85. Mar 01.

2700

Gorringes, Lewes. Worcester 'Royal Lily' breakfast cup/saucer, c1815. £85. Mar 01.

2701

Ambrose, Loughton. Imari ginger jar, hand-painted, phoenix, 22cm high, no lid, some cracks. £85. Mar 02.

2702

Gorringes, Lewes. Volkstedt porcelain figure of a lady, 8in and a classical lady, 8in. £85. June 00.

2703

Locke & England, Leamington Spa. R. Doulton pipe stand, top with match box mount and holes for pipes, imp'd mark and 7324, 12cm. £85. Feb 03.

2704

Locke & England, Leamington Spa. Set 4 National Westminster pigs, Mother, Father, Son and Daughter. £85. Apr 03.

2705

Andrew Hartley, Ilkley. Worcester coffee cup, reeded loop handle, underglaze fret mark, 18thC. £85. Feb 03.

Prices quoted are hammer prices which excluded the buyer's premium. Adding 15% will give an approximation to the buying price.

2706

Gorringes, Lewes. Clarice Cliff plate with landscape decoration, 9in. £85. Apr 00.

2707

Canterbury Auc. Galleries, Kent. Royal Doulton, The Orange Lady, HN1953, 8.5in, green printed mark to base, imp'd date code 4th October 1940. £80. Aug 03.

2708

Richard Wintertons, Burton on Trent. Bretby Art Pottery playful kitten. £80. Aug 00.

2709

Gorringes, Lewes. Mid Victorian porcelain christening jug with floral swags, 9.5in. £80. Apr 00.

2710

Sworders, Stansted Mountfitchet. Minton low tazza, green transfer printed gravy tureen, cover (knop repaired) stand and ladle, an Ashworth ironstone plate and a Carlton tray. (4) £80. Apr 01.

2711

Woolley & Wallis, Salisbury. 2 Chinese porcelain plaques in black/red with political propaganda, 25 x 36.5cm. £80. Sep 00.

2712

Woolley & Wallis, Salisbury. Chinese wucai vase, 19thC, 31cm. (the top reglued) £80. Sep 2000.

2713

Dockree's, Manchester. Late 18thC Newhall scalloped lozenge shaped teapot 9in wide. £80. Sep 00.

2714

Woolley & Wallis, Salisbury. Small Chinese cruet pot, two panels of watery landscapes, Kangxi, 1662-1722, 9.5cm. (the lid missing) £80. Sep 00.

2715

Woolley & Wallis, Salisbury. Japanese dish, with 3 panels of the 'three friends', Pine, Prunus and Bamboo, late 19thC, 53.8cm. £80. Sep 00.

2716

Woolley & Wallis, Salisbury. Japanese porcelain vase, with Shoki and Oni in combat, sgd., 31cm and a Fukugawa Imari vase, 14cm, late 19th/early 20thC. £80. Sep 00.

2717

Gorringes, Lewes. Early 19thC Staffs lady archer with bow and quiver, 7in. (neck restored) £80. Oct 00.

2718

John Taylors, Louth, Lincs. Chintz ware sugar pot, cake stand & jam pot. £80. Jan 01.

2719

Gorringes, Lewes. Early 19thC meat plate printed with panels of pagodas, floral ground, 17in. £80. Apr 00.

2720

Andrew Hartley, Ilkley. 19thC Sampson porcelain famille rose mug, initialled and dated 1762, 5in high. £80. Oct 99.

2721

Andrew Hartley, Ilkley. Early 19thC Spode pearlware plate, with a view of the Tiber, Rome, 9.5in. £80. Apr 01.

2722

Gorringes, Lewes. French earthenware dish moulded with Huntley & Palmers biscuits, 8in. £80. June 00.

2723

Woolley & Wallis, Salisbury. Chinese famille verte tankard, Kangxi, 1662-1722, 14cm. (cover lacking, body cracks) £80. Sep 01.

2724

Hamptons, Godalming. Royal Worcester blush ivory pot pourri, brown printed mark, shape No. 1326, date code 1903, 10cm. £80. Sep 01.

2725

Woolley & Wallis, Salisbury. Royal Doulton stoneware jug, applied Persian warriors in white bas reliefs, imp'd mark, late 19thC, 20cm. £80. Sep 00.

2726

Woolley & Wallis, Salisbury. Samson box, decorated with fish amidst water weeds and mounted on an inkwell, late 19thC, 14cm. £80. Sep 00.

2727

Gorringes, Lewes. Victorian Minton Chinese Marine pattern opaque china meat plate, 16.5in. £80. Oct 00.

2728

Trembath Welch, Great Dunmow, Essex. A c1800 Swansea crocodile patt. deep bowl, 31cm dia. £80. Nov 99.

2729

Woolley & Wallis, Salisbury. Continental porcelain mug, '2,4' mark, 19thC, 13cm. £80. Sep 00.

2730
Biddle & Webb, Birmingham. Whieldon type pottery frog, 3.5in long. (s/d) £80. Sep 01.

2731
Gorringes, Lewes. Majolica 19thC Continental jardiniere, 9.5in. £80. Dec 00.

2732
Gorringes, Lewes. Clarice Cliff dish with a blossoming tree, 9in. £80. Dec 00.

2733
Sworders, Stansted Mountfitchet. Rhenish blue and grey salt glazed stoneware bird whistle, 4in. £80. Apr 01.

2734
John Taylors, Louth. Ridgeways 'Homemaker' tureens, plates. £80. Feb 01.

2735
Ambrose, Loughton. Staffs pearlware font, figure of Christ surrounded by angels, 44.5cm. £80. Feb 02.

2736

Gorringes, Lewes. Dresden quatre lobed cabinet cup and saucer, fete gallant panels, yellow ground. £80. Feb 01.

2737
Gorringes, Lewes. Pair of 19thC jasper urn shape vases, pierced covers, 6.75in. (one heavily restored) £80. Feb 01.

2738

Thos Mawer & Son, Lincoln. Clarice Cliff. 'Viscaria', bowl printed factory marks, 22cm dia. £80. Apr 02.

2739
Gorringes, Lewes. Macintyre vesta holder with armorial of 'The Buffs', 3in. £80. Feb 01.

2740

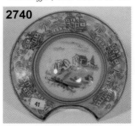

Thos Mawer & Son, Lincoln. Tin glazed barbers bowl with blue buildings, trees and bridges, 26cm. £80. Apr 02.

2741
Tring Market Auctions, Herts. Early Cantonese vase, incised and enamelled decoration, handles slightly af, 9.25in high. £80. Sep 02.

2742

Locke & England, Leamington Spa. 19thC Parian ware blue painted relief moulded jug of Venus rising from the waves, reg. mk. for Charles Meigh, 1856, 23cm. £80. Sep 02.

2743

Gorringes, Lewes. Early 19thC Staffordshire figure of a lady holding a basket of flowers, 7.5in. £80. Mar 01.

2744
Tring Market Auctions, Herts. Pair of Continental faience bowls, one with a woman and a church, other with a man and castle, bases marked 'N' in blue, 4in dia. £80. May 02.

2745

Thos Mawer & Son, Lincoln. Royal Dux Bohemia 1590, posy holder figure group, 28cm high. £80. Nov 02.

2746
Andrew Hartley, Ilkley. Staffs pottery Prince Albert, 19thC, 10.25in. £80. Feb 03.

2747

Woolley & Wallis, Salisbury. Small white glazed Meissen model of a lady, mid 18thC, 6cm. (chips) £80. Sep 00.

2748

Thos Mawer & Son, Lincoln. 19thC cheese bell and stand, 28cm high, impressed mark 1882 HO. £80. Feb 03.

2749

Andrew Hartley, Ilkley. Set of three 19thC Spode pearlware plates with an Arcadian landscape, 8.25in and a pair of similar Spode plates, Italian pattern 8.5in. £80. Aug 00.

2750

Hamptons, Godalming. Paragon china coronation plate, with The Royal Coat of Arms, printed marks, 26.7cm. £80. Nov 01.

2751
Andrew Hartley, Ilkley. Staffs pottery group of a couple with a deer by a tree, 19thC, 7in high. £80. Feb 03.

2752
Trembath Welch, Great Dunmow, Essex. Late 19thC Doulton Burslem moulded china jug with a hunting scene, 14cm. £75. Nov 99.

2753
Gorringes, Lewes. Clarice Cliff Viscaria pattern pot, 31in. £75. July 00.

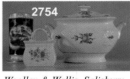

2754
Woolley & Wallis, Salisbury. English porcelain, a spill vase, 10.5cm, (restored) a small basket 5.5cm long and a sugar bowl, pattern No 13, 1st half 19thC. £75. Sep 00.

2755
Sworders, Stansted Mountfitchet. Two Wedgwood Keith Murray cream tankards, with blue printed marks, 12.2cm. £75. Oct 03.

2756
Gorringes, Lewes. Amherst Japan pattern bowl with floral decoration, 10.5in. £75. Apr 00.

2757
Amersham A. Rooms, Bucks. Early 19thC Wedgwood yellow stoneware teapot, lid finial fashioned as a wheatsheaf, imp'd. £75. Sep 03.

2758

Woolley & Wallis, Salisbury. Parian pot pourri, 'Copeland' impressed, 2nd half 19thC, 10cm. £75. Sep 00.

2759

Gorringes, Lewes. Set of three 19thC Copeland plates, 10in. £75. Apr 00.

2760

Amersham Auction Rooms, Bucks. Late 18thC Worcester porcelain bowl, in cobalt blue, 7.5in. £75. Aug 02.

2761

Sworders, Stansted Mount-fitchet. Two Beswick Beatrix Potter figures, 'Miss Moppet' & 'Anna Maria'. £75. July 01.

The numbering system aids the editorial analysis at the beginning of each section as well as providing a reader reference.

2762

Edgar Horn, Eastbourne. Royal Doulton 'Welcome Home' HN3299. £75. Dec 99.

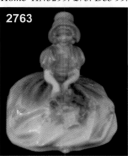

2763

Sworders, Stansted Mount-fitchet. R. Doulton 'Monica' HN1467, 4.25in. £75. July 01.

2764

Gorringes, Lewes. Victorian stone china meat plate, 15.5in & a similar plate. £75. July 00.

2765

Sworders, Stansted Mount-fitchet. Royal Worcester plate, 6in. £75. May 01.

2766

Gorringes, Lewes. Rye pottery mug with raspberries in relief and a Grays Pottery silver lustre jug. £75. Sep 00.

2767

Lambert & Foster, Tenterden. Royal Copenhagen figure of 'Perch' No. 1138, 8in x 3.5in high. £75, Dec 02.

2768

Sworders, Stansted Mount-fitchet. Victorian toilet bowl, by Stock Sons & Taylor, Birmingham. Rd. No. 19753. (poor condition) £75. Apr 01.

2769

Gorringes, Lewes. Early 20thC Dresden vase, 7in. £75. Mar 01.

2770

Sworders, Stansted Mount-fitchet. Graingers Worcester dolphin and shell stand, no. 49/G6021, 4.5in high and a Royal Worcester shell dish, no. G172. £75. Apr 01.

2771

Sworders, Stansted Mount-fitchet. Mettlach Art Nouveau stein, and another, approx 7.5in high. £75. Apr 01.

2772

Gorringes, Lewes. Victorian commemorative jubilee plate, 9.5in and an Edward VII coronation mug, 3.5in. £75. Oct 01.

2773

Locke & England, Leamington Spa. Royal Doulton figure 'A Gentleman from Williamsburg', HN 2227, 17cm. £75. Apr 03.

2774

Cheffins, Cambridge. Mid 20thC Carlton ware sugar caster modelled as a pixie cottage, 13.5cm. £75. Sep 01.

2775

Amersham Auction Rooms, Bucks. Clarice Cliff 'China Harvest' vase, handle as fruit, printed Newport backstamp, 13in wide. £75. June 02.

2776

Sworders, Stansted Mount-fitchet. Three Beswick Beatrix Potter figures, Cecily Parsley, Ribby and Mrs Flopsy Bunny. £75. July 01.

2777

Sworders, Stansted Mount-fitchet. 19thC Imari plate, 14in dia. (chip) £75. Apr 01.

2778

Locke & England, Leamington Spa. Early 19thC creamware plate, with poem in Dutch and inscribed H C Swart, 1813, 25.5cm dia. £75. Jan 03.

2779

Locke & England, Leamington Spa. Two T. G. Green Church Gresley pottery pudding basins. £75. Dec 02.

2780

Woolley & Wallis, Salisbury. Staffordshire spaniel, mid 19thC, 8cm. (re-glued to the base, small chip) £75. Sep 00.

2781

Andrew Hartley, Ilkley. Lloyds porcelain spill vase as a pair of swans with chickens, 19thC, 4.5in. £75. Feb 03.

2782

Lambert & Foster, Tenterden. German porcelain 'Shoe' wall pocket, cherub on toe, with roses & leaves, 9in, AF to (bocage). £75. Aug 99.

2783

Amersham Auction Rooms, Bucks. Late 18th/19thC Davenport, biscuit fired, tan coloured preserve pot and cover, allover basketweave, integral saucer base bears impressed stamp for 1793-1810. £75. Sep 03.

2784

Gorringes, Lewes. 19thC Delft vase with lovers in a landscape, marked AO, 19in. (chip and crack) £75. July 00.

2785

Locke & England, Leamington Spa. Royal Doulton figure, The Old Balloon Seller, HN 1315, 19cm. £75. Apr 03.

117

Hammer Prices £75-£70

2786
Thos Mawer & Son, Lincoln. Pr. early 19thC Staffs brown transfer plates, military sketches, maker SH & Co, c1830, 27cm. £75. Feb 03.

2787
Sworders, Stansted Mount-fitchet. 2 early 19thC pottery plates, and a Davenport plate with enamel floral sprays, 10in. (3) £75. July 01.

2788
Potteries Specialist Auctions, Stoke. Royal Doulton jug, Chelsea Pensioner, D6817. £72. Mar 03.

2789
Cheffins, Cambridge. Mid 20thC Hummel type bell boy cruet, inscribed Excelsior, suitcase pepper and salt, blue V mark, 12.5cm. £70. Dec 00.

2790
Gorringes, Lewes, Sussex. Beswick Jemima Puddleduck naturalistic lamp base, 7in. £70. Feb 2001.

2791
Lambert & Foster, Tenterden, Kent. Beswick 'Dachsund', 13in x 10.5in. £70. Aug 2001.

2792
Gorringes, Lewes, Sussex. Moorcroft lily ashtray, 4.5in. £70. June 2000.

2793
Gorringes, Lewes, Sussex. Royal Worcester blush porcelain tyg with flowers, 2.25in. £70. Sep 2000.

2794
Dee, Atkinson & Harrison, Driffield. Shelley part tea set, melody patt., Rd No 823343. (16) £70. Dec 00.

2795
Woolley & Wallis, Salisbury. Majolica oval jardiniere, 353 moulded mark, late 19thC, 38cm. £70. Sep 00.

2796
Gorringes, Lewes, Sussex. R. Worcester Crown ware lustre vase, 5in. £70. June 00.

2797
Hamptons, Godalming. Paragon china silver jubilee loving mug, Royal coat of Arms, portrait and flags, gilt handles, printed marks, 13cm, No 77 of 750. £70. Nov 01.

2798
Gorringes, Lewes. Worcester dish with exotic birds on the branches of a tree, crescent mark, 4.75in. £70. Sep 00.

2799
Gorringes, Lewes. Hummel figure, The Photographer. £70. Oct 00.

2800
Gorringes, Lewes. 19thC willow pattern chestnut basket, 10in. £70. Oct 00.

2801
Gorringes, Lewes. Modern shaped teapot, Golly playing cricket, 8in. £70. Oct 00.

2802
Gorringes, Lewes. Royal Doulton vase, fruit on a blue ground, 6in. £70. June 00.

2803
Wintertons Ltd, Lichfield. Beswick polled Hereford bull. £70. Nov 00.

2804
Andrew Hartley, Ilkley. Early 19thC Spode pearlware plate, with a castle in a chinoiserie landscape, 9.75in and an 18thC Spode plate and dish. (3) £70. Apr 01.

2805
Biddle & Webb, Birmingham. Japanese ovoid vase with panel decoration. £70. Sep 01.

2806
Gorringes, Lewes. Royal Copenhagen figure, calf recumbent, 1072. £70. Feb 01.

2807
Sworders, Stansted Mount-fitchet. Two 19thC copper lustre jugs, 6in. £70. Apr 01.

2808
Gorringes, Lewes. Royal Crown Derby Japan pattern pot pourri, pattern No 503, 5.5in. (rim chip) £70. July 00.

2809
Sworders, Stansted Mount-fitchet. Taylor Tunnicliffe 'Greek' tobacco jar and lid. £70. Apr 01.

2810
Wintertons Ltd, Lichfield. 18thC Chinese Nankin Cargo blue/white teabowl/saucer, prunus blossom, diaper rim border. £70. Nov 01.

2811
Thos Mawer & Son, Lincoln. Vienna porcelain plate, three figures in a landscape, entitled verso 'Mione und Amor', 25cm. £70. Apr 02.

2812
Thos Mawer & Son, Lincoln. Staffs greyhound facing left, 13cm high. (minor chips to ears) £70. Apr 02.

2813
Woolley & Wallis, Salisbury. Chinese famille verte vase, figures in an interior, Kangxi, 1662-1722, 47cm. (extensively damaged) £70. Sep 00.

2814

Sworders, Stansted Mount-fitchet. Three Beswick Beatrix Potter figures, 'Fierce Bad Rabbit', 'The Old Woman who Lives in a Shoe' and 'Tommy Brock'. £70. July 01.

2815

Potteries Specialist Auctions, Stoke. Chameleon Ware squat vase with Greek Key pattern, 80/126, 7in. £70. Mar 03.

The illustrations in these pages are in descending price order. The price range is indicated at the top of each page.

2816

Thos Mawer & Son, Lincoln. Pair of Staffordshire King Charles chimney ornaments, 23cm. £70. Feb 03.

2817

Woolley & Wallis, Salisbury. Chinese famille rose teapot and cover, 18thC, 14cm. (the spout reduced) £70. Sep 00.

2818

Amersham Auction Rooms, Bucks. Late 19thC Staffs group, 13in. £70. Oct 02.

2819

Locke & England, Leamington Spa. Spode pottery 'Chinese Rose' pattern dressing table trinket set. £70. Nov 02.

2820

Thos Mawer & Son, Lincoln. Royal Crown Derby, pattern 1123, 23cm, printed mark, date cipher 1915. £70. Feb 03.

2821

Andrew Hartley, Ilkley. Staffordshire pottery figural spill vase, a stag and hound, 19thC, 9.5in. £70. Feb 03.

2822

Lambert & Foster, Tenterden. Poole Pottery vase decorated by Audrey Heckford, shape no 401, 1930/40s. £70. Dec 99.

2823

Gorringes, Lewes. Wade earthenware figure, Old Nannie, seated, wearing a pinafore, 9.5in. £70. Mar 03.

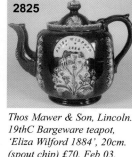

2824

Gorringes, Lewes. Chinese glazed and bisque figure of an Emperor and attendants, 7.75in. £70. Apr 01.

2825

Thos Mawer & Son, Lincoln. 19thC Bargeware teapot, 'Eliza Wilford 1884', 20cm. (spout chip) £70. Feb 03.

2826

Gorringes, Lewes. 18thC Canton sparrow beak cream jug, 4.5in. £70. July 00.

2827

Gorringes, Lewes. Burmantofts majolica novelty vase, crocodile with open mouth, 6.5in. £70. Sep 00.

2828

Gorringes, Lewes. Victorian majolica dish, moulded leaf decoration, 14in. £65. Sep 00.

2829

Woolley & Wallis, Salisbury. Delft trencher salt, 18thC, 9cm long. (rim chip 2.2 x 6mm) £65. Sep 00.

Hammer Prices £70-£65

2830

Clarke Gammon, Guildford. Clarice Cliff Aura pattern jug. £65. Sep 01.

2831

Gorringes, Lewes. Susie Cooper coffee pot, and a Victorian blue and white cream jug marked Dresden Opaque China. £65. July 00.

2832

Gorringes, Lewes. Early 19thC porcelain teapot stand, 6.5in. £65. June 00.

2833

Ambrose, Loughton. Zsolnay Pecs heart shaped dish, 13cm long. £65. Feb 02.

2834

Gorringes, Lewes. 19thC Spode stone china meat plate with flowers, rocks, bugs and a fence, 12.5in. £65. Apr 00.

2835

Sworders, Stansted Mount-fitchet. Royal Doulton 7 piece coffee set, 'Syren' D.5102, pot 8.25in high. £65. Dec 01.

2836

Gorringes, Lewes. Victorian Staffs highland lady with spaniel, 7.5in. £65. Oct 00.

2837

Wintertons Ltd, Lichfield. Beswick Friesian Bull, 'CH Coddington Hilt Bar'. £65. Nov 00.

2838

Lambert & Foster, Tenterden. Susie Cooper part tea set decorated with turquoise stars, (20) af. £65. Dec 02.

2839

Sworders, Stansted Mount-fitchet. Satsuma vase and a Satsuma Koro. (no cover) £65. July 01.

2840

Gorringes, Lewes. Moorcroft anemone pattern dish, paper label, 3.5in, an oval vesta holder with hibiscus, paper label, 3in. £65. Apr 01.

2841

Gorringes, Lewes. Plaue (German) porcelain floral dish supported by three cherubs, 5.5in. £65. Feb 01.

119

Hammer Prices £65-£60

2842

W & H Peacock, Bedford. Pair of hand painted pottery giraffe figures. £65. Dec 02.

2843

Gorringes, Lewes. Pair of Dresden porcelain busts of children, 3in. £65. Mar 01.

2844

Tring Market Auctions, Herts. 19thC faience jardiniere, one side painted with a seated lady the other boats on a lake, lion mask handles, museum rim repairs, 8.5in. £65. Sep 02.

2845

Tring Market Auctions, Herts. Pair of bisque figures of Chinese street vendors, af. 3.5in high. £65. Nov 02.

2846

Tring Market Herts. Pair of Staffs figures of Scottish gardeners, one with small chips, 9.25in. £65. Sep 02.

2847

Gorringes, Lewes. 1960s Kenneth Quick studio pottery dish with trailed decoration, 17in. (chipped) £65. Apr 01.

2848

Gorringes, Lewes. Samson famille rose armorial plate, 11in. £65. Oct 00.

2849

Amersham Auction Rooms, Bucks. Clarice Cliff pottery vase, printed Newport factory mark, 7in high. £65. Nov 02.

2850

Andrew Hartley, Ilkley. Goldscheider terracotta wall mask, stamped marks and imp'd 6764, 10in. £65. Dec 99.

2851

Lambert & Foster, Tenterden. Blue/white fruit bowl 'Abbey' design, 10.5in. £65. May 00.

2852

Gorringes, Lewes. Worcester style vase with reserve of ho-ho birds, 10in. £65. Sep 00.

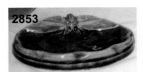

2853

Lambert & Foster, Tenterden. Royal Doulton. W H Dish, blue ground, decorated with a 'moth'. £65. June 03.

2854

Gorringes, Lewes. Royal Worcester blush porcelain shell dish. £65. June 00.

2855

Dee, Atkinson & Harrison, Driffield. Pair of blue/white Pearlware plates, c1800, 6.75in dia. £65. July 99.

2856

Gorringes, Lewes. Early 19thC child's plate, alphabet border, with a furniture removal scene. £65. Apr 00.

2857

Gorringes, Lewes. Dresden cream jug with landscaped and floral panels. £60. Sep 00.

2858

Gorringes, Lewes. Victorian parian figure of a boy skating, 9in. £60. Oct 00.

2859

Lambert & Foster, Tenterden. Noritake fruit set comprising bowl 10in, & six dishes 6.5in. £60. Aug 99.

2860

Lambert & Foster, Tenterden. Royal Worcester bamboo basket, pattern no. 858. £60. Dec 99.

2861

Lambert & Foster, Tenterden. Clarice Cliff, Newport Pottery Co, 4 plates with green border and flower and leaf design. £60. Dec 99.

2862

Gorringes, Lewes. Late 19thC French 2-handled cup and saucer with portrait medallion on royal blue ground, 5in. £60. Apr 00.

2863

Woolley & Wallis, Salisbury. Two Chinese green glazed pottery tilework figures, the longest 37cm, both damaged. £60. Sep 00.

2864

Woolley & Wallis, Salisbury. English bone china dessert service, pattern No 366, c1830-40. (some rubbing) £60. Sep 00.

2865

Woolley & Wallis, Salisbury. Chinese polychrome European subject sparrow beak jug, a Dutchman, his wife and a deer, 18thC, 9cm. (cover lacking) £60. Sep 00.

2866

Woolley & Wallis, Salisbury. Three Pilkington's Lancastrian bowls, two with mottled green glazes, Nos 3067 and 2465, third with mushroom coloured glaze, all with impressed mks., 20thC, 26.5cm (the largest) £60. Sep 00.

2867

Woolley & Wallis, Salisbury. Unusual Carlton ware biscuit barrel formed as a curling stone, printed mark, 20cm. £60. Sep 00.

2868

Gorringes, Lewes. Moorcroft vase with hibiscus on a white ground, 5in. £60. Oct 00.

2869

Gorringes, Lewes. Moorcroft orange lustre inverted baluster vase, 3.75in and a Moorcroft Pottery book by Atterbury, signed by Walter Moorcroft. £60. Oct 00.

2870

Woolley & Wallis, Salisbury. 2 small Wedgwood lustreware octagonal bowls, one cracked, printed marks, Z4827 and Z4831, early 20thC, 6.5cm. £60. Sep 00.

2871

Amersham Auction Rooms, Bucks. Late 18thC tin glazed earthenware plate, blue painted floral decoration, 11.5in. £60. Apr 01.

2872

Gorringes, Lewes. Aynsley cream jug and sugar bowl with fruit by N. Brunt and a Wedgwood jasper ware milk jug, 4.5in. £60. Feb 01.

Prices quoted are hammer prices which excluded the buyer's premium. Adding 15% will give an approximation to the buying price.

2873

Lambert & Foster, Tenterden. Two blue and white flower pattern Delft chargers, 12in and 13in. af. £60. Oct 01.

2874

Thos Mawer & Son, Lincoln. Two Royal Staffordshire Clarice Cliff Biarritz plates 'Love in a Mist', printed mark. £60. Apr 02.

2875

Thos Mawer & Son, Lincoln. Staffordshire cottage, royal blue roof, orange chimney, 21cm high. £60. Apr 02.

2876

Gorringes, Lewes. Set of six miniature monkey band figures, 3in. £60. Feb 01.

2877

Gorringes, Lewes. 1930s Sadler novelty mottled green and blue teapot in the form of a racing car, 9in. £60. Mar 01.

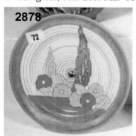

2878

Thos Mawer & Son, Lincoln. Clarice Cliff. 'Orange Capri', Bizarre tazza, electro plated stand, 23cm, printed factory marks. £60. Apr 02.

2879

Ambrose, Loughton. Pair of female majolica figures in the form of flasks each seated on a dolphin. £60. Feb 02.

2880

Amersham Auction Rooms, Bucks. 1920/30s Staffs painted pottery pastille burner, as a cottage, 5.5in high. £60. June 02.

2881

Gorringes, Lewes. 18thC Chinese green, aubergine and ochre painted figure, 5in. £60. Apr 01.

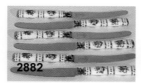

2882

Locke & England, Leamington Spa. Set of six Royal Crown Derby porcelain handled tea knives. £60. Nov 02.

2883

Tring Market Auctions, Herts. 17thC Dutch tile of an archer with bow and arrows painted in blue, green and ochre, 5in square. £60. May 02.

2884

Locke & England, Leamington Spa. 19thC English porcelain baluster vase. £60. Nov 02.

2885

Potteries Specialist Auctions, Stoke. Royal Doulton. Winnie the Pooh, I've found somebody just like me. £60. Mar 03.

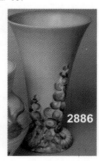

2886

Amersham Auction Rooms, Bucks. Clarice Cliff pottery vase, My Garden pattern, bears a painted Clarice Cliff and a Newport factory mark, 9in high. £60. Nov 02.

Hammer Prices £60-£55

2887

Thos Mawer & Son, Lincoln. 19thC Staffordshire porcelain tea service with gilt pale yellow and grey panels, (29). £60. Feb 03.

2888

Gorringes, Lewes. Royal Copenhagen figure, Faun (large) 2609. £60. Feb 01.

2889

Gorringes, Lewes. German porcelain group of a baby and black poodle on a pink cushion, 4in. (tail and four fingers missing) £55. Feb 01.

2890

Gorringes, Lewes. Royal Copenhagen figure, Bear Walking, 2841. £55. Feb 01.

2891

Gorringes, Lewes. Signed Satsuma box and cover with floral decoration, 4in. £55. Apr 02.

2892

Gorringes, Lewes. Dresden quatre lobed cabinet cup and saucer with marine and floral panels. £55. June 00.

2893

Lambert & Foster, Tenterden. Capodimonte style, cupid and shell, porcelain ornament. £55. Dec 99.

2894

Woolley & Wallis, Salisbury. Carlton ware dish, printed factory mark, 28cm. £55. Sep 00.

2895

John Taylors, Louth. Early 19thC dessert plate. £55. Jan 01.

2896

Gorringes, Lewes. Clarice Cliff Secrets pattern biscuit barrel with lug handles and replacement wooden cover, 6in. £55. Sep 00.

2897

Gorringes, Lewes. Victorian Mason's ironstone water jug decorated with oriental figures, 7in. £55. Oct 00.

Hammer Prices £55-£50

2898

Sworders, Stansted Mount-fitchet. Pair of Brannam pottery vases, impressed C. H. Brannam Ltd, Barnstaple, 8in high. £55. Apr 2001.

2899

Andrew Hartley, Ilkley. Early 19thC Rogers pearlware plate, with the Zebra pattern, 9.75in. £55. Apr 01.

2900

Sworders, Stansted Mount-fitchet. Beswick Beatrix Potter figure, Mr Benjamin Bunny and Peter Rabbit, 4in high. £55. July 01.

2901

Tring Market Auctions, Herts. Royal Worcester stand of blush apricot ground, gilt shaped border, year marks 1912, 7.5in. £55. Jan 03.

2902

Potteries Specialist Auctions, Stoke. Chameleon Ware vase in the House and Willow pattern on a yellow ground, 6.5in high. £55. Mar 03.

2903

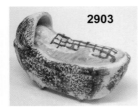

Gorringes, Lewes, Sussex. 19thC Leeds (?) baby in a cradle group with red and green sponged decoration, 3.5in. £55. Mar 2001.

2904

Sworders, Stansted Mount-fitchet. Five Wedgwood Eric Ravillious Persephone side plates, and two handled bowl. £55. Apr 01.

2905

Sworders, Stansted Mount-fitchet. Beswick Beatrix Potter figure, 'Mrs Tiggy Winkle Takes Tea', 3.25in high. £55. July 2001.

2906

Biddle & Webb, Birmingham. Three Royal Doulton jugs of musketeers, D'artagnan, Aramis and Athos. £55. Feb 02.

2907

Tring Market Auctions, Herts. Staffordshire figure group of a young man and woman, she holding a bird on her right arm, he wearing a plumed hat and a plaid, 8.25in high. £55. Mar 2002.

2908

Gorringes, Lewes. Locke & Co., Worcester. Cauldron painted with a peacock, signed H Wall, 4in and a similar tyg. £55. June 00.

2909

Gorringes, Lewes. Davenport Japan pattern bon bon basket with mock bamboo handle, 3in. £55. Feb 01.

2910

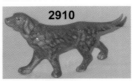

Lambert & Foster, Tenterden. Fieldings Devon Ware, Staffs, England. Figure of a 'Retriever'. £50. Dec 99.

2911

Woolley & Wallis, Salisbury. Royal Worcester Nautilus vase, a puce mark, No 101, c1901, 17cm. £50. Sep 00.

2912

Woolley & Wallis, Salisbury. Pearlware plate, 2/21 impressed, early 19thC, 18cm. £50. Sep 00.

2913

Thos Mawer & Son, Lincoln. Crown Devon. Set of three graduated taper cylindrical jugs, 16cm, 18cm and 20cm high, printed mark. (gilding rubbed) £50. Apr 02.

2914

Gorringes, Lewes. Samson armorial tea caddy and cover, 4.25in. £50. Oct 00.

2915

Gorringes, Lewes. Hadley's Worcester ewer vase with pink roses, 209/10, 5.5in. (handle repaired) £50. Dec 00.

2916

Tring Market Auctions, Herts. 19thC Cantonese famille rose vase. £50. Jan 02.

2917

Gorringes, Lewes. Old English porcelain sugar bowl, cover and stand with floral decoration. af. £50. Dec 00.

2918

Gorringes, Lewes. Continental porcelain plaque with figures drinking in a tavern, 4 x 2.5in. £50. June 00.

2919

Gorringes, Lewes. Victorian Whieldon type majolica pineapple jar and cover, 5in. £50. Apr 00.

2920

Woolley & Wallis, Salisbury. Pair of Chinese green glazed parrots, standing on yellow, grey and green rockwork, the feathers detailed in black, 20thC, 25cm. £50. Sep 00.

2921

Gorringes, Lewes. Goebel parian bust of Napoleon, 6in. £50. July 00.

2922

Gorringes, Lewes. Moorcroft dish, anemones on a green ground, 8.5in. £50. Dec 00.

2923

Lambert & Foster, Tenterden. 19thC vase in colours with figures in garden landscape, 31cm. af. £50. Jan 03.

2924

Woolley & Wallis, Salisbury. English porcelain pink lustre milk jug and matching bowl, no marks, early 19thC. £50. Sep 00.

2925

Thos Mawer & Son, Lincoln. Clarice Cliff. 'Water Lily', bowl modelled in relief, printed factory mark, 20cm wide. £50. Apr 02.

The numbering system aids the editorial analysis at the beginning of each section as well as providing a reader reference.

2926

Amersham Auction Rooms, Bucks. Late 19thC Staffs pottery figure of The Prince of Wales, wearing a floral patterned waistcoat, 14.5in high. £50. Oct 02.

2927

Andrew Hartley, Ilkley. 19thC pottery relief moulded jug in pale blue glaze, body as a frieze of bacchanalian figures amongst trailing vines, 10in. £50. Aug 00.

2928

Gorringes, Lewes. 3 Hummell child figures, largest 3.5in. £50. Oct 00.

2929

Gorringes, Lewes. Mintons Guinness combined vesta and ashtray, 5in. £50. Sep 00.

2930

Tring Market Auctions, Herts. Emery Victorian transfer printed one pint load line measure bearing Government stamp, each side with a reserved description, 4.5in, af. £50. Mar 03.

2931

Richard Wintertons, Burton on Trent. Brewery advertising match striker, 'Bass in Bottle', maker Mintons, 7cm. Restorations. £50. Apr 03.

2932

Woolley & Wallis, Salisbury. Royal Doulton red flambe glazed bottle vase, decorated around the body with a church in a landscape, paper label and printed factory mark, 21cm. £50. Sep 00.

2933

Sworders, Stansted Mount-fitchet. Beswick Beatrix Potter figure, Mr Alderman Ptolemy, 4in. £50. July 01.

2934

Lambert & Foster, Tenterden. Chelsea Pottery pattern dish, monogram AD, 40cm wide. £50. June 03.

2935

Sworders, Stansted Mount-fitchet. Three Beswick Beatrix Potter figures, Timmy Willie from Johnny Townmouse, Tailor of Gloucester and Benjamin Bunny. £50. July 01.

2936

Gorringes, Lewes. Clarice Cliff sugar sifter with metal top and moulded flowers, 6in. £50. Dec 00.

2937

Amersham Auction Rooms, Bucks. Late 19thC Japanese porcelain blanc de chine group of 2 theatrical figures, 6.25in high. £45. Sep 01.

2938

Potteries Specialist Auctions, Stoke. Pendelfin. Maud Rabbit, in green and black. Out of production. £45. Apr 03.

2939

Sworders, Stansted Mount-fitchet. Lithophane mug commemorating Bishop's Stortford 1902 Coronation. £45. July 01.

2940

Tring Market Auctions, Herts. 18thC pottery figure of a recumbent lion, txfr printed in u/g blue with a diaper cell pattern, glaze chips, 2.5in long. £45. May 02.

2941

Gorringes, Lewes. Pair of Bretby vases painted with storks, 9in. £45. Apr 00.

2942

Locke & England, Leamington Spa. Royal Crown Derby Imari polar bear paperweight, printed mark, 11cm. £45. Apr 03.

2943

Woolley & Wallis, Salisbury. Caughley mug, 'Fisherman' pattern, no mark, (rim chips and star crack to base) 11cm, and a Worcester teapot, crescent mark, (damaged) both c1770-80. £45. Sep 00.

2944

Gorringes, Lewes. Pair of Chinese blanc de chine models of kylin, 5in. £45. Apr 01.

2945

Gorringes, Lewes. Graduated set of three jugs with silhouette decoration, largest 6.5in. £45. Apr 00.

2946

Dee, Atkinson & Harrison, Driffield. 3 pieces of Gouda, a jardiniere, 4.5in, inverted baluster vase, 5.25in, and a double handled sugar bowl, 2.5in. £45. Apr 01.

2947

Wintertons Ltd, Lichfield. Pair of Chinese Export blue and white porcelain plates, c1790, with Oriental land-scapes, 9.5in. £45. Nov 01.

2948

Gorringes, Lewes. Continental porcelain plaque of an angel after Raphael, 3.75 x 2.5in. £45. July 00.

Hammer Prices £45-£35

2949

Gorringes, Lewes. Carltonware 6 piece rouge royale coffee set. £45. Oct 00.

2950

Gorringes, Lewes. Late 19thC Dresden cabinet cup and saucer. £45. July00.

2951

Gorringes, Lewes. Beswick Ware courting couple wall pocket, 8.5in. £40. July 00.

2952

Gorringes, Lewes. Clarice Cliff Celtic Harvest jug, 8.5in. £40. Sep 00.

2953

Locke & England, Leamington Spa. 19thC Staffordshire pottery pastille burner modelled as a cottage, 17.5cm high. chimney restored. £40. Oct 03.

124

2954

Gorringes, Lewes. Continental porcelain figure of a lady holding a basket of flowers, 8in. £40. Apr 01.

2955

Woolley & Wallis, Salisbury. English porcelain plate, no marks, mid 19thC, 24cm. £40. Sep 00.

2956

Gorringes, Lewes. Beswick model of a stag, 12in. £40. June 00.

2957

Gorringes, Lewes. Late 19thC French oval porcelain plaque painted with cherubs, 3in. £40. July 00.

2958

Gorringes, Lewes. German blanc de chine parrot on a gilt ball, 8in. £40. July 00.

2959

Gorringes, Lewes. Pair Derby dishes, 10in. £40. July 00.

2960

Ambrose, Loughton. Limoges coffee pot and sucrier, pink decoration, and associated pot and cover. £40. Feb 02.

2961

Sworders, Stansted Mountfitchet. Two Beswick Beatrix Potter figures, 'Little Pig Robinson' and 'Mrs Rabbit and Bunnies'. £40. July 01.

2962

Lambert & Foster, Tenterden. Coalport, Ladies of Fashion, 'Mary' Jack Glynn 11/95, 7in. with certificate. £40. Nov 99.

2963

Locke & England, Leamington Spa. Wedgwood classical collection 'Inspiration' figure, modelled by Jenny Oliver, 1997, 31cm. £40. Apr 03.

2964

Tring Market Auctions, Herts. Early 19thC porcelain inkwell, 1.5in. £40. Nov 02.

2965

Amersham Auction Rooms, Bucks. Royal Doulton china sandwich plate commemorating the Battle of Hastings, with scene from the Bayeaux Tapestry, 17.5in wide. £40. July 02.

2966

Richard Wintertons, Burton on Trent. Mintons Brewery advertising ashtray, 'Say Allsopp', 12cm. £40. Apr 03.

2967

Gorringes, Lewes. Pair of 19thC Wedgwood crescent dishes with floral decoration, 14in. £40. Apr 00.

2968

Woolley & Wallis, Salisbury. 7 Chinese bowls, 3 in famille rose enamels and 4 blue and white, all 18thC (2 cracked) and 3 Canton enamel teabowls and saucers, 19thC (damages). (13) £40. Sep 99.

2969

Gorringes, Lewes. French porcelain figure of toby the dog, 2.75in. (lid of a box) £40. Apr 01.

2970

Sworders, Stansted Mountfitchet. Poole Pottery freeform pattern tankard, inscribed '5/NN', impressed 126, printed factory marks, 10cm high. £40. Oct 03.

2971

Sworders, Stansted Mountfitchet. Moorcroft inkwell and cover, with fruiting branches, lacks well, impressed Moorcroft, restore, 11cm. £40. Oct 03.

2972

Ambrose, Loughton. Limoges pink and gilt enamel part tea service. (7) together with a Noritake pink and gilt basket. £38. Mar 02.

2973

Gorringes, Lewes. Royal Worcester miniature blush porcelain mug painted with flowers, L037, date code 1906. £35. Dec 00.

2974

Sworders, Stansted Mountfitchet. Newhall trio, in the 'boy in the window' pattern. £35. July 01.

2975

Gorringes, Lewes. Pair of 19thC Staffordshire agate glaze mugs, 4in. (1 af) £35. Dec 00.

2976

Sworders, Stansted Mount-fitchet. Green glaze pottery soup tureen, 20thC, 10.5in. £35. July01.

2977

Sworders, Stansted Mount-fitchet. Qianlong plate, a bowl and two saucers. £35. July 01.

2978

Sworders, Stansted Mount-fitchet Liverpool pearlware plate, 8.25in. £35. July 01.

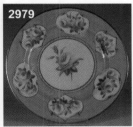

2979

Woolley & Wallis, Salisbury. English porcelain plate, prob. Rockingham, no marks, c1820-30, 22cm. £35. Sep 00.

2980.

Woolley & Wallis, Salisbury. Chinese famille rose European subject globular teapot and cover, 18thC, 12cm. damaged. £35. Sep 00.

2981

Lambert & Foster, Tenterden. Royal Copenhagen, duck on base, no 1192. £35. Dec 99.

2982

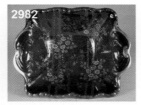

Woolley & Wallis, Salisbury. Crown Devon dark red lustreware square bowl, printed mark, pattern No. 5009, 24.5cm. £35. Sep 00.

2983

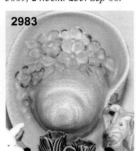

Crows, Dorking. Beswick straw hat wall pocket. £35. July 01.

2984

Locke & England, Leamington Spa. Royal Doulton figure 'Humpty Dumpty', limited edition, No 957/1500, c1998, 13cm, boxed. £32. Apr 03.

2985

Tring Market Auctions, Herts. German porcelain jardiniere, pierced sides threaded with a painted ribbon and decorated with pink roses within a gilt border, mark of Max Roesler Rodach to base, 5.5in high, slightly af. £32. Mar 02.

2986

Gorringes, Lewes. Royal Worcester blush porcelain dish painted with irises, No. 1706, 4.25in. £30. Apr 01.

2987

Gorringes, Lewes. Royal Crown Derby Japan pattern fluted dish, No. 2451, 6in. £30. Dec 00.

2988

Gorringes, Lewes. Flight Barr & Barr plate, purple vine leaves, parcel gilt, 8.5in £30. July 00.

2989

Gorringes, Lewes. Beswick figure of John, a conducting pig no. PP1 and a Beswick dinosaur. £30. Apr 00.

The illustrations in these pages are in descending price order. The price range is indicated at the top of each page.

2990

Gorringes, Lewes. Modern Belleek vase in the form of an owl, 8in. £30. Oct 00.

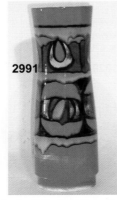

2991

Locke & England, Leamington Spa. Poole Delphis pottery vase. £30. Nov 02.

Hammer Prices £35-£25

2992

Lambert & Foster, Tenterden. 'Oriental vase' pattern blue and white basin, 34cm. af. £30. May 02.

2993

Tring Market Auctions, Herts. 18thC blue and white tile in oak frame, biblical subject, 5in square. £30. May 02.

2994

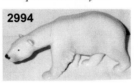

Lambert & Foster, Tenterden. Royal Copenhagen, polar bear, no. 320. £30. Dec 99.

2995

Gorringes, Lewes. 18thC Staffordshire enamel patch box with love motto, 1.5in. £30. Oct 00.

2996

Gorringes, Lewes. Pair of Chinese green glaze vases and covers decorated with flowers, 6in. £30. July 00.

2997

Gorringes, Lewes. Royal Doulton Titanian octagonal dish, 7.5in. £30. June 00.

2998

Gorringes, Lewes, Sussex. Moorcroft clematis vase, (badly cracked) 5.5in. £30. Mar 2001.

2999

Gorringes, Lewes. Coalport quatre lobed gilded pink cup and saucer, A5844, (restored handle) and a tea bowl and saucer with swallows amidst bamboo on a gilt ground, A2334. £30. Dec 00.

3000

Lambert & Foster, Tenterden. Staffordshire flat back spill vase, Shepherdess playing a harp with sheep at her feet, 33cm. af. £30. |May 02.

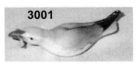

3001

Lambert & Foster, Tenterden. B & G figure of a 'seagull' with fish in beak, 5.5 x 2in high. £28. Dec 99.

3002

Lambert & Foster, Tenterden. Figure of a dancer in green bikini top and tiered skirt, 6.5in. £25. Dec 99.

Hammer Prices £25-£5

3003

Woolley & Wallis, Salisbury. Copeland earthenware mug and saucer, 'John Arkwright', 'Presented in Commemoration of the Coming of Age of John Hungerford Arkwright, July 12th 1854 Hampton Court', printed and impressed marks. £25. Sep 00.

3004

Gorringes, Lewes. Early 19thC porcelain mug with printed and titled 'Worcester from N.W'. £25. Sep 00.

3005

Lambert & Foster, Tenterden. Royal Copenhagen, seagull, no. 1468, 2.5 x 5in. (PH 60/70) £25. Dec 99.

3006

Tring Market Auctions, Herts. Majolica comport moulded with a bird and prunus on a beaded turquoise ground, grey basketweave border, af, 9in. £25. Sep 02.

3007

Lambert & Foster, Tenterden. Royal Copenhagen, rabbit, no 4705, 3 x 3.5in. (JG 50/60) £25. Dec 99.

3008

Gorringes, Lewes. Early 19thC sauce tureen, lion knop, 7in. af. £25. Sep 00.

3009

Fellows & Sons, Hockley, Birmingham. Victorian leaf moulded jar, interior with pink glaze, not marked, 12cm. (s.d. and repairs) £25. Oct 03.

3010

Ambrose, Loughton. Noritake tea service. (20) £22. Feb 02.

3011

Lambert & Foster, Tenterden. Beswick alsation CH. Ulrica of Brittas, 5.5in. £22. Dec 99.

3012

Crows, Dorking. Sylvac green top hat with cat seated on rim, dog below. £20. July 01.

3013

Gorringes, Lewes. Late 18thC Worcester tea cup. £20. Oct 00.

3014

Gorringes, Lewes. Victorian Staffordshire figure of a man holding fruit, (cracked) 7.5in. £20. Mar 01.

3015

Gorringes, Lewes. Royal Worcester blush porcelain side plate painted with flowers, 4.75in. £20. Oct 00.

3016

Ambrose, Loughton. Salt glazed stoneware jug, relief moulded with a coat of arms indistinctly signed, possibly 'GRES', Walton, Guernsey, 21cm high. £20. Feb 02.

3017

Gorringes, Lewes. Pair of Royal Worcester hors d'oeuvres dishes from a set of four, 9in. £20. Apr 01.

3018

Woolley & Wallis, Salisbury. Pair of bone china low stands, unmarked, mid 19thC, 23.5cm. (one cracked) £20. Sep 00.

3019

Gorringes, Lewes. Pair of German porcelain prams, 4in. £20. June 00.

3020

Gorringes, Lewes. Oak framed pomade pot lid, The Fish Seller. £20. June 00.

3021

Thos Mawer & Son, Lincoln. Pair of Staffordshire seated King Charles spaniels, 22cm high. £20. Feb 03.

3022

Woolley & Wallis, Salisbury. Chinese blanc de Chine figure of Wen'Ch'ang, standing on rockwork, accompanied by his attendant K'uei-Hsing, 18thC, 33cm. (damages) £20. Sep 00.

3023

Crows, Dorking. Sylvac vase with swan. £15. July 01.

3024

Crows, Dorking. Two Sylvac Scottie dogs. (one af) £15. July 01.

3025

Gorringes, Lewes. Pair of late 19thC German porcelain costume figures, polychrome decorated with floral encrusted bases, 8in. af. £15. Oct 00.

3026

Woolley & Wallis, Salisbury. White glazed Cozzi porcelain group, no mark, 2nd half 18thC, 22cm. (extensively damaged) £10. Sep 00.

3027

Lambert & Foster, Tenterden. USSR ceramic figure of a baby donkey. £10. Oct 01.

3028

Lambert & Foster, Tenterden. USSR ceramic panda, 4in x 3.25in. £10. Oct 01.

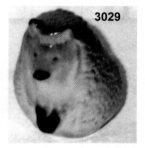

3029

Lambert & Foster, Tenterden. USSR ceramic figure of a hedgehog. £10. Oct 01.

3030

Ambrose, Loughton. WRN Burslem handpainted part dinner service, yellow and red geometric decoration, together with a British Anchor Ware cake stand. £8. Mar 02.

3031

Ambrose, Loughton. Collection of ceramics, including nine Wedgwood Imperial porcelain plates, a part tea service, and other items. £5. Mar 02.

Index

Factories can be identified by the emboldened entries. The names of patterns, paintings and figures are in italics.

Glossary of Terms

agate ware Earthenware or stoneware imitating stratified agate. Associated with Whieldon from the 1740s and later imitations.

alabaster ware A kind of bone china with similar translucency.

albarelli Waisted maiolica drug jars mainly from Italy. There are a number of examples illustrated. See the **Index**.

amphora Two-handled ancient urn-shaped earthenware vessel for wine or oil.

Arita ware Japanese porcelain from the Hizen province. In Europe from the mid 17thC.

Astbury wares 18thC white-glazed stoneware and red earthenware particularly known for early pew-group figures.

bamboo ware From 18thC a fine stoneware suggesting strips of bamboo lashed together with cane.

bargeware Colourful earthenware suggesting canal boat painting.

basalt High quality fine stoneware from 1760s usually black and capable of decoration with encaustic colours.

Bellarmines German brownish saltglazed stoneware bottles from 17thC onwards, with a relief ornament of a mask of the infamous Cardinal Bellarmine.

bianco-sopra-bianco White ornament in slight relief on tin-enamelled earthenware.

biscuit, bisque Single-fired unglazed wares.

bocage Flower or tree support behind a figure or group.

body Basic clay mix in earthenwares and stonewares. (see also paste)

bone china From 1794 (Spode) the hard-paste porcelain ingredients combined with their equivalent weight in calcined bone.

cane ware Fine cane coloured stoneware from c1770.

celadon ware From the Sung Dynasty, (960-1280) a porcelanous ware with a whitish body and a hard, restrained green, feldspathic glaze. Check **Index** for examples.

ceramic All fire-baked clay vessels.

china A misnomer generally attaching to English bone china because of its relationship to Chinese hard-paste porcelain.

creamware A fine quality light-density earthenware which evolved from the 1740s.

Delftware Tin-glazed earthenware associated with Delft in Holland, providing a fine white surface for painting.

earthenware Opaque clay wares, porous after firing and for most purposes requiring a glaze.

Elers red ware Fine stoneware made by the Elers Brothers in England from 1688.

faience The French name for tin-enamelled wares. Equates to delft or maiolica.

fairings Cheap novelties originally sold at fairs during the 19thC.

famille rose Chinese porcelain enamel decoration dominated by the colour pink.

famille verte Chinese porcelain enamel decoration dominated by the colour green.

flambé Imitates Chinese wares in a wide range of brilliant flowing glaze colours.

lead glaze Application of powdered lead ore to the ware, dipped from c1750. Leadless glazes from 19thC to avoid the health hazard.

hard-paste porcelain Chinese or 'true' porcelain. First made in Plymouth in 1768 and exploited at New Hall as hybrid hard-paste.

Imari English name for Japanese Export porcelain made at Arita and shipped from Imari.

ironstone china A strong earthenware originally patented by C.J. Mason in 1813.

Iznik Turkish pottery made at Iznik in Istanbul.

Jackfield wares Brownish red earthenware covered in a lustrous black glaze, associated with Jackfield, Shropshire.

jasper Fine stonewares from 1774 needing no glaze. Usually in solid colour or two-tone.

maiolica The Italian equivalent to delftware or faience.

majolica A corruption of the word maiolica. Colourful relief-moulded ware in naturalistic shapes, evolved at Minton in 1851.

mocha ware Cheap tablewares imitating mocha stone.

Palissy ware Applied ornaments of figures, grotesques, lizards, ferns etc. in high relief.

parian A vitrified porcelain suggesting whitish Grecian marble. (Introduced from 1842 by Copeland & Garrett)

paste In porcelain, the basic material mix. (see also body)

pâte-sur-pâte Literally paste on paste to produce a cameo effect.

pearlware The light-density earthenware which replaced creamware. Excellent for blue transfer printing.

pottery The general term for earthenwares and stonewares as distinct from porcelain.

saltglaze Glassy glaze applied to stoneware by throwing salt into the kiln.

sang de boeuf An ox blood glaze using metallic compounds.

Satsuma Japanese pottery as distinct to porcelain. Popular with Victorians and imitated in Kyoto.

sgraffito Scratched or incised ceramic ornament.

slipware Earthenware ornamented with slip, i.e. a creamy watered-down clay.

smear-glaze An invisible glaze applied to domestic parian as a vapour.

soapstone porcelain A soft-paste type containing 35-45% steatite.

soft-paste porcelain Fragile and costly glass frit type, made from 1740s until eclipsed by bone china. A hybrid hard-paste porcelain intervened, lasting from 1780s to about 1813.

sprigged ornament Relief ornament shaped in separate molds and applied before firing.

stoneware Clay mixed with sand or flint. Fired at a higher temperature than earthenware and impervious to liquids.

terracotta Literally baked earth - a soft unglazed and porous earthenware. Usually reddish.

tortoiseshell ware In earthenware, imitating the shell, developed by Thomas Whieldon in c1750. Often known as Whieldon Ware.

transfer-printing The process of transferring a pattern from tissue paper, applied with coloured ink to an etched copper plate and hence to ceramic ware.

Whieldon Ware Either agate ware, tortoiseshell ware or green glaze or cauliflower ware.